Best wishes

Barbara Kay

OVER THE WALL

TRIALS AND TRIBULATIONS OF A JAILBREAKER

BASED ON A TRUE STORY

BARBARA KAY

This book is *based* upon a true story. It was crafted from a handful of notes written by Walter when he was in his late 70's and is reliant upon his recollections. The work contains *fictional crimes, composite and representative characters and dialogue.* Some names and persona's have been changed for legal reasons and / or to protect identities. In the case of re-created identities, any resemblance to actual persons, living or dead, is purely coincidental.

Photograph of Walter, aged 25 years, reproduced by kind permission of the *Shropshire Newspapers* and *Shropshire Archives*-Reference WJ29/10/1961

Depiction of The Dana in Shrewsbury reproduced on front cover by kind permission of *Joel Campbell* - The Campbell Group of Companies and *Trevor Osborne* - The Trevor Osborne Property Group

ISBN: 978-0-9957697-0-0

Publisher: Barbara Kay

Barbara Kay asserts her moral right to be identified as the author of this book.

Personal messages from Walter

Dedications
To my wife, who taught me there is only one judge who really matters, and it is not my fellow man, it's myself.

To Ann, who sadly passed away in 2013 and didn't get to see my book published. She would have loved it!

With thanks to
My son, Richard, for patiently reading every word and providing constructive criticism.

My son, Jason, for being my drinking buddy down the pub at odd times when my powers of recall hit a brick wall.

Friends who listened to my ramblings and continued to encourage my endeavours.

All the characters in my story 'cos without the likes of them there would be nothing to write about.

Barbara, who made sense of my scribbled notes and fashioned them into this wonderful book

Finally, you, the reader. I hope you enjoy it; get lost in my world and share my experiences. Brace yourself, it's a bumpy old ride!

Walter Groom

Prologue

It is said that man is the author of his own destiny and I suppose it's true but a single word or event can shape decisions made along the way. Those decisions affect the paths we tread, the people we meet, the jobs we do and ultimately the way in which our lives, and the lives of those around us, unravel.

I was born on 17th December 1935. One of seven children, I had two sisters and four brothers. Nine of us squeezed into a small three bed Council House in the Black Country. Mostly I recall being hungry all the time and the cast off clothing, always too big or too small. Left to my own devices I hardly ever attended school. My Dad favoured the buckle end of his belt or a whack with the broom as chastisement for any misdemeanor.

This book charts my life, over a period of twenty years, from the age of fifteen. I'd just started work as an apprentice toolsetter and remember feeling very proud walking home with my first pay packet. I'll never forget the sense of utter misery when my Dad told me it wasn't enough and I would have to leave the job.

That single event changed my life forever.

Chapter 1

THE CYCLE BEGINS

I look up at the tiny window. It seems smaller now than when I was standing on the ground. I shift my weight from one foot to the other and almost topple off Bishop's shoulders. I start to shiver but am not sure if it's the feeling of dread which has suddenly rushed from my head to my toes or the cold night air striking at my bones. I've only got one coat and it's on the ground where I carefully placed it a few moments ago. I glance down to check it's still there.

"What you doin'?" whispers Bishop "get on with it."

"It's too small, I won't be able to get through" my voice sounds thin and squeaky.

"Bollocks, you ain't backing out now." Bishop grabs both my feet and thrusts me upwards.

Johnny Bishop is a big bloke and local villain. You don't argue with him if you want to stay out of hospital.

Him and his sidekick, Billy Taylor, had come on me in the Table Mountain at the top of the town that Saturday morning. It's a small cafe with wood effect formica tables, red leatherette chairs and a juke box next to the counter where cheery, red faced, Doris does the best bacon sarnie for miles. It's a sort of meeting place for the local lads where you can make your cuppa last for hours and listen to the latest hits.

"You wanna earn some quick money son?" Bishop leaned over from his table. He must have been listening to me tell my mate, Rob, how I'd taken my first wages home yesterday. Rob had been dead jealous when I got the job as apprentice toolsetter at Johnny Fellowes. It's a job for life he'd said and I was so proud when I took the money home. The pay packet contained £1.2s.6d but my Dad had flown into a rage saying he'd kept me all my fuckin' life, it wasn't enough and I could get more boiling tea on the building sites.

The likes of Bishop and Taylor had never spoken to me before but I knew their reputation, everybody did. Bishop, in his mid twenties, always dressed snappy in the latest gear and flashed the cash. His shock of blonde hair and blue eyes meant the girls hung round him like flies. Taylor, the older one, gaunt and thin lipped, rarely cracked his face and had staring eyes that looked straight through you. A vicious man with scars to prove it...

"Push up the catch and open the window wide, you can do it" encourages Bishop.

"Is he in yet?" I can hear Taylor's voice coming from the end of the alley where he is keeping watch.

My left hand eases through the tiny gap, lifts the catch and pulls the window open. I hold onto the frame, haul myself up and go head first through the opening.

I know what to do once I'm in. Bishop and Taylor had told me to go to the back door of the factory and open the bolts. That's all I have to do to get my twenty quid.

The window is high and I land clumsily, trying to do some sort of forward roll.

A powerful mix of fear and excitement sets my heart racing. The pounding in my ears grows louder and every nerve in my body jostles for position. All my senses are on high alert. It's incredible. I've never felt so alive.

The floor is cluttered and I trip over something almost as soon as I've stood up. Where's the door? Swallowing hard, I pull the handle. As it opens a harsh creaking fills the silence. I catch my breath. Did Taylor mention a Nightwatchman? Squeezing through the smallest of gaps I step into a corridor.

Bishop's voice is in my head. "Turn left out of the room" he'd said, "the door you want is at the end."

Feeling my way along the walls I creep swiftly along the dark passageway. Tiny shafts of moonlight trace the outline of a huge, ill fitting door. This must be it.

There are four hefty bolts, three of which go across to the frame. They slide easily enough, but the one into the floor, it just won't seem to budge. Bishop and Taylor are outside. I'm frantically trying to wrench the floor bolt.

"What the fuck's he doin' in there?" I hear Taylor ask and then Bishop "he ain't strong enough to get the bolts, let's fuck off."

My hands are sweating. I can't get a grip. Panic stricken, I give the floor bolt one almighty tug and fall backwards as it gives.

"Now fuck off." Taylor hands me twenty one pound notes and pushes me outside. I stare momentarily at the money. I can't believe it. My Dad only brings home £8 a week for five twelve hour shifts at the brickyard.

Shoving the dosh into my trouser pocket I run like hell down the alley. At the end I peer out from between two red brick walls but quickly dodge back into the shadows when a lone car passes. As its engines purr into the distance I'm off and running again. The cold wind takes my breath. I leap up and punch the air. I feel great. I did it.

It must be about three in the morning and I will have to sleep in the coalhouse but come tomorrow, I'll show my Dad, I'll show him. A shudder stops me dead in my tracks. Something's missing…I've forgot my jacket! Gotta go back.

Staring apprehensively into the darkness, I creep slowly towards where my coat is lying, still neatly folded and exactly where I'd left it almost an hour earlier. What a dickhead. Sighing with relief, I grab it and head for the safety of the coalhouse.

Well, we call it the coalhouse but there's only ever one bag of coal in there and a few logs that me and my brothers collect from over Bevans' fields. Dad locks up at 10 o'clock sharp so I've taken to leaving an old coat off the bed on the back of the coalhouse door. Coats that are any good in our house are pawned on a Monday and fetched out again on Fridays. When they get too tatty for the pawnshop they end up on our beds.

I lift the latch and creep in taking the big old coat off the hook. It's got furry lining and a huge collar that envelops me as I snuggle into it. Sitting propped with my head against the wall I soon drift off to sleep.

"You comin' in or what?" my younger brother, Roy, stares at me from the coalhouse door.

Blinking in the daylight, I ease myself up and instinctively check for the wad of notes. A silly great grin spreads from ear to ear as my fingers close around the paper bundle. I'm bursting and dash to the adjacent privy where a stale smell of urine greets my nostrils. I screw up my nose and try not to breathe.

Three strides bring me through the scullery into the parlour, where floor boards peek through holes in the lino, faded floral patterns adorn the walls and a solitary picture of Our Lord, Sweet Jesus, watches over us all.

Mom stands bent over a large wooden table that dominates the centre of the room. She's pouring tea into Dad's tin mug. Pearl, my older sister, sits absently reading one of the newspapers that form a tablecloth, waiting for her tea which will be poured into an old jam jar. Barry, the little 'un, rocks back and forth on the shabby brown sofa that lines the back wall. Malcolm, Mike and Marje must still be in bed.

Dad is reading his newspaper in the easy chair closest to the fire. Being Sunday, there's no work at the brickyard. He glances at me and grunts something. I look at him sitting there with his thin, weather beaten face and small pig like eyes that never smile. My gaze is drawn to the thick leather belt holding up his baggy trousers.

Memories of the times he'd hurt me with the buckle end of that belt and chased me round the table with the broom come flooding back. I never knew what I'd done wrong and he always caught me. I hate him, the bastard.

My stomach's turning cartwheels at the thought of what I'm about to do but the money gives me a strange sense of power.

I reach into my pocket, grasp the wad of notes and throw them onto the table. "You wanted some fuckin' money? Well now you got it, and there's more where that came from."

I'd never sworn at my Dad before. There is a moment of stunned silence. The newspaper slides from his lap. Briefly our eyes meet as without a word, he reaches across to snatch the money. Pearl sits open mouthed while Roy, who is 13, grins and runs upstairs to tell the others. Mom frowns and carries on pouring the tea. She knows the pub will see most of it!

Can't go back to toolsetting at Fellowes but if I do a few more jobs with Bishop and Taylor then I can have the flash clothes and maybe get a bird. I hang round at the café until two days later they come in. Feeling braver now I make a beeline to their table and ask Bishop straight out if there's a chance of another job. He smiles, leans back on his chair and looks at Taylor, who doesn't smile but nods and so it looks like I'm in luck.

Job follows job and pretty quickly I become one of the lads with cash to flash. When I take home bags of food and tell the coalman to fill up the coalhouse my brothers and sisters laugh out loud, a sound not very often heard in our house. The expression on Mom's face when I produce some proper cups and a pretty wipe-clean cloth for the table is priceless.

On my 16th birthday I enjoy a trip up town with my mates, Rob and Steve, to buy some new gear. My pinhead suit, crisp white shirt, snazzy tie and silky white scarf make me feel great as I turn this way and that to admire myself from all angles in the mirror.

"You look the bee's knees mate" says Rob as he stands beside me.

Rob is like me, thin and wiry. We both have olive skin and jet black hair although mine is a lot thicker. Steve is about the same height, 5'9" but thick set with fair skin and light mousey hair which is sort of wild. We still ain't got no birds but the new gear might help.

Because I am so slim and wiry my services for entry through small windows are now in great demand. I think I'm not doing anything bad because I'm not actually pinching anything myself. Bishop and Taylor put a word in for me with some other local villains and between them I am kept busy most every night.

Bishop and Taylor stick to doing factories, that's their thing, but Mad Jack and Dave like to rob the big houses on the main road. To my mind this is more risky but I give it a go. Trouble is, whilst Bishop and Taylor carry 'dusters' in case of bother with other villains, Mad Jack and Dave like to be tooled up with flick knives. They keep on at me to get one.

"Why don't you wanna get a flick then Watt?" asks Mad Jack.

I'm named after my Dad, Walter, but everyone has shortened it to Watt since I was a nipper.

I hadn't noticed them come into the café because I'd been standing at the Jukebox with my back to the door. They didn't even sit down and came straight across. Don't really want a knife. I've seen enough fights up town with knives and dusters. I don't want any part of that.

"Cos if you get nabbed with a knife you get more time, I ain't daft."

Mad Jack throws me a dark look from beneath the quiff of curly brown hair that lops onto his forehead. At 6'2" he towers above me.

The brown eyes narrow as he lowers his voice and bends to whisper in my ear. "But you ain't gonna get copped with us. Me 'n Dave got a job on tonight. You want in?"

Dave, who is leaning against the Juke Box, looks on encouragingly, his big frame filling out the huge gabardine mac. "How much?" I hear myself ask.

"Thirty" offers Dave, reaching in front of me to press a record selection.

"What about Fifty?" I'm chancing my arm.

"Forty" says Mad Jack. "Be outside the Globe at one" and with that they leave. I head back to the table.

"You ain't working with them are you?" Rob sounds a bit worried. "They're mad, him with the dark hair stabbed somebody up town the other week!"

I stare into my teacup. "I know, but money's money ain't it."

"Why don't we do a job ourselves?" Steve's got a glint in his eye. "Three more teas over here Doris."

We huddle together over the table. "What about Connor's shop, we could get the fags and booze 'n sell it round the estate" suggests Steve.

"I ain't doing it" says Rob straight away. "My Mom 'ud kill me". His Mom doesn't like me and whenever I called for him she'd always say "he's not in" and shut the door. I'd wait on the corner and sure enough, five minutes later, he'd come running up the street with that wicked grin on his face.

Steve lowers his voice and leans forward. "You've been on enough jobs Watt, you done shops before ain't you?"

It's true. Over the past few months I've been with most of the local crooks and got into factories, houses and shops. It never ceases to amaze me why people leave their top windows open so the likes of me can crawl through. I've shimmied up drainpipes and crept over roofs to get to where I needed to go but never actually taken anything, apart from the money given to me for getting in and opening the door.

This is different. Already feeling the buzz, it doesn't take me long to consider, "OK, let's do it."

Steve laughs and drinks down the rest of his tea in one gulp. "Come on, let's walk past and have a look see."

Connor's is a lock up shop round the corner from the Police Station. Most crooks steer clear because of that but it has rich pickings of booze and fags.

That night me and Steve 'do' the shop.

It's his first job and although it's not mine I can hardly contain my excitement at the thought of how much money we'll get for all this stuff as we fill our rucksacks with packets of fags and bottles of booze. Much more than the forty quid Mad Jack and Dave had offered.

Oh God! I'm rooted to the spot. I glance at my watch. It's 1.30 a.m.

"What's up?" whispers Steve.

"Mad Jack. I'm dead" I whisper back. "Look, let's go, we got enough." I'm already leggin' it towards the storeroom rooflight where we had jumped down. Getting back out is another matter but with the help of a chair and lots of pushing, pulling and cursing, we manage to ease ourselves and the rucksacks up and through.

Telling Steve to carry the stuff to mine and wait for me in the coalhouse, I sprint round to the Globe which is only a couple of streets away. They might be waiting for me. I was wrong. They hadn't waited for me then, but they sure as hell waited for me the next day.

There is a narrow gulley which cuts through from our estate to the main road. Big weeds and brambles tumble into it from between gaps in the fences which line unkempt gardens along its length.

I'm strolling through when Mad Jack suddenly steps out to block the way. His big frame spreads across the gap and fills me with dread. I turn to leg it but Dave appears at the other end. Nobody speaks. Mad Jack lunges at me with a blow to the stomach which doubles me up and sends me reeling. His fist smashes into my back as I fall in front of him.

Dave comes running and kicks me in the ribs as I'm lying on the ground. Can't breathe. The pain is excruciating. I've been in some fights and brawls with other lads my own age but nothing like this.

Mad Jack pulls me to my feet. The tattooed swallow on his right hand flies towards my face. There's a flash of something bright. Must be a knuckleduster. I try to defend myself from the rain of blows but it's useless. Blood gushes from my nose. All I can think is my new suit will be ruined.

Dave's parting shot is another taste of shoe leather. "Nobody let's us down son, nobody, you cost us a grand last night." I'm lying dazed and bloody in a heap. The familiar 'click' of a flick-knife sharpens my senses. Mustering every last ounce of strength I claw desperately at the fence. Mad Jack watches my efforts with some amusement. I only have eyes for the blade. In one agonizing movement I'm on my feet. Ain't strong enough to fight. Can't run. I'm gonna die.

Dave places his hand on Jack's arm. "No need for that, eh."

Slowly I sink to the ground and slump against the fence. Laughter rings in my ears as they walk off dusting down their gabardine macs. Eventually I manage to stagger home.

Had planned to sell the fags and booze myself but I'm so beat up that I can't even get out of bed. Steve starts touting it to all and sundry.

We don't know who grassed but the cops get wind that he's selling knocked off stuff and follow him back to mine. Mob-handed they raid the house. A search reveals the unsold gear which is still in the coalhouse. It's all very noisy and frantic as we are cuffed. Mom shouts at them to leave me alone as they drag us off to the local nick, Bilston Police Station.

I spend the night locked up. "Press this button, son, if you want the toilet" the Sergeant says as he bangs the cell door shut. The key turns. It's a sound you somehow never quite get used to.

The cell is about 8ft by 6ft and has nothing in it apart from a bench-like bed with a very hard mattress. I can't sleep and stare at the walls, which by morning, seem to be closing in on me. Little did I know then that the next 15 years would see me in many different police and prison cells. They all have one thing in common. You can't walk out when you want. I suppose that's the idea!

I am questioned the following day by two hefty plain clothes cops. They tell me Steve has admitted everything but I don't believe them and say nothing. It's a sort of code that Bishop and Taylor had instilled into me. If you get nabbed say nothing, no matter what. I'm determined not to grass.

One of the cops goes out of the room. The other one comes round the table to where I'm sitting, grips my arm like a vice and yanks me out of the chair. He throws me against the wall and punches me in the stomach. I am only just recovering from the beating I took a few days ago and by Christ it hurts like fuck.

"Come on lad" he says smirking at me "the stuff was found at your place, admit it." He lands another blow and I double up but keep my mouth shut apart from the groan which escapes my lips.

Grabbing my hair he jerks my head back. "You been in a fight?" he asks, pointing at the cuts and bruises on my face, "don't try and say I did those." He let's go and punches me in the back. I lurch towards the table and feel the sharp end of his boot as my legs are kicked from under me.

He drags me up and slams me against the wall. I watch him pull back his fist and wince as it connects with my ribs. "What other jobs you done then, what about Jones's lock up last week?"

My head is reeling and my whole body seems to be on fire.

"Bet you and your mate have been at it for months haven't you?" he asks, "come on, I'll get it out of you one way or another."

Another punch to the stomach followed by a kick to the knee and I'm on the floor again.

"Think about it son" he says as he leaves the interview room.

I slump into the chair, lean on the table and wonder about Steve.

A while later the other cop comes in with a brown folder under his arm and a cup of tea in his hand. I'm parched and hope it's for me. "You'll be needing this" he says pushing the tea towards me. I gulp it down. He pulls a packet of fags from his jacket pocket and offers me one. I don't smoke but take one anyway and slide it behind my right ear like my Dad.

"Now then lad" he says, placing the folder on the table and pulling up a chair opposite. "We know you did Connor's shop." I stare back at him. "Your mate has confessed and says it was all your idea." My idea, ha, that's a laugh, if I hadn't listened to him I wouldn't be here now, I'd have gone with Mad Jack 'n Dave and saved myself two beatings.

"You've been seen around with Bishop and Taylor" good cop leans back on his chair "are they in on it?" I stare at him blankly. "No" he pauses, "it's not their MO is it" he says "you and your mate did this on your own didn't you."

"Look lad" he pulls a piece of paper from the folder. I can see it has a lot of writing on it. "If you own up to these jobs we'll go easy on you. That's how it works see. You help us and we help you. It'll mean a lighter sentence when you get to Court and we get to clear our books of all these unsolved crimes." He waves the list in the air. I keep my mouth shut and my eyes firmly fixed on the empty cup in front of me. Oh how I could do with another cuppa.

When he realizes I'm not going to say anything he gets up and heads towards the door. "I'll have to let my colleague back in to *question* you further" he says.

We both know what he means by the word question and it ain't nothing to do with words. This is my first taste of police brutality.

I'd heard about cops beating people up to get confessions but never really believed it. In fact, until a few months ago I wanted to be a copper myself but wasn't tall enough, so I went for the toolsetter's job instead.

Despite further beatings I don't say anything but they charge me anyway and my fingerprints are taken.

A couple of days later I appear at the local Magistrates Court. There is a tunnel which runs underground from the Police Station to the Court. This is the first time I've seen Steve since we were arrested. "You ain't said nothing have you?" I ask as we climb the steep steps to the dock.

"No" he replies wearily.

We are refused bail because the Police are 'continuing their enquiries'.

It's a relief when, after two days, I'm finally taken from the cell for further questioning. I've only been out for a wash each morning and to use the toilet. I feel like climbing the walls!

The same two cops are waiting for me in the interview room but the atmosphere is different this time. They look smug. "Got you bang to rights" says the one who had beaten me up the other day.

It turns out that my fingerprints were found on the rooflight at Connor's although I don't know how because I'd taken to wearing gloves after the first couple of jobs with Bishop and Taylor. Steve's prints were all over the stolen stuff and the gear had obviously been found at my house.

There isn't much option but to plead guilty and on the following day at the Magistrates Court we are bailed to appear at Stafford Quarter Sessions for sentence. My Uncle Harry, a local and respected businessman, supports my application for bail, saying I can stay with him.

It's great living with my Uncle Harry. He keeps the Globe Hotel which is next to the Police Station and opposite the Theatre Royal in Bilston Town .There are always interesting people, like actors, staying here. Harry also lets me have use of the function room so I go out and buy a record player and some records. Very soon I'm undercutting the local dance hall and charging mates one shilling entrance fee. It's a nice little earner.

Being a little earner isn't good enough though and I continue my life of crime. My brief has told me to expect a custodial sentence. I'm going down anyway so it can't get any worse. Steve doesn't want to be involved and I don't see him again until the Quarter Sessions.

Stafford Court is a huge imposing place. From the dock it seems like the Judge is miles away but his voice booms and reverberates around the wood panelled walls as he sentences me and Steve to three years Borstal training.

I am transported in a Black Mariah, together with Steve, to Winson Green Prison in Birmingham for assessment and allocation, where we are classed as Young Prisoners, YP's for short.

Once at the prison we're escorted to 'reception' and told to strip. There are about ten of us, all shapes and sizes. Clothes and personal possessions get boxed up, details written down and I'm asked to sign a form. We are taken into separate cubicles for a bath in three inches of tepid water. Still naked, we line up and step forward, one by one, to see the doctor.

It's comical watching the others but not so funny when my turn comes. With the aid of a small torch he carries out his inspection. Hair, mouth, ears, armpits and last but not least he asks me to cough before checking my dick and balls. Don't know exactly what he's looking for but whatever it is I ain't got none. Back into line, we are ushered through to collect our prison clothing and a bedroll which consists of two sheets, a pillowcase and one blanket.

Many doors are unlocked and locked behind us on route to the separate YP wing. Everything looks grey. There's a lot of banging and shouting which seems to echo in this lofty building. Thankfully, YP's have single cells.

"In you go lad" says the sour faced screw nodding towards the door. Along the left hand wall stands a steel framed bed with lumpy palliasse mattress and stained pillow. I chuck my bedroll onto it. Opposite there's a small wooden table with a chair drawn up underneath. In the far corner is a sort of triangular shaped table, on top of which sits a jug and bowl, and beneath that is a shelf for soap and stuff.

CLANG. The solid steel door slams shut and my stomach sinks as the key turns. Grim reality hits home. Adjacent to the corner table a small mirror hangs precariously at an angle and I move to straighten it. There's a book on the table and I pick it up. It's a bible.

The cell, which measures about 10ft by 8ft, smells of stale urine and body odour. There is a small high window with bars on the outside. Reaching up I try to push the slider but it only budges about an inch.

It's terrible. I am locked in this stinky cell for twenty three long hours a day. The other very short hour is spent in the exercise yard. We are allowed three books a week and I've read 'em all in two days. I resort to counting the bricks for something to do and after that, to relieve the boredom, I take to reading the bible.

Meals are collected from the centre and taken back to our cells. There is a pot for pissing in and anything else you need to do. Slop out is twice a day, bathing is once a week. I am allowed one visit a month but no-one comes to see me.

It's a dismal place and the only respite is a Church service on Sundays. Although I'm not particularly religious I look forward to this.

Young prisoners have to sit behind the ordinary cons and on the second Sunday I'm on the front row of YP's. We are all saying the Lords Prayer and I can hear cons chanting "give us this day our daily cob, lead us not into temptation and deliver us from the Police Station." It makes me laugh out loud.

Next thing I know a screw grabs me by the scruff of the neck and hauls me back to my cell. He is joined by another screw on the way and once inside they punch hell out of me. I'm not allowed to attend any further Church services.

Two weeks later, after one month in Winson Green, I find myself standing in the Governors office. He tells me that tomorrow I am going to a closed Borstal in Rochester, Kent where I will serve out my sentence. A glimmer of a smile plays about my lips because I am *ooohhh* so glad to be getting out of here.

Steve is sent to Portland Borstal and I don't see him again for three years. The next time we meet we are both grown men with different experiences to share.

The drive down to Rochester is long and it's hot inside the Black Mariah. I have my suit on now, which is creased from being kept in the box for a month at Winson Green but it's nice to feel normal for a bit, even though I am in handcuffs.

There's a young copper with me and he drones on about his latest escapades with various girls. Not what I want to hear when I'm going to be locked up for the next three years.

I hear the creaking of heavy gates as we pull up at what must be the entrance. It seems ages before we stop again. The rear doors are finally opened and I clamber out. Ah, at last, a breath of fresh air. A tiny shaft of sunlight hits my face. Grey stone walls surround me. Bleak and foreboding. So…this is Rochester.

Chapter 2
GETTING FED AND GETTING FIT

"Here you go then" says the young copper who had sat with me in the Black Mariah. He undoes my cuffs and hooks them onto his belt. "I'm back up to Brum and on the town tonight with the girlfriend" he winks at the screw who is signing the handover document and then walks off whistling.

The reception room is similar to the one in Winson Green prison and the procedure is virtually the same. I am told to strip and place my clothing into a box. This time I take greater care when folding my suit. It's going to be in there for a long time!

"You've been allocated to Hawk House" the screw tells me when I return from the bath and visit to the Doc. "You will wear this at all times" he says giving me a bright red badge and pushing the Borstal uniform and bedroll across the counter. The uniform consists of navy blue tunic style jacket which is belted at the waist, trousers to match, blue striped shirt, a tie and shiny black boots. I am also given some shorts and a pair of plimsolls.

Another screw takes me outside into a large central courtyard which is surrounded by two and three storey buildings. "Which one is Hawk House?" I ask, curious as to where I'm going.

"You will address *all* Officers as *Sir*" he barks, keeping his eyes fixed straight ahead.

I don't speak again and just follow him to the next building where we go through a locked door into what will be my home for the next two years and eight months.

All the cells appear to be single ones, which is a relief to me. I was worried about ending up with a cellmate who didn't like girls! I had heard some horror stories whilst at Winson Green about bullies preying on the weaker cons to scrub out their cells, run errands and provide sexual 'housewifely' services. The weaker one is then called an 'Old Joe'.

Cells line each side of a central area which has benches and tables set up down the middle. At the bottom end I can see a billiard table and dart board. There is also a table tennis table. Looking up I can see there are a further two landings.

The screw stops and nods his head towards an open door. In fact I've noticed that none of the cell doors are locked.

"Get yourself settled Groom" he says, and then glancing at his watch, "tea will be up in 15 minutes." He doesn't lock the door and I feel better already.

The cell is about the same size as the one in Winson Green but at least it smells clean in here. The layout is much the same with a metal framed bed, table 'n chair and small corner unit housing the big tin jug and bowl. I notice some wooden pegs and, after depositing the bedroll, hang up my jacket. A pisspot juts out from underneath the bed and a black bound bible lies neatly placed on the table. I relax onto the bed and lay staring at the barred window. Out of the corner of my eye I see the black bound book. If I have to read a bible many more times I'll be a fuckin' vicar!

Five minutes later there is a sudden burst of noise, heavy footsteps and loud chatter. I poke my head out and see lots of Borstal boys charging through the main door. Some are wearing red badges like me, others have blue or green and the odd one or two have white.

"Whatcha" says the small guy entering the cell next to mine. "I'm Arthur but you can call me Titchy, everyone else does." It's obvious he's a scouser by his accent. Titchy stands about 5'6" short with a cheeky smile and he has a certain spring in his step. I like him immediately.

"I've just got here, I'm Watt Groom."

"I'm going for a quick brush up" he says, exiting his cell almost as quickly as he had entered it, this time carrying a rolled up towel under his arm. I tag along with Titchy to the recess, located at the end of the row of cells, where there is a line of sinks which are already being used. He plonks his towel down and introduces me to a few of his mates. Behind us I can see there are toilet cubicles and also a large communal shower area. It's great to take a leak in a proper toilet for a change.

"Sit with us if you want" says Titchy as we stand in the queue for food at the end of the central hall. He nods towards a table which is already occupied by three others. We take our steel trays, now filled with some sort of goulash, and sit down.

"This is Watt" Titchy nods at me as he greets the others. "PJ, Lofty and Del" he says pointing at each one in turn. They look up briefly and carry on eating. Actually the food smells good and I'm really hungry. There's not much chatter until everything has been cleared off the tray. I notice that Titchy, PJ and Lofty have the red badges like me but Del is wearing a blue one.

"What you in for then" asks the one called PJ. He is a stocky bloke from London, a bit older than me, with blonde hair, steely blue eyes and a fair complexion. His biceps are literally bulging out of his shirt.

"Shop breaking" I reply. "What about you?"

"I was set up, I never did nothing." The others start to laugh.

We take our dirty trays back up to the servery and Lofty suggests a game of cards. "It's association 'til nine" he tells me. Lofty, as his nickname suggests, is very tall and gangly. He is quite young looking with thin mousey hair and lots of tattoos, on his hands, up his arms and on his neck.

During the card game we all get chatting and I find out about the badges. Newcomers, like me, have the red ones, called Probs. Keeping out of trouble means moving onto the Blue a lot faster. Leaders get a white one and those nearing discharge wear a green 'dizzi' badge. I also discover there are four wings, called Houses and the other three are Nelson, Rodney and Blake.

Regular sporting activities take place and competition between the Houses is fierce. Once a month there is a film and on special occasions the cons are allowed to put on a show. I am glad to be told the library has no restrictions on the number of books borrowers can take out and it gets even better, there is a gym. I have never been in a gym before and PJ says he will show me the ropes.

"The Governor will see you tomorrow" says Del "he'll ask you what work you want to do. You don't always get what you want mind, it depends on where they need people." Del is probably about 20 with dark eyes and a mop of curly black hair. He only has a few months left to serve and is looking forward to his home leave which is due soon.

"What do you think is best?" I ask him. After all he's obviously been here the longest, 'cos he's wearing the blue badge.

"Well, you seem to like your food and you ain't got much fuckin' meat on your bones so if I were you I'd go for the kitchens." He smiles at my reaction of licking my lips.

"I went for the bricklaying but it's crap" says Titchy "outside in all weathers, freezing your bollocks off most of the time."

Association is soon over and we go back to our cells which are locked at nine o'clock. Lights go out at ten. After buffing up my boots, as Del had warned me to, I think it isn't so bad and sleep soundly for the first time in ages.

I am startled by a loud bell and then someone shouting "Come on you lazy bastards" as the clanking of key meeting cell door grows nearer. Must be very early 'cos it's still dark outside.

Upon hearing the order to "slop out" I leap out of bed and head for the door with my pisspot. We line up outside the cells, in our underpants, and once given the word, progress towards the recess where the pots are emptied. Back to the cells where towel, soap and shaving gear is collected before returning to the recess for wash and brush up.

"It's parade next" says Titchy, "so just shorts and plimsolls, and don't forget what I told you last night about the bed."

I struggle to remember exactly what he'd told me but strip the bed and fold everything as neatly as I can. Sheet blanket sheet, like a sandwich, I think he said. I place the pillow on top and put it all in a pile at one end.

We line up again outside our cells. All the cons are silent and standing to attention as the screws move along banging doors and shouting, "Stand up straight, eyes front, what do you call this?"

My own inspection goes without comment so I must have got it right.

"On the double" bellows a screw and we start trotting on the spot and then, at some command I can't quite catch, everyone turns and we march in an orderly fashion out of Hawk House to the central courtyard.

I can see guys pouring out of the other Houses and there is a Drill Instructor shouting commands. I follow the others as best I can. We march back and forth, up and down and round again.

After about twenty minutes I am just getting the hang of it when another Instructor takes over and we start doing PT exercises and when I say PT exercises, I fuckin' mean PT exercises. Finally the instructor yells "fall out."

My legs ache from all the squatting and I'm struggling for breath. Then it's back to Hawk House for breakfast. I'm not sure about all this physical stuff but the food here is great.

Immediately after breakfast I am told by one of the screws to wait in my cell. A while later I am escorted out and across the courtyard to the Governors office.

Marching…everywhere we go we're marching.

The Governor does not look up when I am marched into his office.

"Now then Groom" he says, still not raising his head from the document in front of him, "you are sentenced to three years training. My Officers will conduct your training and I expect you to co-operate."

"Yes Sir."

"There are several training courses here and you will have the opportunity to obtain a qualification. Did you have a job before you came here?"

"No Sir." He appears to be ticking things off a list. I think this might be the opportunity to mention my preference, "but I would quite like to work in the kitchens."

Eyebrows raised he glances at me.

"Sir," I add quickly.

"There is an opening in the bakery where you can train for City and Guilds in Baking and Confectionary."

He makes a mark on the paper. I don't think I'm expected to reply.

"You are allowed one letter a week and one visit a month" he pauses for a moment, "stay out of trouble Groom and make good use of this opportunity."

"Yes *Sir*" I say with emphasis on the *Sir*. That's the way they seem to like it.

"Take him away" he nods to the screw standing behind me.

I am marched directly to the bakery and Officer Brannigan, the silver haired screw in charge, gives me a white coverall. "These are called your 'whites'" he tells me. The smell is delicious and I smile, breathing it in deeply. Did I make the right choice or what?

The bakery supplies all the bread, cobs, pastries and cakes for Officers and cons alike. The first thing I learn is how to scrub the wooden moulding tables.

The water is very hot and the scrubbing brush very hard but when I've finished the wood is almost white. Officer Brannigan seems pleased. He's the best screw I've come across and takes a liking to me.

That evening, after tea, PJ takes me over to the gym. He has been here about two months and tells me that he used to work out at home. Looking at his biceps I believe him.

"You gotta get fit in here else you get taken for a fuckin' cunt" he says as he gets ready to press some enormous weights. "See him over there," he nods in the direction of a huge guy who is standing by the wall bars. "Hunkus, you gotta watch out for him. He's on the next landing up, two along from Del."

Hunkus must notice us staring at him and walks over. At 6'3" he towers above me.

"You fuckin' looking at something?" he shoves his face about an inch from mine.

Although my legs feel like jelly, I don't move and just stare back at him.

PJ steps forward. "I was just explaining stuff. He's never been in a gym before."

Another heavily built guy makes his way across thinking something might be going off. I know he's from Hawk House 'cos I've seen him at mealtimes. "What's to do lads?" he asks in a thick Welsh accent.

"Nothing Taffy" says PJ "this is the new chap, name of Watt, came in yesterday."

Loosing interest Taffy moves away but Hunkus takes a long time looking me up and down before swaggering back to the wall bars.

"Taffy's the daddy of Hawk" PJ tells me, "but Hunkus wants it. Trouble is Taffy is an ace at Judo and Hunkus is a bit wary."

"So there'll be a fight then?"

"Yeh, but that's the least of your worries considering the way Hunkus was eyeing you up." PJ carries on pressing his weights. I start to worry.

Later that night while getting ready for bed I glance down at my thin frame. I know I've got the heart of a lion, now all I need is the body to match. I go to sleep with PJ's words ringing in my ears, 'you gotta get fit in here else you get taken for a fuckin' cunt.' I resolve to get fit!

I settle into the Borstal routine quite quickly. Del shows me the 'canteen' which is a cell converted into a sort of shop. Earnings are marked down in a book and we can 'buy' such luxuries as toothpaste, sweets, chocolate and tobacco.

I have no earnings yet but scan the shelves until I spot the liquorice, a favourite of mine, and lick my lips in anticipation. A few sweets are like a lifeline because it's something to look forward to. Come the end of the week I'll be in here like a shot.

I go to the gym during most association periods. There is a PT instructor and he shows me how to use the equipment. I enjoy the vaulting horse and learning how to do somersaults and suchlike. With PJ's encouragement I begin to make some progress on pressing weights.

Working in the bakery is great, mainly because there are regular breaks for tea, with as much sugar as you want. Officer Brannigan says I am the best moulder he's had in a long time. I am quietly chuffed to be learning all about the different dough mixes and working towards a City and Guilds qualification.

I write home and can imagine Mom proudly telling the neighbours how her son is learning to be a Baker. She writes back once or twice but then I'm not really expecting replies every week. I send the first of many Visiting Orders (VO for short) but it's a long way from Bilston to Rochester and I resign myself to the fact that they won't come very often, not least because they can't afford to.

I don't forget how Hunkus had looked at me in the gym but a couple of weeks have gone by since then and I put it to the back of my mind. I've spotted him looking at me on the odd occasion during mealtimes or at the gym, but our paths don't really cross that much.

Then, without warning it happens.

I want to borrow a book off Del. He had been telling me over breakfast about a great Western he'd just finished. It sounded like a good read and so, on the way back from gym tonight, I decide to pop and get it. Del doesn't seem to be around the billiard table, which is his favourite haunt, so I head up to his cell.

Lost in thought and whistling away I climb the steel staircase to the next landing. Del's is the fourth one along and I am almost there when the huge frame of Hunkus suddenly appears and blocks my way.

"I need your fuckin' arse in here" he growls, nodding towards the door of his cell.

I freeze.

"What you waiting for you little cunt" he makes a move to grab me.

"Fuck off" sort of comes out of my mouth.

"I said, get your fuckin' arse in here, I hear you're good at scrubbing" he laughs and lunges at me "you can scrub my cell out and then we'll see what else you're fucking' good at." He makes a thrusting motion with his hips leaving no doubt as to what is on his mind.

I might as well have a go 'cos I just know he's gonna give me a pasting so I land a punch to his jaw and start to pummel him in the ribs. Hunkus gives me a body punch and smashes me in the face. I'm no match for him and go down.

I'm desperate not to become his, or anyone else's Old Joe, so despite the searing pains in my jaw and ribs, I jump back up and start punching and kicking him. He lifts me off my feet and throws me against the wall.

"You little fucker" he growls, landing another punch to my stomach. I'm doubled up again and he kicks me into his cell.

The commotion brings other cons and screws to the landing. Cons like to see a fight so the Officers have difficulty getting through. Meanwhile I am being used as a punchbag and there is blood everywhere.

"Next time you cunt, just get your fuckin' arse in here when I say so" hisses Hunkus as the screws finally charge into the cell.

Only two words stick in my head, 'next time'.

Hunkus, being an old hand, tells the screws I have a grudge against him and as I am on *his* landing and in *his* cell I must have started it.

If I wasn't in so much pain I could almost laugh. My head is screaming 'look at the size of me and the size of him' but my mouth stays shut. Two screws haul me off to the 'Block'. Cons had told me about it but nothing could have prepared me for the hard regime I was about to experience.

The Block is the smallest of the buildings surrounding the courtyard and I wonder what awaits me as two screws half drag me there. Cons say that once you've been down the Block you never want to go again.

My jaw hurts and my ribs hurt even more. A trickle of blood

runs from my nose but I can't wipe it away because both my arms are being held.

"Groom, Walter, Hawk House" barks the screw as he hands me over to the Officer who is waiting at the entrance.

"Attention" he roars, "on the double, quick march" his face only inches from mine.

Can't he see I'm in pain and bleeding? Well, obviously not. I try to comply with the command. If I look half as bad as I feel, then its fuckin' bad.

Another screw joins us as I am marched past the cells to the bath-house. The layout is similar to Hawk House only it's much smaller and, although a couple of tables are set out in the central area, there's no sign of any billiards or table tennis.

"You've got five minutes" yells the one screw as he shoves a soap and towel into my hand. After a very quick, tepid, bloody bath, I take a leak and am marched to a cell. I'm told to go inside and bring out the chair. What on earth's coming next?

"Leave your tie and boots on the chair 'til morning Groom."

The familiar sandwich lies folded on the mattress and the black bound book is waiting for me on the table. I make the bed and crawl in feeling very sorry for myself but with an even stronger resolve.

Next morning it's up before the lark as usual. I can see there are only four of us in the Block as we stand outside our cells waiting for inspection. None of the other three are from Hawk but I recognise the 'daddy' of Rodney, an Irish guy by the name of Gallagher. He's not very tall but has a reputation of being like lightening with his head. They say he's a bit of a nutter (ha ha).

Inspection doesn't take long. There's almost as many screws as cons down here but these screws are definitely different. I don't know in what way yet but they look tough and mean and are built like the proverbial brick shithouse.

After a bollocking for not buffing up my boots, even though they had been locked outside my cell where I couldn't get at them, the four of us are marched outside, at the double, for PT.

The Block has its own walled yard which is completely separate. We are told to continue doubling on the spot whilst the one screw shouts as loud as he possibly can. "You are here for punishment and fuckin' punishment you will get." If anyone was handing out awards for yelling then these screws would definitely win.

Two screws take it in turn to give us demonstrations and shout instructions as to what is required and which particular muscle or part of the body is being exercised.

At the end of the first exercise my legs have gone numb and my back feels like it is breaking. At the end of the second my chest throbs and my head thinks my arms belong to someone else. At the end of the third exercise breathing is an effort and at the end of the fourth, I think I'm dead. So this is what they call punishment PT.

If anyone slows down they get a kick in the legs or a prod in the ribs. Same happens if we can't respond immediately to the question of which muscle or part of the body is being worked.

It's hard to memorise all this stuff, rectus abdominis, pectorals, deltoids, intercostals, biceps, triceps, hip flexor, latissimus dorsi. It becomes apparent from what is said that these screws are ex-Marines. I just knew there was something different about them.

We sort of half stagger and half march back to the Block for breakfast. I am more than pleased to see that rations are the same and wolf down the porridge. It's not bread and water then, thank God for that.

"Is the PT like this every day?" I ask Gallagher as we stand at the urinal.

"If you think this morning's been bad, wait 'til later."

After a short break in our cells, we line up again and 'on the double' march back outside, this time to the woodyard at the rear of the Block. All I can see is a pile of thick tree trunks. The screws set up jacksaws and, with one con on each end, we begin to cut the logs.

"One, two three, four. One, two, three, four" the screw shouts to set the rhythm. It's very physical work and after the earlier PT session it only takes thirty minutes or so for us to feel knackered and slow down but the screws are having none of that.

When the command "Rest" finally comes, I am relieved but my relief is shortlived as we line up for more PT.

Gallagher looks over and laughs. I can't believe it. Call this rest! Every half hour we go from jacksaw to PT and back again for two hours.

During dinner the Governor carries out his daily visit. He asks if we have any complaints and surprise, surprise, nobody says anything.

A brief relax in the cell passes far too quickly. I think I'll never make it for six weeks here. What about my work in the bakery, will I be allowed back after this? And then there's Hunkus. I feel my face setting harder and throw myself into the jacksaw with new vigor.

"That's the way, keep it up" shouts one of the screws, "one, two, three, four."

And that's how I get through the next six weeks.

One by one the four of us leave the Block. The six weeks had seemed like forever but I have grown fitter and stronger.

There has been plenty of time to think in the evenings because after tea we are locked up. No association period, no leisure activities and no library books. All we do is eat, sleep, work and PT. In between reading the bible and counting bricks I have resolved to get the bastard, even if it kills me, I'll get him.

I am marched from the Block to Hawk House in time for breakfast exactly six weeks after being hauled out of there. PJ looks up and nudges Del as I come through the main door.

I notice Del's green 'dizzi' badge as he stands and motions me over to their table. Lofty and Titchy, who are walking back with their breakfast trays, give me a wave. I'm not interested in them 'cos I've only got one thing on my mind.

I spot him sitting at his usual table right down the bottom end. My eyes never leave his head as I make my way through the tables. I calculate that I'll make it from half way down and casually walk that far. Then I break into a run.

He isn't expecting it, I can tell by the look on his face as his mouth drops open. I don't speak or give him time to speak. I just take a flying leap at him from the end of the table. He is knocked back but throws me off sideways and stands up.

I hear the cons shouting "fight, fight" as they close in around us and the shrill whistles of the screws as they try to get through. I jump up and nut him then follow with a couple of good punches to the ribs. He grabs my shirt and holds me there. The last thing I see is the giant fist of Hunkus coming my way.

The screw seems surprised at my arrival down the Block. "Not you again Groom, you've only just fuckin' left."

I grimace. "Yes Sir."

My jaw is really sore and I guess I'll have a few bruises tomorrow but it was worth it just to see the look on that bastards face.

This time there is only me and another guy down the Block for the first week. Now we have one ex-Marine each so to speak. The physical training is intense but I'm hungry for it and throw myself into the hard regime. I'm on a mission.

Press-ups using one hand and then thumb and forefinger, jump squats, chest exercises, sit ups, the list is endless and all the time I feel myself becoming fitter. I don't get so breathless or ache so much afterwards and my muscles are beginning to show as they become toned.

The six weeks seem to fly past and soon I am back at Hawk House. This time they keep me over the Block until after breakfast so I go straight to the bakery for work. Officer Brannigan is not pleased, I can tell by the way he doesn't look up as he hands me my 'whites'.

"Now then lad" he says "you've been away for twelve whole weeks. I thought you wanted to learn something useful so that you can get a job when you leave here. If you carry on like that..." his voice trails off and he shakes his head as I follow him through to the bakehouse. I like him and feel I've let him down but inside there is a torrent of rage that needs release.

I go through the motions for the rest of the day and although Hunkus has looked my way as if to say 'come and try again if you want' during dinner and again at tea, I decide to wait until association.

"You're like a cat on a hot tin roof" says Del "come and have a game billiards with me."

"Nope, I'm off to the gym."

Del stares at me in disbelief. "I should think you've had enough PT to last a lifetime over the Block, why do you want to go to the gym tonight?"

I just look at him and he knows.

"I'd come over with you Watt, but it's my home leave this weekend and I can't do anything to put the kaibosh on that."

"Anyone for the gym?" shouts one of the screws.

There are about fifteen of us and I take my place in line, towards the end, about six behind Hunkus. Cons appear to be whispering to each other on the march over and a few cast furtive glances towards Hunkus and me. I'm clenching my fists, My heart starts to race. PJ is directly behind me and must sense something because he leans forward and whispers "watch your back."

We get to the gym and, along with cons from other Houses disperse to different equipments. Hunkus and a new guy I don't know head towards the weights. I stand on the mat near the vaulting horse and watch them.

Other cons are beginning to get wind that something is going off but Hunkus and his mate seem oblivious as they start pressing weights. Taffy goes over to Hunkus gesturing him to get off the weights. He isn't happy and for a moment I think 'the big one' is about to kick off, but Taffy is still the 'daddy'.

Hunkus makes his way to the wall bars. If I can pin him against them I've got more chance so in the blink of an eye I'm right there. He turns. His head cracks against the bars as I jump up and put the nut on him.

"What the fuck…" he growls as I land a punch to the body and one to the jaw in quick succession. His forehead starts to bleed where I've broken the skin. Cons gather round to prevent the screws getting through.

Hunkus tries to grab me but I'm much lighter on my feet now and dodge the giant hand easily. I punch him in the stomach. A sharp pain in the middle of my back takes my breath. I whirl around to see the new guy who had been with Hunkus. He lands one on my jaw as the big man kicks at my legs. I'm down and the two of them are raining blows to my head and kicking fuck out of me.

I look up to see PJ and Taffy pulling the new guy off. This is between me and Hunkus. I can feel the warm blood streaming down my face as somehow I roll to the side and stand up.

Hunkus runs at me, head down, smashing into my ribs. We both go reeling onto one of the mats. Cons follow the fight, forming a tight circle and egging us on.

My only advantage is being fast, so when Hunkus is half stood up, I land a punch to his head. My fists seem to have a lot more force than the last time we fought and his head goes back. Blood splatters everywhere. He rallies with a huge body punch. I double up and go down.

Whistles ring in my ears as screws arrive in droves to break up the fight.

"Fucking hell Groom," says the Officer down the Block, "what is it with you?" He eyes me up and down, "you waging a war out there?"

I can feel crusts of dried blood on my face. My knuckles are red and sore. Every inch of my body aches. After a bath, albeit in three inches of tepid water, I crawl into bed and a warm glow of satisfaction creeps over me. I did a bit better this time. Next time I'll nail the bastard.

Another six weeks of gruelling jacksaw and punishment PT follow but my body is building up now. I'm getting fed and I'm getting fit. There is only one focus to my life, to beat Hunkus.

I throw everything I've got into the PT and don't groan like the others when we have to 'double up' whilst sawing. I push myself to the limits. The other cons think I'm mad.

The screws like it though and towards the end of the six weeks, one of them, Officer Atkins, becomes curious as to what is going on. When I tell him there's a big bully who thinks he can get the better of me he shows me some extra exercises and I do them in my cell at night after lock up.

I've been down the Block for a total of eighteen weeks and it's now mid December. In a couple of days it will be my 17th birthday. I'm hoping for a letter or something from home. Do I really want to spend Christmas in the Block? It's a question I ask myself on the march back to Hawk.

It's breakfast time and when the lads wave me over, I decide to join them. Hunkus, at his usual end table, raises his head and gives me the stare but I just stare back and sit down.

The screws are keeping a close eye, waiting for something to kick off. I watch them watching me.

Titchy, PJ and Lofty fill me in on what's been happening. Del has been discharged, lucky beggar. My mates can see the difference in me and I can tell PJ is impressed as he feels my bulging biceps.

"There's a show tonight" says Lofty. "While you've been down the Block some of us have been rehearsing. It's dead funny, well you'll see for yourself, everybody's coming, we're setting the chairs out later, before tea."

"Are you in it as well?" I ask PJ

His face contorts. "Are you kidding mate?"

We make our way towards the main door and form a line, then hi-ho, it's off to work we go.

"Birthday soon lad" says Officer Brannigan as he hands me my 'whites'.

"Yes Sir, I'll be seventeen on the 17th."

Officer Brannigan knows everybody's birthday. He must make it his business to find out. On their birthdays cons working in the bakehouse have an easy day and there is always a cake to share out during the last tea break. He certainly has a soft spot, old Brannigan.

Birthdays had never been celebrated much at home. It was just another day as far as my Dad was concerned and Mom was always too busy and too worried trying to make ends meet. But at Christmas we did get an orange and a couple of nuts at the bottom of a sock.

It's the 14th today and as I leave the bakehouse my thoughts turn from home to Hunkus. He's never far from my mind. I've got to take the fight to him and show I'm not scared. I need to get the job done 'cos if I don't every bully in the place will be after my arse. I ain't gonna be anybody's Old Joe.

I'm fit and fast so this time I might get the better of him. At the end of the show tonight is as good a time as any, everybody will be a bit relaxed. The thought of it sends the adrenalin rushing through my body.

Lofty was right, the show is very funny. It consists of cons doing different comedy sketches, some dressed up as tarts and vicars, that type of thing. The laughter is prompted mainly by scenery falling over and cons forgetting their lines. There is some singing and dancing, if you can call it that, with one of the cons playing the piano. He ain't half bad either.

The show lasts for about an hour after which everybody has to pick up their chair, form an orderly procession and stack them on the stage. As I move forward in the queue I look round to find Hunkus. He is the last but one in line. Perfect.

The screws are standing by the door at the other end, laughing and discussing the show. I stack my chair and move across the stage to where the film projection stuff is kept. I hang around pretending to tie my bootlaces until I see him coming.

As he gets closer I stand up and step forward. The guy behind him scurries off stage. Out of the corner of my eye I can see the screws are still engrossed in their conversation.

"What the fuck…" Hunkus looks shocked, "ain't you had enough?" He throws a punch but it misses as I duck and retaliate with a good 'un to his side and one to the jaw.

He lunges forward to grab hold of me but I dodge to the left, land another punch to his ribs and skip round behind. As he turns I smash him again in the face and see him wince. Blood starts dripping from his nose. He delivers one that sends me reeling and I crash into the chairs.

Hunkus takes a running kick at my leg and punches me in the stomach. I'm trapped. There's nowhere to go. An almighty blow lands on my chin but I smash another to his head. Whistles echo. Pounding boots thunder across the wooden floor. Strong arms pull us apart.

"It's him, Sir, he started it, I saw everything" exclaims the guy who had been last in line, his stubby finger pointing at me. "He was waiting at the side of the stage Sir."

Hunkus smirks.

I'll wipe that fuckin' smirk off his face if it's the last thing I ever do. The screws drag me down the Block for what will be my fourth time in succession.

Chapter 3

GETTING EVEN

"I don't believe it" exclaims the screw "at this rate you'll never get the fuckin' blue."

"Yes Sir." My shoulders slump as I limp into the Block, only too well aware that my progression through the badges is at a standstill.

Holding onto both sides of the bath and trying to keep my left leg straight, I ease myself gently into the water. There's a big red swelling around my knee, bruising is already apparent along the calf and just breathing makes my ribs hurt.

I trace a line with my fingertips around the puffiness of my right eye. Leaning forwards I cup some water in my hands and splash it over my head. I've just got to beat the bastard next time.

A stranger's face greets me in the mirror next morning and my left leg feels like someone has strapped a ton of lead to it. A searing pain shoots through my knee every time I bend it. Marching outside takes supreme effort and even before we start the PT I know it's going to hurt bad.

When the order comes for squats I take a deep breath, set my face and grit my teeth through the pain barrier as I go down. Just focusing on one at a time gets me through and eventually the PT session comes to an end.

I can see Officer Atkins studying me during breakfast. He is the screw who had shown me some extra exercises towards the end of my last spell. He nods at me as if with some respect. After breakfast we go to our cells for half an hour before the work party and I'm lying down when he walks in. Surprised, I struggle off the bed and stand to attention.

"I was a champion boxer in the Marines. You done any boxing Groom?"

"No Sir."

"I can show you a few moves if you like" he offers

"I'd appreciate that Sir."

Atkins nods. "See you after tea tonight then."

There are six of us down the Block this time, me, another new arrival 'Spider' from Nelson House, and four others who will be going out before Christmas.

'Spider' is a wiry kid with short spiky hair and a big spiderweb tattoo on his back.

"They call you Spider 'cos of the tattoo?" I ask him during dinner, which today is shepherds pie followed by steamed pudding with custard, my favourite.

"Och no, I only had that done a few months back, it's 'cos I can climb up places where others cannae get" he leans over "and I'm fast see."

I discover he originates from Scotland but joined a gang doing over big houses in London, which is where he was caught. He talks so fast it's hard to understand what he says sometimes. Turns out he's having the same trouble with my Black Country accent so we both laugh and agree to speak more slowly.

His real name is James but he prefers to be called Spider.

"What happened to you then?" Spider takes a closer look at my right eye, through which I can hardly see at the moment.

"It was this or Old Joe."

His eyebrows rise. "You're Watt from Hawk?"

I carry on eating and just nod.

"You're the one who keeps on coming down the Block, everybody's talking about it."

Steely determination gets me through this day. I'm in constant pain. What sheer relief to see my bed. I've no sooner flopped onto it than Officer Atkins walks in.

"You need to protect your face Groom. There are certain places to aim your punches at" he gives me a knowing look "and I'll teach you what I can."

I'm totally drained and not what you'd call light on my feet tonight but I appreciate what he's doing and try to take it all in.

"You can practice this in your cell" he shows me several body punches, hooks and upper cuts.

"I gotta get the bastard Sir." The thought of Hunkus makes me clench my fists, "I won't give up, even if it kills me."

"I know lad, I know" Atkins looks at me. "You done any weights?"

"Yes Sir, I've been to the gym here a few times."

"There are no weights in here Groom but you can try pressing the bed which will give you good upper body strength."

We both look at the bed.

"Go on then" he gestures towards it.

I scramble underneath the metal frame and grab both bottom rails, one in each hand. "It's just like pressing weights in the gym, breathe in first" Atkins tells me.

I do as he says and find myself lifting the bed, not very high and it's wobbling a lot as I set it back down with a clang.

"Don't forget the warm up and cool down. It's important. Organize your workouts so that each muscle group gets a rest period between exercises, remember what I've told you" Atkins turns and starts to walk out my cell "we don't want to see you back here again Groom" he grins and winks.

And so I start an extra regime of shadow boxing, press ups, push ups, squats and suchlike during lock up. Hardest of all at the beginning is pressing the metal bed frame which is heavy and cumbersome but after a week or so, no problem.

My days are filled with jacksaws and punishment PT. My nights are filled with exercising in the cell. I start to feel *really* good. My eye has returned to normal and the leg is not bothering me any more.

There is only me and Spider left down the Block for Christmas. The others have all gone back to their Houses. I get a card and letter from home on Christmas Eve. Mom writes that she will come to see me with Roy and Pearl in the summer, which gives me something to look forward to.

It's a relief to know there's no work on Christmas Day and the dinner is great. Following the Governors daily visit we are taken to watch a filmshow. Me and Spider have to sit separate from the other cons, right at the back, but it makes our day.

Back in the cell, I'm buffing up my boots when thoughts of home come creeping in. I picture little Barry scoffing his orange and nuts and Mom pouring the tea. I wonder if Rob's got a bird yet.

A while later I hear the familiar sound of the spyhole being flicked. Briefly looking up from my press-up I wonder if it's Officer Atkins on the other side of the door. It'll be lights out soon but that makes no difference. I carry on with my routine regardless.

I've been down the Block for a total of twenty four weeks and when I finally emerge from *this* six week period, I'm super-fit and ready to take on anyone.

I literally bounce into Hawk ready for breakfast and can see Lofty and PJ already tucking in. Titchy is still at the servery and I join him with my tray.

"Watcha Watt, I was thinking of renting out your cell" he jokes "you've been away so long."

I notice that Titchy is wearing a blue badge, one step nearer to getting out.

"When'd you get that?"

"Couple of weeks ago" he flashes me one of his cheeky grins "some of us try to be good, or is it we don't get caught."

On the way to the table I look for Hunkus. Our eyes meet. He is watching me. The screws are watching both of us. Nothing changes.

"Good to see you Watt, you're looking fit" remarks PJ, as Titchy and me plonk our trays down.

"Yeh, I'm ready for the bastard now" I see the way they're looking at me and quickly add "but this time I've got a better plan."

"Well, thank fuck for that" says PJ "things have been going off while you've been down the Block."

"It's Taffy" explains Titchy, "he's trying to stop the Old Joeing. Hunkus and his cronies don't like it."

Taffy, who is sitting two tables down, looks across at the mention of his name. He holds up his hand in greeting and I nod an acknowledgement. He doesn't know it yet but he is a vital part of my plan.

"You're fit to burst out of that shirt." Lofty feels one of my biceps and I tense the muscle so that he can feel the strength.

PJ leans forward just as the bell rings "What's the plan then?"

"Talk tonight" I grab my tray and scrape back the chair. For now all I want is the warm, sweet smell of the bakery and a nice cup of tea with plenty of sugar.

"You lucky beggar, working in the warm" Lofty turns as we stand in line with our dirty trays "spare a thought for me today, out on the friggin' garden party."

"It's enough to freeze the bollocks off a brass monkey out there" says Titchy "I'm building a fuckin' wall but I have to keep knocking it down and fuckin' starting again, fuckin' bricklaying, why didn't I go for the kitchens" he shakes his head and we all laugh.

Officer Brannigan gives me a disapproving look as he hands me my 'whites'.

"I'm glad to be back Sir." I'm trying to get into his good books. You would only ever speak when spoken to with any other Officer and never, ever speak first, but old Brannigan is different.

"Well, I'm glad to hear it Groom, does this mean that you'll be here for more than one day every six weeks?" his face breaks into a crinkly smile.

"I don't intend going back down the Block Sir" I say with some conviction because it's true.

The day flies by and Officer Brannigan is pleased when I ask to take a course book to my cell. Truth is I like it in the bakery and there is something about the thought of getting a qualification that feels good.

During evening association PJ, Lofty, Titchy and me gather at one of the tables and I explain my plan to get Hunkus. I feel fast and fit. After one or two arm wrestles PJ pronounces that my upper body strength is "fuckin' awesome."

"When?" asks Titchy.

"I'm going to leave it a week or so, let the dust settle, the screws are watching us both like hawks."

There is a murmur of agreement and Lofty produces a pack of cards. He shuffles and starts to deal them out.

"Can anyone join in?"

Without looking up I know it's Taffy. What a stroke of luck. He usually goes to the gym during association and I was going to speak to him tomorrow night. The news that he is trying to get rid of the Old Joeing means he'll probably be on side.

Although Taffy isn't the biggest built or hardest looking bloke he has the edge because of his judo skills. Word has it that he can just put one finger on you in a certain spot and its curtains. Everyone gives him a wide berth and he's still the 'daddy'.

"How you doing Lofty?" Taffy sits himself down. Lofty works with him on the outside party where they grow all the vegetables and stuff.

"I'm good." Lofty gathers up the cards he has just dealt and reshuffles them.

Titchy, Lofty and PJ look at me as if to say, 'go on then'. Well, there's no time like the present.

"I might need your help in a few days" I lean forward and hold Taffy's eyes.

Taffy shifts his weight on the uncomfortable chair. "How's that then?"

I tell him my plan and what I need him to do, which in truth isn't much, but it's necessary. Lofty deals the cards. Nobody speaks

Taffy leans back on his chair studying his hand of cards and studying me even harder. "You got some fuckin' balls, you know that?" he says, placing his cards, face down on the table. "I'm in" he grins "who's the other guy gonna be?"

PJ hunches forward on the table, "It's me."

I keep my head down for the next week or so. During association I go to the gym every alternate evening which is an important part of the plan. The screws need to believe my actions of either staying put or going to the gym is normal behaviour for me.

Every night, after lock up and lights out, I relentlessly continue with my fitness regime. For me it's a way of life now and I have come to enjoy the way it makes me feel.

The screws seem to be relaxing their hawk-like vigil and although I've spotted Hunkus watching me at times, I have ignored him.

It's 14th February today, Valentines Day, and a lot of the cons are joshing about the cards they've received from home. Titchy gets one from his girl with a lipstick kiss on it which he passes round at breakfast. "It'll be round my dick tonight" he laughs, grabbing it back off PJ.

"It's gonna be tonight," my tone breaks the laughter.

Instantly the mood changes and Lofty looks up from his porridge. "You want me to tell Taffy?"

I nod.

Titchy glances across the table, serious now, "make it fuckin' good."

There's a new guy in the cell on the other side of Titchy, name of 'Porky', whose life is being made a misery by Hunkus. Titchy has told me that he hears him crying most nights.

I feel my face harden. "Don't worry mate, by the time I've finished with the bastard, he'll wish he'd never been fuckin' born."

At tea Taffy gives me the nod and I know it's on. I begin to focus on the task ahead. For the first time since I've been here, the food on my tray seems unappetizing and I move it around, eating little. A full stomach is the last thing I need right now. I'm eager for teatime to be over.

Hunkus would usually go to the gym during association. That's where Taffy comes in. It's his job to get Hunkus to go to his cell instead and the nod from Taffy tells me that this part of the plan is in action. Taffy, being the 'daddy', is the only one who can make this happen.

Lofty and Titchy move towards the billiard table where they will create a distraction when the time comes.

PJ, Taffy and me sit at a table outside my cell going through the motions of playing cards. My eyes are everywhere, watching the screws, watching Hunkus.

The target gets up from his table and I lean forward, which is the cue for PJ and Taffy to fold the game.

Hunkus climbs the steel stairs to his cell. Porky trails behind. A feeling of hatred rises through my body. Porky, so named probably because he's a bit on the podgy side, walks as if he's going to the gallows. His head hangs down and his arms are limp at his sides. Poor bastard. I catch my breath and clench my fists.

PJ and Taffy stroll casually towards the stairs chatting. My eyes never leave Hunkus as I start to follow them. So this is it. The adrenalin rush is incredible as I reach the top. It's all very quiet up here and the screws don't have a clue.

Hunkus goes into his cell. Like lightening Taffy pulls Porky back, putting a finger to his lips and motioning him to scarper. The frightened rabbit doesn't need telling twice.

"Fuckin' hurry up" growls Hunkus from inside the cell "get your arse in here."

PJ darts past the open door and positions himself further along the landing. Taffy stands to block anyone from coming up the stairs and I walk into the cell. Now there's just me and him. I shut the door behind me.

Hunkus is sitting on the bed undoing his trousers. He's expecting Porky.

He looks up as I strike the first blow. I'm surprised at just how powerful it is. His head jerks back. He flails about. Like a flash I'm punching into his side and ribs before smashing him in the face. Blood splatters onto my shirt from an open cut under his right eye.

The big man looks dazed. He shakes his head and rallies, moving his huge frame off the bed. I dart behind, leap onto the mattress, and as he turns, launch a massive blow to the body followed by three fast jabs to the chin

Hunkus hits out but I'm too quick for him, ducking and dodging. Blood is pouring down his face now. I skip to the other side of the cell.

"You had enough yet? You want me for a fuckin' Old Joe do you?" I jump up and put the nut on him. He reels backwards. I follow with a body punch and upper cut. Hunkus goes down in a crumpled heap.

"Get up you bastard."

Hunkus puts one hand on top of the table and draws himself up. He throws a left. My arm blocks his and I bang him one in the gut to remember with a couple to the head for good measure. Timber cracks and splinters as he crashes into the wooden chair.

There is a fair bit of noise going on. I'm hopeful that mates who can be trusted are being as rowdy as they can in association tonight. All the time I'm listening for shrill whistles but I needn't have worried. We are not disturbed.

"You fuckin' picked the wrong one with me you bastard." I grab his shirt collar and punch him full in the face, once, twice…over and over. His head lurches from side to side. "I never, ever, give up, you hear me?"

Sprawled at my feet, bleary eyed and beaten, Hunkus raises a hand. It falls to rest awkwardly on the floor.

"Unless you want some more of this," crouching low I shove my fist into his face, "you don't so much as fuckin' speak to me again."

He shakes his head in submission and mutters "no more."

I look at this giant of a man lying slumped against the wall. He might have the bulk but he ain't got the power, the fitness, the speed or the sheer iron will. He's just a bully.

The cell is in total disarray. Walls are splattered with blood and the chair is broken. Several books and stuff that had been on the table is now strewn all over the floor. Buttons are missing from my ripped and bloodstained shirt. What must I look like?

Reaching the door I tap lightly twice, which is the signal that I'm done. Nothing happens for what seems like an age and I have visions of being carted off to the Block again. It's a relief when the knock finally comes. I open the door and walk out.

The three of us stand on the landing for a moment. Loud voices from the direction of the billiard table begin to quieten. Taffy grins and heads for the stairs.

PJ says he's glad to see I'm in one piece and ushers me into a nearby cell which has been commandeered by Taffy. In the corner there is a jug of water, small slither of soap and a comb.

"Be quick." PJ pulls a spare shirt from under his jacket, "thought you might be needing this."

He walks out and leans on the rail to keep watch and wait for me. I pull the battered shirt over my head and take a quick wash. As I comb my hair in the tiny mirror I can see that Hunkus never managed to land one on my face. I was too fast for him. The only telltale sign is my right hand which has started to swell and the knuckles are red raw.

"Shove that in your pocket" says PJ, who gives me the once over as I join him on the landing.

We make our way down the stairs and swagger towards Lofty and Titchy at the billiard table. Taffy gives me a thumbs-up before turning back to his game of darts.

I can hardly contain myself. I'm grinning like a Cheshire cat and feel like somersaulting across the room or vaulting all the tables. Cons who are 'in the know' give me the nod and there is some cheering and laughing. Puzzled screws frown at each other.

"Looking good mate" Lofty pulls back his cue to take a shot.

"Yeh great," still grinning I give him a flash of my right hand.

Lofty raises an eyebrow and breaks into a lop-sided smile. "Bugger it" he says missing his shot.

"By the way this is Pete" Titchy nods towards the guy standing alongside him, nervously puffing a cigarette, and who I only know as Porky.

With that the bell goes to mark end of association and we head for our cells. On the way a few cons pat me on the back and others get out of my way. I like it and do a sort of shadow box through my cell door, punching the air, "*yes.*"

I flop onto the bed and grab a liquorice. One sharp flick sends the treat soaring. I catch it in my mouth. The taste is sweeter than ever.

No training tonight. Might do a bit of reading. There's a western full of blood and thunder which has been sitting next to the bible for months. Glancing at my reddened hand, I feel a warm sense of satisfaction.

Getting even ain't easy but it sure feels good. Nobody messes with the Groom. At last I can go to sleep and not have Hunkus on my mind.

Without realizing, I had built a reputation. Problem is there's always someone who wants to take it and make it their own.

Chapter 4

THE BARON

"Punching the wall last night were we, Groom?" asks Officer Gregg as he walks past to carry out the cell inspection. There is no denying my right hand looks a mess. Skin is broken all along the knuckles and the back of my hand is still quite puffy.

"No Sir."

Officer Gregg is one of the nicer screws and there aren't many. In his forties, he tends to speak rather than shout, which is a novelty in itself.

Emerging from my cell he studies me for a moment. "Try and keep out of trouble Groom, eh."

"Yes Sir."

He shakes his head, pushes the horn-rimmed spectacles back up his nose and moves on.

Hunkus looks decidedly worse for wear this morning. During PT it's impossible not to notice the gaping cut, black eye, and bruises on his face and upper torso. In fact his nose appears to be broken. In any event, he doesn't so much as glance my way, which is fine by me.

Later, as I make my way towards the breakfast servery, there are a lot of winks and knowing looks from other cons. I'm waiting in the queue and spot Pete (aka Porky) about six in front, chatting with another guy. Pete calls me forward and the other six cons move out of the way.

"This is Bones" Pete nods his head towards the lanky guy standing next to him. "I gotta thank you for what you did last night."

"No need to thank me mate, I did it for myself, not you."

46

The kitchen orderly gives me a smile and extra porridge. This can't be bad. PJ and Titchy are already seated and I walk through the tables to join them. Lofty stops on the way to chat with a thick set guy they call 'the Baron'.

I'm already tucking in when he slides onto the chair opposite. "Everybody's talking 'bout you and Hunkus." Loves a bit of gossip does Lofty. He frowns at his tray and then at mine, "hey, how come you got all that porridge?"

"Well I ain't complainin', perhaps he fancies me."

This amuses everyone and PJ almost chokes. "Word has it that Hunkus was cleaning his cell well into the night."

"It was a right state, blood everywhere, mostly his," I pull a face.

Taffy plonks his tray down. "He won't be bothering *you* again anytime soon. Don't like bully boys and there's too many of them in here."

I lower my voice and lean forward as Taffy sits down. "What about the shirt I left in your mates cell?"

"No problem. Whitey works in the Laundry, took it with him this morning." He gives me a wink "very handy if you've got a bloodstained shirt or two!"

"No more tears from next door then?" I turn towards Titchy. His mouth is full so he just shakes his head.

"What's with the Baron?" enquires PJ

"He's looking for another carrier" Lofty looks round "anyone game?"

"Don't smoke," I pipe up.

There's only Taffy who smokes on this table and he doesn't bother with baroning himself, although he could if he wanted. Somehow I don't think he's gonna be anyone else's carrier.

"Nobody interested then?" Lofty asks again. We shake our heads.

There are three barons in Hawk but the main man is the guy Lofty has just been chatting to. It's an offence, so getting caught means extra time being added to your sentence.

Smokers don't do so well in here. A few days after payday they've puffed their way through the meager amount wages will allow them to buy and are on the cadge for smokes, burn, snout, bacca, or two's up. The 'canteen' stocks tobacco because proper cigarettes would be too expensive. Black Shag, considered to be the strongest, is favoured by most of the cons. It's rolled in paper to form a cigarette and dog-ends are undone and re-used.

The Barons lend out say half an ounce for three quarters back or a quarter ounce for three eighths back and so on. Then, on paydays, they collect and lend it out again. It's a vicious circle for the smokers. Anything over 2oz in a tin is confiscated by the screws so the Barons need carriers.

I glance across at the Baron. Don't smoke myself so if I saved my wages for a few weeks I could buy a 2oz tin. For 2oz I would get 3oz back in just one week. Seems pretty easy to me. Could trade the bacca for stuff I actually wanted myself, like proper toothpaste instead of that powder stuff, nice scented soap that actually gives a lather or tinned pears and sweet, creamy condensed milk.

"Any good at footie Watt?" asks Titchy, bringing me out of my thoughts, "Grogan is looking for recruits because two of the players for Hawk went down with leg injuries last week."

"You missed most of the fun when you was down the Block" Lofty adds.

"Anyone I know in the team?"

"Nah, Grogan said none of us was good enough." Lofty eyes my tray which is still half full of porridge. "We all tried 'cos practice is on a Saturday, anything's better than work."

"Might give it a go then."

Officer Grogan is one of the instructors at the gym. I'll speak to him tonight in association. I'm fit and fast so I might be good enough. I like it in the Bakery but if football practice can take me outside at the weekend I'll have some of that.

"What on earth is wrong with your hand Groom?" Officer Brannigan glances at the broken skin as I start to put on my 'whites'.

What can I say?

"Come with me." I follow him to the box where plasters and suchlike are kept. "You need to keep those knuckles covered when you're working."

"Yes Sir."

He looks at me hard, "I thought you were going to stay out of trouble lad."

"I am Sir."

"You know you could earn a good honest living out of this if you pass the examinations. Everybody needs bread. You'd never be out of work."

I can't let my mind run too far into the future. Getting out and getting a job seems like another world almost. Just getting an extra bit of sugar for my porridge is a feat in itself. In this place it's survival of the fittest.

It's pay day today and as soon as it opens, at the start of association, I make my way to the 'canteen'. I ask for some liquorice, a tube of toothpaste and some sugar. The screw puts it on the table. "No, I've changed my mind, I'll just take the liquorice Sir." He huffs and puffs but puts the toothpaste and sugar back. I have a plan. It's gonna be hard but my rewards will come later.

Walking back to my cell I notice a big built guy hanging about near the door. I've seen him around with Hunkus, name of Jonah, I think. Can't say why but I just know what he's after. Scanning for screws I notice there are two by the billiard table and another one is shouting about something on the landing above. Good, all screws are otherwise engaged!

Jonah has spotted me now and our eyes lock. He comes at me but I'm more ready than I look and dodge the punch. I land a hard blow to his stomach which doubles him up. He staggers backwards into my cell. In hot pursuit I smash him in the face as he straightens up. No words are spoken. He's still holding his stomach as he exits the cell. I pop a liquorice.

"Anyone for the gym?" shouts the screw.

Lofty has decided to stay and have a game of darts. He shakes his head. PJ, Taffy and me join the line. As soon as we get to the gym I head for Officer Grogan. He's in his mid thirties, about 5' 10", with light brown hair and a moustache. Standing there I can see he's a fit bloke, his body well toned.

"What can I do for you Groom?"

"I've heard you're looking for volunteers for the football team Sir."

"You're from Hawk aren't you, ever played before?"

"Yes Sir," I lied. How hard can it be? I'd played a bit at school. Well it would be a bit, 'cos I hardly ever went. Mom said the School Board Man spent more time at our house than I spent at school. I'd often climb up onto the roof and watch him come along the street. He spotted me once but of course couldn't get at me. I remember him wagging his finger saying he'd be back. The only lesson I liked was English. The teacher was very kind to me. She brought me some shoes once.

"You look fit Groom," Officer Grogan looks me up and down. "Come for practice tomorrow and I'll have a look at you. Where do you work?"

"Bakery Sir."

"I'll have a word with Officer Brannigan then."

"Thank you Sir." I'm having second thoughts now. Brannigan won't like it one bit.

Joining PJ at the weights I spot Hunkus over by the wall bars. Our eyes meet. He looks away. That'll do me.

* * * *

"Football team, attention" shouts the screw. Fourteen of us march over to the practice ground. Each one of the four 'Houses' have their own trainer and section of the field. Officer Grogan, organizer of the whole thing, is also in charge of Hawk. He instructs those who have been before to "carry on." They know what to do.

There's just me and 'Bones' doing a try out today. As his nickname suggests, Bones is about 6'2" and so thin. To be truthful he ain't very healthy looking and his skin has a sort of pallor to it. He looks a bit comical with his basin hair cut.

"You're Porky's, sorry Pete's mate aren't you?"

"Yes, we arrived here at the same time."

I am surprised when he opens his mouth because he talks so posh.

"Right then Groom, let's see what you can do" shouts Officer Grogan, "You too Bone."

I thought he was called Bones because of his lanky build, not his surname, but it suits him on both counts. I've never met anyone so posh before, except the lady in the big house on the main road, where I used to go begging for scraps as a nipper.

I'm not much of a football player but I can run fast and I'm fit. Officer Grogan tells me that he can train me on the ball. I'm in. Bones is phenomenal. He can do all sorts with the ball. He's definitely in.

The training is intense but I'm used to that and actually enjoy it. Better still, it gets me outside every Saturday.

"So you've joined the football team Groom" Officer Brannigan greets me the following morning. We work seven days a week in the Bakery, well six for me, at least until the football final.

"Yes Sir, Hawk was short of players." I think this excuse might make it sound better for me, but he doesn't look pleased.

"Mmm" is the only response I get. "Bring that course book back tomorrow Groom, ready for some class work."

Monday dawns. I always scrub and clean my cell twice a week, usually Monday and Thursday. Immediately after PT but before breakfast I make my way to the recess and collect a galvanized bucket and soap. It doesn't take long and fifteen minutes later I'm returning to empty the dirty water.

I hear raised voices and turn the corner just in time to see 'the Baron' raise a bucket and smash it down on this other con's head. Blood spurts everywhere from a big gash. The con is screaming and clutching his head. The bucket ricochets off the tiled wall with a resounding clatter, and rolls to a halt near my feet. 'The Baron' rushes past, almost pushing me over.

"Keep this shut" he raises his finger to his lips and glares at me.

The con falls to his knees, still screaming, trying to stem the blood with both hands. It's no use. He takes one hand off his head and looks at it which seems to send him into a heightened state of panic. Blood is streaming down his face and spurting all over the white tiled walls.

I hear the familiar shrill whistles as screws race towards the recess. I'm stood standing here with a bucket in my hand. This con is kneeling in front of me with a big gash in his head. I'm in the wrong place at the wrong time.

"Groom stay where you are," Officer Gregg commands, as Officer Harris slaps a towel on top of the con's head and tells him to hold it there.

"Better get this one over to the Hospital Wing," Harris addresses Gregg as he helps the con to his feet, "you'll be alright West, it's only a scratch."

West doesn't look convinced and his legs visibly shake as he stands up.

"Was it Groom?" Officer Gregg nods in my direction.

I look at West. West looks at me. He doesn't know what to do now. He's obviously frightened of 'the Baron' but he looks absolutely terrified of me.

"I slipped Sir."

The screws look at each other, at West and then at me. I'm trying to avoid eye contact with anyone.

"As you were Groom, go about your business." Gregg motions me out of the recess. I don't need telling twice, quickly replace the bucket and head for breakfast.

"What the fuck was all that about?" asks PJ at the servery.

"There was this West guy getting a fuckin' bucket over the head from 'the Baron'. Blood everywhere mate. The screws thought it was me."

"I'm watching you Groom," Officer Harris interjects as we make our way to an empty table with our trays. Oh no, not again.

He's not kidding either. I notice that everywhere I go and everything I do for the next couple of weeks is very closely monitored.

I'm keeping my nose clean, bakery all day, gym most evenings, working out in my cell during lock up, football practice on Saturdays, (I'm getting quite good) and most important of all, saving my earnings. I didn't even have any liquorice last week.

After a month I decide to buy 2oz of Black Shag. "Didn't think you smoked Groom." The screw scribbles in his book and hands me the tin.

"Have I got enough left for some soap Sir?"

He raises his eyebrows and puffs hard "Soap as well is it?"

"Yes please Sir, if I've got enough."

"You've got enough, just about, anything else?" he says pushing the soap across the table. He seems to be looking at me a bit hard and I'm wondering why. Then it hits me.

"Oh yes, I need some fag papers and matches Sir."

"Thought you might," he smiles and produces them from inside his hand. "You're spent up now Groom. NEXT."

I've been watching the smokers for this past month and I know who goes where to get their extras. There's also a good trade to be had in sugar which is what I'll get with next week's wages.

Pete and Bones can be trusted. They smoke quite heavily and so does Taffy. They've got mates who smoke too. Watch out Baron, here comes the Groom.

A few nights later, during association, I stay in the Wing and have a game darts and billiards. This is where most of the smokers hang out. I watch fascinated as Bones lights up with a tiny slither of a match. The cons split one match into eight with their razor blades. Amazing.

Payday was three days ago so this is a good time. When I pull out an ounce of bacca and start to make a big fat roll up Taffy starts to laugh.

He's a bit older than most of the cons in here and knows my game.

"Can you spare a bit of that then?" asks Bones

"How much do you need?"

"Half ounce?"

"Three quarter back on Friday then." I give him the half ounce and he's well chuffed.

Pete has the other half ounce and I have to pick up the other ounce from my cell which soon goes amongst the other cons. Come Friday I'll have made a fifty percent profit. Can't be bad. Come Friday I'm also going to need carriers because of the 2oz rule.

The bigger my empire grows, the more carriers I'm going to need. Therein lies the problem. I decide to start with Pete and Bones, if they're game, 'cos at least they can be trusted.

I'm back in Officer Brannigan's good books again, working hard and memorizing what I can from the coursebooks. In the Bakery we have classroom sessions once a week in the afternoon. Because of missing so many lessons whilst down the Block I'm going to have to wait until next time to sit the examinations.

The wheatgerm and the endosperm," I'm telling PJ over tea when Lofty interrupts.

"Sperm you say, sounds friggin' horrible to me. Is that what we're eating?" he holds up his bread and studies it.

PJ shakes his head.

"I'm going to be working in the greenhouses next month," Lofty proceeds to tell us. "You should see the stuff we planted, it's shooting up now."

"How's the football practice coming Watt?" PJ changes the subject, 'cos once Lofty starts talking about vegetables there's no stopping him.

"We've got our first friendly soon. Then the matches proper will start and the finals at the end of April. Bones is just great. You wouldn't think it to look at him, but honest mate, he's fuckin' unbelievable."

"We've got a chance of winning then. Might take some bets" says PJ.

"We're gonna walk it."

It's soon Friday again and I'm waiting outside the canteen during association for those who had borrowed bacca from me. I get my three ounce back. I'm up and rolling. Another couple of weeks and I can buy some more as well.

Pete and Bones have agreed to be carriers. They will each carry one ounce of mine in their tins. In return I've told them they can use what bacca they want out of the ounce and I won't charge them any interest. But it has to be there for me when I need it. That's the only stipulation.

I see the Baron glancing in my direction once or twice during the next week but don't take much notice. Come Friday, as usual, I am outside the canteen to collect my dues. Now I've got a total of four and three quarter ounces, two myself and one each for Pete and Bones, so I need another carrier.

I'd watched West come back from the Hospital Wing with his head bandaged and puffing away like a good 'un. I don't know what went on between him and the Baron, but anyway, I ask if he'll carry for me. He's a bit wary at first but when I tell him that my carriers don't pay any interest, he readily agrees.

So here I am having a game of table tennis with Taffy. It's his new thing. I'm hopeless and we're having a right laugh when up walks 'the Baron' and two burly cons. Right away I can tell by their body language that this ain't no social call. Here we go again, another bully.

"You," he says nodding in my direction. Slowly I place the bat on the table and walk round to where they're standing. Taffy moves to stand beside me.

"Don't fuckin' muscle in on my carriers." The Baron bends down so that his nose is almost touching mine.

"It's a free Country ain't it?" My eyes narrow and I stare at him.

"Not in here pal, you fuckin' back off. You ain't big enough to play with the big boys yet."

"Is that so? Well I ain't backin' off and if you wanna fuckin' play, come on then, now if you want." I'm hissing at him through clenched teeth. My face has set hard and I shove it as close to his as I can.

There have been no raised voices so as to alert the screws. Just a confrontation. "Watch your back" he growls. Then, nodding at his two henchmen, the three of them walk off. Somehow I don't think I've seen the last of him.

"Watcha Watt," Titchy comes over from his game of cards. "Got a visit from my girl on Wednesday, can I borrow some of your Brylcream and Imperial Leather?"

"Yeh, go on then. What are mates for?"

Titchy rubs his hands together. "She ain't been for a couple of months, can't wait."

"Gonna give her a kiss from me. Doreen isn't it?"

"Yes it is and no I won't." Titchy and his girl have been sweethearts since school. They are both 18 now and he has another 12 months left to do. He's looking forward to home leave and the green 'dizzi' badge.

Taffy and me rib him about his girl and then it's back to the cells for lock up. I ain't had a girl yet. Hard to imagine what it'll be like. I close my eyes. For now my right hand will have to do.

On Tuesday, just at the end of association, Titchy comes round to mine to borrow the gear so it's in his cell ready for tomorrow's visit. He's so excited.

"Soon as I get out we'll get married" he tells me "My Grandma says we can live with her 'til we get a place of our own. I'm made up." He flashes that cheeky grin of his and bounces back to his cell with Brylcream, Imperial Leather and I've thrown in a tube of toothpaste so he'll be able to breathe on her.

"I want 'em back tomorrow, don't forget, it's only lends," I shout after him.

Next day after work I pop in to see Titchy before tea. He's sitting on the bed with his head in his hands. Well, I suppose it's hard to see your loved one go off without you.

"Don't worry mate." I was going to say 'this next few months will fly past and then you'll be getting married', but the look in his eyes as he raises his head tells me there's something more than just feeling homesick. Perhaps she didn't turn up.

"She's got someone else" his voice sounds hoarse and broken.

"Tart" it's all I can think to say.

He doesn't seem to hear me and carries on, his speech coming in fits and spurts. "She wouldn't listen to me Watt,…I told her it isn't long,…if she could just wait,…we can sort it out. She said not to write." He looks up at me as if for some word of encouragement.

"I'd write if I were you mate." It's what he wants to hear and his face brightens a bit. "After all, she did come a long way, she could have just written a letter. She must have wanted to see you." He brightens a bit more.

"I'll do it tonight. Tell her I love her and that."

"You comin' for tea then?"

"Nah, I can't face any scran. I'll start my letter," he grabs some paper and pulls his chair to the table. "What shall I put?"

"No good asking me mate, I never had a girl, just put what you said, you love her an' that." I make my way over to the corner table for the Brylcream, toothpaste and soap. "You could try writing her a poem," I suggest and leave him sitting there staring at the blank wall for inspiration.

I'm walking back into my cell when PJ comes rushing over. He doesn't usually rush anywhere so I can tell there's something bad going off. "It's Taffy, he's in the Hospital."

"What the fuck happened?"

"Lofty just told me. Somebody sliced him over the head with a spade. His eye popped out. Blood everywhere. Taffy won't say who did it so nobody else is saying either."

I can't take it in. "Did Lofty see it? Where's Lofty now? Must be bad. His eye out?" Not waiting for PJ to answer and not really expecting him to, I'm outside the cell looking for Lofty who is busy telling the tale to a crowd of cons gathered opposite.

"Hey Lofty" I shout and motion him to come over.

"Better tell Titchy," PJ moves towards the cell door.

"No, leave him, I'll tell him later."

Lofty comes across and into my cell. PJ and me sit on the bed while he takes the chair opposite and proceeds to tell us the details of what happened.

Apparently Taffy had been sent to the shed for a tool of some sort. Whoever it was must have been hiding with a spade and chopped at Taffy's head as he emerged. Poor bloke never stood a chance. Lofty hadn't actually seen it happen so he don't know who done it. The cry, he said, was like a cat caught in a mangle, and, together with several other cons and screws, he'd found Taffy laying there in a pool of blood. "You could see the bone and everything. His eyeball was hanging right down on his cheek! I'm telling you it was friggin' gruesome."

"It's a wonder he ain't dead," I shake my head in disbelief.

Lofty is itching to get back amongst the other cons so he can carry on telling the tale. "Coming for tea then?" he asks, making for the door.

"See you later mate." PJ looks at me. "Wonder if we'll be allowed to see him? Do you think they've took him to an outside Hospital or the one here?"

I shrug my shoulders. "I'll ask Gregg tomorrow morning, if he's on.

C'mon let's get some tea, I'm starving. I'll tell you about Titchy."

What happened to Taffy is the talk of the place tonight and for a few days to come. Next morning, as Officer Gregg is handing out the razor blades, (issued from a large brown leather pouch which has a corresponding slot for each cell number), I ask after Taffy and whether there is any chance of a visit for me and PJ.

Just before breakfast, when he's collecting the blades back in, Gregg tells me that Taffy is in the Hospital Wing but there'll be no visits for a while. He'll find out how the patient is doing and let me know.

In between times this Saturday is the first friendly game and it's Hawk versus Nelson. Kick off is 2pm and all the cons turn out to watch and cheer on their mates.

I'm playing on the right wing because I can run fast. Bones, the top scorer, is our secret weapon. But this is only a friendly and Grogan has told us not to worry too much about winning today.

"Tactics lads," he tells us "don't let the opponent know all your strengths." Doesn't mean much to us though. We just want to win everything.

Nelson House and Hawk House teams come onto the field to a roar of support from the cons. It's a great feeling to be part of it. The weather is cold and it's been raining most of the week so the pitch turns into a mudbath pretty quickly. There's a lot of slipping and sliding going on 'cos the boots we have are not the best. Still, at half time we are 3 – 0 up. Our goalkeeper is a huge guy by the name of Dan. Between him and Bones we're onto a winner. In the final moments Bones takes a shot from 20 yards out. Amid uproar the game ends 5 – 4 to us. Carver, the 'daddy' of Nelson, has been playing in goal and is boo'd off the pitch by his own House. He doesn't look happy and starts swearing at the referee. Spider, who has given his all in the half back position, looks across, rolls his eyes and laughs. "We'll beat you next time."

"Got any burn Watt?" asks Dan as we're getting changed. Being so big and powerful a lot of people are wary of him but he wouldn't hurt a fly.

"How much you need?"

"Half ounce."

I promise to sort him out at teatime. Having just offloaded mine

I'll need to get some from one of my carriers before tea. Bradley's only been carrying for me a few days, so he's still got the full ounce.

After a shower I make my way to his cell which is on the top landing. He's sitting at the table writing a letter as I walk in and the teatime bell rings.

"Need half."

Bradley, who is about 6', pushes the chair back, stands up, and sort of squares up. His body language tells me everything I need to know. He glares down at me and points to his nose, "best take it out of…"

I don't give him time to finish 'cos I know what's coming. *He* doesn't.

Quick as a flash and twice as deadly I put the nut on him. He staggers backwards clutching his face. I punch him in the ribs a couple of times, good hard punches. He ain't pointing at his nose anymore, he's pointing towards the corner table where the bacca tin sits. I grab it and leave him leaning against the wall. Life ain't easy. I'm one carrier down.

Reaching the tea queue I look for Dan, and spot him at the other end, next table up from Hunkus. I give him the nod. Just then all hell breaks loose as a con, two in front of me, leaps over the servery and smashes his tray in the face of one of the cooks. A fight breaks out. There's blood splattering all over the food from the deep gash that has appeared on the cook's nose. Ugh. What's with the tea now then? We can't eat that.

The screws, whistles blowing, break up the fight and we are sent back to our cells whilst the place is cleaned and fresh food prepared. Later, during association, I slip Dan the half ounce.

Next morning Officer Gregg tells me that a visit to the Hospital Wing has been arranged for me and PJ next Thursday, during what would be our association time. He tells me Taffy is doing well and that his eye has been saved. This is all good.

"We'll find out who did it and get 'em" I tell PJ and Titchy during breakfast.

Titchy is studying his porridge hard. I know what's going through his mind. He needs to keep his nose clean so he can get home to sort things out with his girl. He told me he'd written a love poem like I suggested but she hasn't replied yet.

"Don't worry Titchy, we know you gotta stay out of it." He seems relieved.

"Taffy might not know who did it" says PJ, and then "this porridge is disgusting, got any sugar on you Watt?"

"Word's out…it was Carver" Lofty's tray clatters onto the table as he joins us. "Something to do with Taffy trying to stop Old Joeing in the other Houses as well as Hawk. Carver doesn't like it."

"We'll ask Taffy himself on Thursday, agreed?"

PJ nods. Lofty and Titchy carry on scoffing the porridge. Mine seems to taste a lot better than usual, probably 'cos I've stirred in another two spoons of sugar.

"Give us two's up mate?" I recognize West's voice and turn round as he goes past with a con I don't know.

"This is my pal Dave." West stops and takes what's left of a fag from his mate. Leaning towards me and lowering his voice "he'll carry for you if you want."

"Dave is it?" I stand up.

"Yeh" he offers his hand "I'm alright, you can trust me, honest, I've done it before."

I do need more carriers and he's West's mate. "I'll see you by the billiard table tonight then." West walks off and Dave follows him with half a fag dangling from his lips. I'm glad I don't smoke.

I've got quite a thing going now. People come to me for all sorts, not just bacca. In my cell I've got sugar, tinned stuff, toothpaste, soap, Brylcream, sweets, chocolate, you name it. A regular little shop of sorts. Cons can have some but they gotta pay interest at the end of the week in one form or another.

I'm on my way to the recess and pass a new arrival being shown the ropes by one of the cons from top landing. They stand to one side out of my way. "He's one of them as you don't mess with," advises the seasoned con, nodding in my direction. I smile inwardly but give them the stare. The new arrival looks absolutely terrified. Hunkus fodder.

As my 'business' grows keeping track of everything is the biggest headache. Who had what and when? No good trying to write it down 'cos the screws would find any sort of list during shakedowns.

Later that day Dave is given an ounce to carry. He goes off happy enough. Another face, another name, another number to add to the memory bank.

Chapter 5

THE AVENGER

"Hello Taffy, mate." He looks a deathly colour; well the bit I can see of him in between the bandages wrapped around his head and covering his left eye.

The orderly plumps Taffy's pillows and leaves. A screw sits at the door and tells us we've got thirty minutes, before pulling out the Racing Post and a pen. He's trying to pick a winner. Aren't we all...

"Bought you a bit of choco." I place Taffy's favourite chocolate bar on the bedside table. He gives me a watery smile and it's obvious he's in some pain. I can tell he's still very weak by the way his hand flops on the bed after his initial greeting. I was going to try and crack a joke or two to cheer him up but think better of it.

Me and PJ sit on the chairs which have been placed on the right hand side of his bed. The Hospital Wing is situated in the grounds of Rochester Borstal, only a short march from the main buildings. Each patient has his own room, so apart from the screw at the door, we are on our own.

I lean closer to Taffy and lower my voice. "What happened mate?"

Taffy glances towards the door but the screw is intent on his mission to find that elusive winner. "Bastard Carver. He came at me from behind the shed with a fuckin' spade," he sighs deeply, "I don't want to talk about it."

"We can sort the bastard" I whisper. PJ nods.

"No, don't fret Watt, I'll get him myself. I'm lucky to have my eye you know, after what he did to me." We murmur our agreement.

"Now don't be doing anything, I want him for myself." Taffy seems to be getting anxious so we change the subject to football.

I tell him about the friendly matches we've played and the eliminators coming up. "If we beat Blake then we'll be in the final in three weeks time."

"You might be out of here by then" encourages PJ

"Don't think so, they've said another six weeks."

PJ recounts various incidents including the fight with the cook and having to wait ages for our tea. Taffy's one visible blue eye brightens a bit as he talks about the visit from his wife, Martha.

"She never brings Beth with her because it's such a long way from home," the disappointment is obvious in his voice. Taffy's wife had the baby soon after he was sent here and he's only ever seen photos. His hand fumbles on the bedside table. "Martha brought this with her," he shows us the latest one.

I tell him about Titchy's bird, Doreen, knockin' off some other bloke. Taffy asks after some of his mates and we say we'll try and get another visit. The thirty minutes pass quickly and we're marched back to Hawk.

There's still an hour of association left and we join Titchy and Lofty at the dartboard. After relaying the news about Taffy we get down to it and play a game of doubles. Me and PJ win. Lofty has started to smoke but hasn't quite got the hang of it yet. His fag keeps going out, which is the subject of some hilarity during the game.

Football is the main topic of conversation and there are 'books' being run all over the place. PJ has opened one and I have 2oz on Hawk to win the final.

Our game with Blake is a walkover and we win 5-2. They have some good players but their goalie is rubbish. The following Saturday it's Rodney versus Nelson and for a change I'm watching. The atmosphere is brilliant as we wait for the teams.

I spot Carver as he runs onto the pitch. "There he is the bastard."

"Everybody knows it's him what did Taffy. He's been braggin' about it to some cons on the garden party" Lofty tells us.

I turn to PJ. "He won't be braggin' when Taffy gets hold of him. Fuckin' coward."

The game is 2 -2 when, with a minute to go, Spider plays a blinder. He heads the ball which is picked up by a team-mate who takes it down the field. Spider runs hard and calls for the ball. He flicks it across to their striker who lashes his shot past the goalkeeper and into the net.

The whistle blows. There is uproar. Some cheers, some boo's. That's it then. We're playing Nelson in two weeks time for the cup. Well, Grogan calls it a cup. It's more the size of an egg-cup.

The next two weeks fly by. There's a buzz of excitement and everyone's passing on football know-how. Suddenly all cons are experts. During this time I get a letter from home and Mom says she will visit, with Pearl and Roy, on 6th June, which is just over a month away. I send a VO. It will be my first visit from home, something to look forward to.

Our team is honed to perfection. We've been working on our fitness and stamina. "Cardiovascular endurance and muscle strength is the foundation of overall fitness" Grogan tells us. I still do my cell routine, most nights after lock up, so my fitness is not in question.

The Saturday of the final is a dull, rainy day, which is not the best. There are rousing cheers as we run onto the pitch. A lot is riding on this. Cons have made bets, I've made a bet, but more than that, I want to win. The glory of the cup. I also want to give Carver a bit of a kicking if I can!

The match begins and from the off it's apparent that Nelson are gonna play dirty. Within two minutes one of our players is being carried off with what turns out to be a broken ankle from a flying tackle.

There are boo's as the referee says play on. What's the matter with him? Is he fuckin' blind?

Officer Grogan sends on one of the substitute players, McCauley. It turns out well for us though, because within five minutes he's curled a left footer beyond Carver's reach right into the back of the net. Grogan does a little dance on the touchline.

Goalkeeper Carver looks in trouble again a few minutes later after he clearly handles outside the box when saving another strike. However, the referee rules the ball had struck his shoulder. We play on.

Nelson gets the equalizer when Spider powers in a terrific header just minutes after another header had brought a fingertip save from Dan. The crowd goes mad.

A few minutes later, one of our players is screaming in agony and clutching his face. He was elbowed and gestures to the referee who, surprise, surprise didn't see it. Another substitution, Amos, comes on.

I see an opportunity, run, tackle and gain control of the ball. We have a strategy and stick to it. I pass it to Amos who immediately crosses it to Freddie. I run up the field and Freddie passes it back to me. I flick it over to Bones who outwits four Nelson players in a packed penalty area before calmly slamming his shot past Carver. The crowd is in uproar. Grogan is doing his dance again on the touchline. Score is 2 – 1 to us and stays that way to half time.

Officer Grogan is well pleased with our performance and during the half time break he just warns us to watch out for the fouling.

Moments into the second half Bones sweeps a beautiful right foot shot past the outstretched arm of Carver. Boo's from Nelson supporters. Rousing cheers from Hawk. The pressure is really on Nelson now. Within a few minutes Carver saves a spectacular shot from 25 yards out by McCauley.

Ball back in play and I'm on it. The old one two to Amos and Freddie, then the ball comes back to me. I ain't gonna pass it to Bones or McCauley. I'm running with it. No Nelson players around. Carver, sensing danger and lack of cover, charges outside the box. I kick the ball and take a flying leap at his leg. The ball goes in. "Bastard, that's for Taffy" I growl at him. He goes down with a strangled cry. The referee is over in a flash. "Slipped in the mud Sir."

He blows his whistle, "offside, no goal, play on."

Carver scowls at me and limps back into goal.

McCauley latches onto a loose ball, out-muscles his marker but is brought down by a charging maniac just as he's about to launch a shot at goal. He screams in pain and is writhing in the mud. He has to be stretchered off. The Hospital Wing will be full at this rate.

There's five minutes to go. I know because Grogan has just given us the sign by holding up his hand with his fingers outstretched.

The lad who is marking me has this habit of catching hold of my shirt so I give him a right dig in the ribs as I make a run for the ball. Looking for Amos, he ain't there, I pass it to Freddie who is running up the field on the other side. I can see Bones out of the corner of my eye making his run. Freddie crosses the ball to me and I take it further up the field. This might be our last chance.

I slide the ball past my marker and pass it to Bones who picks it up and strikes. The ball hits the post, amidst cries and boo's from the crowd. Bones looks across, shrugs his shoulders and runs back up the field.

I see the two minute sign from Grogan and remember his words "don't stop playing until the final whistle blows." A bit knackered now,

I manage to put a touch on the ball across to Freddie. Fending off his mark he passes it to Bones, who, to great roars from the crowd, smashes home the last goal of the match.

The whistle blows and Officer Grogan runs onto the pitch congratulating us all. "Well done lads, well done." The cons are still cheering. Carver hobbles past and throws me a menacing look. Nothing, however, is going to spoil this moment.

Cons from Hawk are jumping up and down and the chant 'we won the cup, we won the cup' drifts across the field. From the front row PJ and Lofty give us the thumbs up. Even Titchy manages to forget his troubles for a while, his cheeky face just one big grin.

The Governor presents the cup to our Captain. To tell the truth Snowy ain't much of a player, tending to stay on the sidelines so as to keep himself out of any tackles but Grogan had already made him Captain before Bones came into the side.

Later, back in Hawk, the team is greeted by cheering cons at teatime. The cup is passed around and the mood, for once, is light hearted. Even the screws seem pleased. There's a lot of backslapping but a few glum faces from those running 'books'.

"Come on then PJ, cough it."

"Good job everybody didn't have as much faith as you" he says giving me my winnings.

"We saw you" Titchy gives me a knowing look across the table "slipped on the mud Sir" he imitates my Black Country accent. "Slipped my arse."

Lofty starts to laugh "he was still friggin' limping at the end."

The whole football experience has given a purpose but now I feel a bit deflated as we settle back into the Borstal routine. Still, it's my visit next week and I need to concentrate a bit more on the course work for my City and Guilds.

Visiting day arrives and early afternoon sun is shining bright as I am marched over to Reception block. The room has several small tables and there are lots of Mom's and Dad's, wives and girlfriends, brothers and sisters, all sitting at their separate tables, expectant, happy and sad at the same time.

Mom stands up as I walk in. "Watt," she just says my name and gives me a big hug.

"Sit down please" a screw walks over. We have to sit on opposite sides of the table.

Roy's grown a lot and looks so different. Pearl, with a light in her eyes, tells me about her boyfriend, Tom, and Mom gives me all the gossip about various neighbours. I tell them about the food, the football and the bakery. Pearl can't get over how much I've filled out. Mom complains about the long train journey to get here and in no time at all the screw shouts that visiting is over. I give Mom and Pearl a hug and ruffle Roy's mop of hair.

"Geroff" he laughs and pushes my hand away.

There are hysterical tears at the next table from the wife or girlfriend of the con. She's clinging to him but they are roughly separated by the screw. There's no point in prolonging the agony. Not looking back, I walk to stand in line with the other cons and we are marched out, searched, and then march back to our respective Houses.

I'm in my cell putting a shine on my boots that evening when I get the news.

"You'll never guess" says Lofty walking in. I'm sitting on the bed so I motion him to the chair.

"Carver has bragged once too friggin' often and he's been up in front of the Governor today. One of the screws was in the shed, probably skiving, and heard Carver telling another con about how he got Taffy. He's being transferred to Felton Borstal in Middlesex."

"When?"

"Well I don't know everything."

"Round up some of Taffy's mates," I'm already heading for the door, "I'll get PJ and Titchy. Meet back here in five."

Within minutes we are assembled in my cell. There's PJ, myself, Titchy, Lofty, and four of Taffy's mates, including Whitey.

"Look, we need to get him before he goes to Felton" I open up the discussion. There is a murmur of agreement. "Taffy ain't coming out of Hospital anytime soon, so he won't have his chance. We gotta do it for him." Another murmur of agreement.

"Put that fag out, I can't breathe in here," PJ waves his arms at the smoke. One of Taffy's mates snuffs his fag and shoves the dogend in his pocket. There are eight of us crammed into a small space and we need a plan, fast.

I turn to Lofty. "Is he still gonna be working?" I'm trying to figure out where we can get at Carver. If there are enough of Taffy's mates, together with Lofty, they might be able to get him amid the vegetables.

"I won't know that 'til tomorrow."

"Whitey, I know you work in the Laundry, but what about you?" I ask the other three. Turns out John and Bill work in the engineering shop, handy to know, and the other one, Andy, works on the farm. Not much help there then 'cos Carver works on the garden party.

It comes to me. "Well he's usually at the gym during association. That's the only place we can get him."

"Too many screws" pipes up Andy.

"They're everywhere in case you hadn't noticed" Bill points out.

"You'll need to create a diversion" I wave my arm towards the gathering of cons, "while me and PJ get him."

"I've never been to the gym" says Bill, who is a bit on the hefty side.

"It'll do you good then" retorts John. I'd seen him working out a few times with Taffy.

"We need to act fast 'cos we don't know how long we've got. I say tomorrow night." The others agree. "Get to the gym, give it half an hour and then have an argument, you'll think of something."

The next day Lofty reports at dinnertime that there's been hell to pay on the garden party this morning. Carver is on the warpath. He transfers to Felton in two days time but has heard it's for the nutters and doesn't want to go. It's not like he's got much choice in the matter.

"Don't worry" re-assures Lofty as we leave the table, "me and the lad's will cover your backs. See you tonight."

"Anyone for the gym" shouts the screw. We line up and march over. Me and PJ stick together at the wall bars. John's showing Bill around and explaining the different equipment. Andy and Titchy are using the vaulting horse and Lofty, who is not much of an athletic type, is standing offering his opinion on how they are doing.

Carver is using the weights. He has a couple of frightened looking cons putting 'em on for him. Probably his Old Joes. Carver is talking to Hunkus and they briefly glance in my direction.

The signal is me scratching the back of my head and when Hunkus walks off towards the wall bars on the other side I think now is as good a time as any.

I run my fingers through my hair and start scratching. John and Bill spot me but the other three are too absorbed in what they are doing. I'm impatient and so totally focused on Lofty, Andy and Titchy that I don't see the screw approaching. "You got head lice Groom?"

"No Sir." He walks off chuckling to himself.

I shake my head as John and Bill look across. They carry on with their exercising. The other three are oblivious.

"I'll wander across and have words with them three twats." PJ walks off towards the vaulting horse.

Twenty minutes later and we're on again. This time everyone spots the signal. Lofty starts loudly criticizing the way Andy is vaulting and they square up to each other on the mat. A couple of screws make their way over. Bill and John start a ruck further down the gym and the other screws go off to sort it out.

Carver is bent down rolling his hands around the bar and getting ready to lift the weights. At the sound of a noisy argument he briefly raises his head. In that moment me and PJ are in front of him. His 'helpers' fuck off quick. I bash him in the face, he reels backwards and I almost trip over the weights as I follow up with a powerful punch to the stomach.

Voices are getting louder from the other end of the gym. PJ wants to have a go but I'd told him this is between me and Carver, one on one, for Taffy. Carver pulls himself to his full height and in an instant I put the nut on him. Time spent down the Block with Gallagher, King of the Nutters so to speak, certainly paid off. 'It's all in the flick of the head' he used to tell me.

Carver recoils clutching his face. I smash him in the ribs and, as he goes down, I deliver a vicious blow to his back. He rolls over and gets to his knees.

I step aside 'cos PJ is itching to say goodbye too.

Shakily Carver stands up and lashes out. PJ catches a glancing blow to the chin but sticks a couple to his body and lands a nice one to the jaw. Saliva and sweat sprays everywhere.

Carver is all over the place now and sort of folds into a crumpled heap, his arm lolling lifeless on top of the weights. Grabbing the short black hair I pull his head back and glare into the vacant staring eyes, "that was for Taffy, just so you know." His head flops forward as I toss it away from me.

Me and PJ quietly make our way to the other end of the gym. Lofty and Andy are being given verbals by two exasperated screws. Further down, Bill and John are still arguing and are about to be carted off. As we pass they smile at each other and shake hands. The screws look puzzled and turn to assist their colleagues.

Hearing the whistles, me and PJ laugh as we hit the mats doing press-ups. That night I pop a liquorice before bed and reflect upon the day. It went well, nobody got caught and Carver got no less than he deserved.

Four weeks later and Taffy is back from the Hospital Wing. It's approaching teatime and I'm getting some extra sugar ready for my cuppa when he walks into my cell.

"I heard what you and PJ did," he says offering me his hand "thanks mate."

I beam at him. "No need," but I shake his hand anyway. "Good to see you back Taffy, how you feeling?"

"Not so bad, I keep getting headaches but they told me to expect that."

The scar runs all across the back of his head and down to the eyeline. He still looks a mess and the hair hasn't grown back properly where his head was shaved.

"I wish I'd been able to get him myself."

"You'd have made a better job with them fingers of yours," I make a jabbing motion. Taffy had given us a demonstration once during association 'cos a lot of cons didn't believe him. 'It's all to do with pressure points' he'd said, as he placed his fingers against some guy's neck. Poor bloke went down like a ninepin, out cold.

"Tea then?" Holding the door open, I gesture him through.

During the meal several of Taffy's mates pat him on the back and wish him well. He doesn't really want to talk about what happened but Lofty being Lofty pushes him. "I remember the shooting pain in my head and then nothing, next thing I'm waking up and its two days later!"

"I tell you mate, it was friggin' gruesome. Your eyeball was on your cheek. There was a big flap of skin hanging off your head and I could see the bone. We thought you was dead." Lofty, animated now, as he recounts the tale. "Officer Corns went white, he just blew his whistle and wouldn't go near you 'til the other screws come."

"You're lucky they saved it" Titchy stares intently at Taffy's left eye.

"Mm" agrees Taffy and then, changing the subject, "what's all this I hear about you and Doreen?"

Titchy drones on about Doreen but I've heard enough about her over these last few weeks to write a book so I give PJ the eye and we head off and leave 'em to it. Perhaps Taffy can give him some advice, after all he's married with a kid so he should know what works with the girls.

"Who's that old guy with the grey hair?"

PJ shrugs. I've seen him a few times during association moving between the tables. No sooner have I opened my mouth than he walks across.

"Hello lads, want a chat?"

I'm curious and so the three of us head to an empty table. I'm also a bit wary. He's in his mid 60's so he ain't no Borstal boy and he certainly ain't a screw but he could be after information. Well you never know.

"I just come along and have a chat with some of the lads. Most of you are a long way from home and probably don't get many visits" he explains. "Just call me Pop." He sits down and pulls out two roll ups, "smoke?"

We take one each and slide it behind our ears. He seems a friendly old boy and actually it makes quite a change to talk with somebody about what's going on in the outside world. He's led an interesting life and relates many anecdotes that make us laugh. "See you again then lads, Watt and PJ isn't it?"

"Reminds me of my Grandad," remarks PJ as we walk back to our cells at the end of association.

I recall my own Grandad Burton, Mom's Dad. We didn't see him very often. He worked at the Steelworks wheeling big barrows into the furnaces.

I remember the oily smell of him and his big, powerful arms, which had always fascinated me as I sat on his lap as a nipper.

Waking up this morning I feel as if I've already done a day's work. My dreams had taken me to toil in the furnaces all night.

It's classroom day in the bakehouse. I almost forget my course book and have to dodge back into the cell to pick it up. Classes are held once a week in a room off the bakery. We each have our own lift top desk in which paper and pencils are kept. Officer Brannigan issues the course books from a big cupboard which sits behind his desk at the front of the class. He allows us to take them back to our cells only upon request and he writes it in a ledger.

There is a big blackboard and posters detailing different aspects of bread making line the walls. The one I like best shows yeast with a slogan underneath, 'yeast is a minute fungi'. Old Brannigan tells us that a small pinch of live yeast every day is good for our blood. It tastes horrid but we all have some.

Learning is by rote, and we chant in unison various sayings that should help us get through the written examination. There is also a practical test in which we will have to demonstrate our skills. I am determined to pass but the exam is next year and seems a long way off.

That night Titchy is beside himself. "Whatcha Watt" I am greeted by a huge smile and he's jumping up and down. I guess it must be Doreen. Nothing or nobody else could make him this happy.

"It worked, it worked," he's dancing round my cell waving a letter at me. "She wants a VO, she wants a VO."

His happiness is contagious and I'm grinning from ear to ear. "Glad for you mate."

"It was your love poem that did it."

"You wrote the poem, not me."

"It was your idea though. Fuckin' beauty," he's kissing the letter now.

During tea everyone has to hear about Doreen, so when it's time for association me and PJ head over to the gym, not a favourite haunt for Titchy.

"Any of you lot interested in doing the Christmas show this year?" asks Officer Grogan as he walks round with a clipboard.

"It's only August Sir," PJ gets set to lift some weights.

"I'm just collecting a list of volunteers at the moment. There's a lot to do, scenery, rehearsing. We usually start at the end of September. What about you Groom?"

"Come on it'll be a laugh, let's put our names down." I try and get PJ interested but he just pulls a face.

"I'll put you both down then."

"Fuckin' hell Watt, what'd you go and do that for? Once your names on the list, that's it."

"You heard the man, lots to do, rehearsing and that, we might get time off work."

And so our names are on 'the list' but we soon forget about it and get down to our training. I leave PJ at the weights and head for the vaulting horse. I enjoy the springboard and somersaults. That feeling of flying through the air, momentary freedom. Any sort of freedom is like paradise lost. We're all just marking time.

As we're lining up to be marched back to Hawk I tell PJ that I'm not coming to the gym tomorrow night because I've got a bit of 'business' to sort.

It's the sort of business I don't particularly enjoy but one of my carriers is playing up. He's a new guy on the top landing. I'd asked him for a quarter at dinnertime today but he said he'd used it all, the whole ounce, and I'd have to wait 'til he could buy it back from the shop. He knew the rules. Wait is something I don't do.

He probably thought I'd come after him tonight but I let him stew. He'll be wondering now, which is all the better for me.

Next day I see him watching me, furtive glances here and there but I just get on with what I'm doing. He works in the kitchens emptying bins and comes into the bakery every so often to empty ours. He nods in my direction. I give him the stare. He hangs his head. He thought it was going to be alright. Now he knows different.

"Well then Reggie, where's my bacca?" I'm at the entrance to his cell having followed him up the stairs straight from work.

He backs up against the wall underneath the window. "I'll get as much as I can with my wages on Friday, honest" he sort of pleads. He ain't gone down on his knees yet but it's in his voice. The weakness.

He's a nice kid from Birmingham. Says he went on a job with a local crew and they were interrupted by a nightwatchman. Reggie wanted to leg it but the others waded in and beat the watchman so bad that he almost pegged it.

For a split second I feel sorry for him but there's a lesson to be learned here. "I'll have it now. The ounce." I stand quietly in the doorway with my arms folded.

"But I got none, none at all." Terrified, he stumbles to the corner table and grabs his bacca tin, opening it to show me.

I don't look at the tin. I just hold his eyes. I think he's gonna cry any minute and hope he doesn't.

I set my face and take two steps forward. He flattens himself against the wall and shuts his eyes. I sit on the bed and wait for him to open them.

"Go get me my ounce."

"Where from, how……" his voice falters.

I raise my voice. "Just fuck off and bring me my ounce. I don't care where from or how, sell your fuckin' arse if you have to, just get it."

He stands rooted to the spot. I get up and move towards him. Grabbing hold of his shirt I almost lift him off the ground. My other hand is round his throat. "You got any mates Reggie?"

He can hardly speak because his airway is constricted but manages to croak "Yes." Sweat is pouring off him and he's getting redder by the minute.

I push my face as close as it will get to his. "Fuck off and get me my ounce, now!" I relax my hold and he falls forward clutching his throat and coughing.

I flop onto the bed and pick up one of his library books. A Western, good. I watch him disappear and think I'll give him ten minutes. He's back in five with my ounce.

"I'll borrow this now I've started it." I wave the book at him as I leave. "Thanks."

Back in my cell I throw it on the table for later. I'm a carrier down, but got my ounce back, well there was never any doubt that I would. Business concluded I could go to the gym tonight after all, but decide to stay in Hawk and have a laugh with the lads. Lofty got his Blue today so he'll be in high spirits.

I should have gone to the gym, 'cos tonight is the start of something that stays with me for the next twenty four years!

Chapter 6

GETTING OUT AND GETTING LAID

"Christmas Show volunteers" shouts Officer Gregg. There's a lot of ribbing as me and PJ join the line. Bones and Lofty have signed up too. "Put your fags out lads" shouts Gregg. Lofty and me extinguish our roll ups along with most of the other cons. PJ is among the minority in continuing not to smoke. I've never really forgiven Lofty for giving me that roll up last month. I'd had a bad day dealing with that Brummie kid, and thought 'what the heck'. Now I was hooked. It would be 1976 before I finally manage to kick the habit. Still, we make our own choices.

I've been looking forward to this Christmas Show and spent the last couple of nights thinking up ideas for a comedy sketch. I'm game for anything that relieves the monotony. If last years show was anything to go by we can't do any worse.

Over in the gym, which doubles as a theatre with the stage at one end, volunteer cons from all the Houses gather round. Grogan and Gregg are in charge and this is the first meeting. We are supposed to come up with a few ideas.

PJ just isn't interested so there is no input from him. I recognize the guy who played piano last year, Tony, from Rodney House. I remember he was very good. It turns out he wrote most of the stuff for last years Show and has already done a lot of preparatory work for this year too.

He wants to be a scriptwriter and is working on something he hopes will be published upon his release. Not only does he play piano, he scores the music, writes our scripts and designs the scenery. A sort of One-Man Band really. He's bursting with ideas. Good job, because none of the other cons have got much to suggest. My idea for a sketch is taken on board and Gregg says I can pick who I want to play opposite me. I choose Lofty 'cos I think he's lanky enough for the part and will look good in a big red beard! Lofty himself is not too sure.

The Officers pick cons at random, from those who are not performing, to carry out the tasks of scene building, painting, sewing the costumes and suchlike. Everyone is given something to do.

Rehearsals are once a week on Saturdays. Officer Brannigan is not going to be too chuffed. I tell Pop all about it on his visit the next evening. "Perhaps they'll let you come, you'd like to see my comedy sketch wouldn't you?"

PJ rolls his eyes. "You and your fuckin' comedy sketch."

PJ got landed with sewing costumes. Not something he's too happy about.

"How are you me old china?" it's West on his way to the recess. Pop gets up and greets him. "Are you in this show?"

"Not on your nelly" says West laughing "but I'll enjoy watching."

Rehearsals go well and PJ, together with the other 'seamstresses' make costumes from clothes collected by the screws from a local jumble sale.

Christmas in Hawk is a bit different from the one I had down the Block last year. The screws are lightening up a bit and we will be making some special bread and stuff in the bakery for the Christmas period. I'm really looking forward to it. Old Brannigan, to my surprise, isn't too put out about me having to miss Saturdays in the bakehouse.

The Show is held ten days before Christmas and there is much hilarity backstage as we don our costumes. The 'dancing girls' are getting most of the flack, with their frondy headgear swinging about and cons chanting *where did you get that hat, where did you get that hat*.

The dancers go on first, followed by a guy from Nelson who can do some magic and then Bones tells some jokes and finishes off with *Burlington Bertie* which is half spoken and half sung. Just looking at him makes some people laugh and when he opens his mouth, speaking like the Queen an' all, he brings the house down.

The stage is set for my comedy sketch. It's a Western Hillbilly kitchen with a painted window through which can be seen a big barn. I take my place in the rocking chair by the 'fire' with my knitting. I'm dressed as an old woman in a blue gingham dress, an old cardigan and a sort of bun held on top of my head with some elastic, a bit like old mother riley. Lofty is sitting at a table, pretending to eat some dinner. He's wearing a big floppy hat, bib and braces type overalls and a red curly beard.

Two cons pull open the stage curtains and our sketch starts. We must look funny 'cos there's a ripple of laughter already. I begin rocking in the chair and Lofty picks up his fork.

Speaking in a lazy American drawl I begin.

"Where's your Pa, Son?" I'm rocking and knitting and there's a long pause.

Lofty carries on eating and eventually looks up. "He's in the barn, Ma."

I stop rocking and knitting. Me and Lofty turn and look out the window.

"What's he doin' in the barn, Son?" I start rocking and knitting again. Lofty eats some more dinner and there's another long pause.

"He's hung himself Ma."

I continue rocking and don't look up. "Why don't you cut him down Son?" I'm knitting and rocking but can hardly contain myself from laughing. Here comes the punchline.

Lofty delivers it in the accent he has perfected over the weeks with the help of Tony. Nice and slow Lofty, nice and slow.

"Cos he ain't dead yet Ma."

The place is in uproar. Some cons start whistling. Everyone is in bits. The Governor on the front row stands up clapping. I can see Pop, sitting next to him, laughing and clapping and he gives me the thumbs up when we take our bow.

We exit left and Tony is there to congratulate us before nipping back to his piano ready for the next act, which is four cons dressed as Egyptians, doing a soft sand shuffle.

Me and Lofty get changed and go out front to watch the rest of the Show which concludes with the 'dancing girls' performing a can-can. There are shouts of 'get 'em off, give us a flash and what you doing later'. One thing about this captive audience, they are really appreciative and the whole thing ends with riotous applause.

Officers Grogan and Gregg walk onto the stage and thank everyone for their hard work. They call Tony up to take a bow, 'cos really it's his Show.

The Governor and his visitors, including Pop, leave first. I remember this time last year and as I chat to Tony by the piano. Out of the corner of my eye I can see Hunkus. He's watching me as he waits in line to stack his chair. Four behind him is the Baron. He ain't watching me but I've always got my weather eye open just in case. As Taffy had said, 'need eyes in the back of your head'.

My 18th Birthday comes and goes with some joshing from my mates and a nice bit of cake down the bakery. PJ gets his Blue, on *my* birthday. It ain't fair.

Two days before Christmas I receive a card and letter from home. Pearl is still going out with Tom. Little Barry fell over last week and badly hurt his leg. Marje has been ill with 'flu. Dad's still working at the brickyard. 'Rob called round last week to ask after you,' Mom writes, 'he came with his girlfriend'. Girlfriend! All of a sudden my stomach is plummeting and lands in my boots. I find myself staring at the barred window for what seems like ages.

There's another card. Who's this from? My spirits lift when I see the scrawled signature at the bottom. It's from Pop and he's written a bit of a rhyme on the back. In one of our many chats I'd told him about my love of poetry, not something I would admit to anyone else! On the odd occasions I attended school, my English teacher would call me up in front of the class to recite such classics as 'Jackdaw of Rheims' or 'The Glory of the Garden' which I loved and memorized word for word. Pop's poem is like a breath of fresh air, priceless.

I wish for you your Probs and Blues
Home leave as well for five day spell
Your Leadership just one long kip
Your dizzi too, I wish for you
No kinds of sorts of poor reports
And may you earn a stack of burn
From your mates get two's up straight
Some kindly words from all your birds
And watch your due with every screw
Big mouth shut, don't do your nut
Get out quick, stay out long
Is the burden of my song

Now I've swallowed, time to stop
Merry Xmas, China Pop

Laughing, I nip next door to show Titchy. He's received a card from Doreen and a long letter. She comes every month to see him now and he's made up. Pop's rhyme makes him laugh too. "The power of poems, eh Watt."

"Can't argue with that mate."

Christmas comes and goes. Dinner tastes great. Turkey followed by Christmas pud. PJ remarks on how good the bread is and we get to watch a film in the afternoon. This year it's a Western which is just up my street.

In January it's Titchy's 19th Birthday and he's in high spirits 'cos the Governor's given him his dizzi badge. He'll be going on home leave in March and discharge end of April if all goes well. He now has a permanent grin on his face, which can be quite irritating to those of us who ain't even got our blue yet.

It's the middle of February when Officer Gregg tells me, as he's handing out the blades, that the Governor wants to see me after breakfast. I've been very careful about my baroning and kept my nose clean as far as the screws are concerned. Old Brannigan's pleased with me in the bakery. It can only mean one thing. The Blue.

Officer Gregg marches me across the courtyard to see the Governor and I stand to attention in front of his desk. My clothes and hair are dripping 'cos it's snowing outside.

He looks me up and down. "Well Groom, I'm pleased to hear that you've managed to stay out of trouble since your last spell in the Block. My Officers have given you a good report so I've decided to give you the Blue Badge."

I can see it lying there on his desk. My stomach flips. Motioning me to remove the red one from my tunic, he hands me my Blue. After placing the red one into the drawer he dismisses me. As I turn to march out I just have to break into a grin.

Because I'm with Officer Gregg I feel I can celebrate a bit and punch the air as we emerge into the cold, snowy day. "*Yes.*"

Gregg allows himself a smile on the march to the bakery. At the door he removes his hornrimmed spectacles to clean the snow off them and turns to me, "you got off to a bad start Groom but you've got the Blue now, one step nearer, keep your head down and this time next year you'll be going home."

Home. Freedom. I can't take my eyes off the badge all morning. Old Brannigan gives it a pat and smiles "the Blue eh." He can see what it means to me. Can't wait to show the others and at dinnertime it's all I want to talk about.

"You joined the Blue's at last," PJ nods at my badge.

"I should be getting my dizzi soon" Taffy throws an envious look at Titchy.

"I just wanna get Doreen's knickers off, first thing I'll do," Titchy grins across the table and then shuts his eyes as if imagining it, which makes the rest of us feel, well, just fuckin'jealous.

"Lucky beggar. Is she a good shag then?" asks Lofty, leaning forward across the table towards Titchy expecting some juicy titbits.

"Oh yeh, she fucks good alright, does everything" Titchy grins and winks at Lofty, "you know what I mean."

Lofty squirms on his chair. His right hand disappears under the table. He looks uncomfortable and Taffy laughs. "Well you did ask, best keep your mind off it if you ask me. When's your home leave then Titchy?"

"Three weeks. Every day seems like a week."

"It was a bit like that in the Hospital. It'll soon pass."

I dip my cob into the gravy and get on with my shepherds pie. They're all going out before me. I've still got another twelve months to do.

Taffy was right, the three weeks soon pass and we decide to stay in Hawk for Titchy's last night before Home Leave. He's like a pea in a colander.

"I need some of that scented soap Watt," he comes dashing into my cell after tea. "I've been using it every day for a week now and that bit I had has gone." I pass him some soap. He dashes off again.

We play cards, darts, billiards, everything to keep him occupied, otherwise he's just gonna explode. Pop comes over and reminds Titchy that, although it's hard, he must come back.

Just before lock up we give him a list of what we'd like brought in. Lofty wants a dirty mag. Doesn't everybody? A single picture flies round like wildfire and you can get a quarter ounce for a one night lend. Taffy needs some decent razor blades, his facial hair is tough and he can never get a clean shave with the ones they issue in here. PJ asks for a bit of cream for his dry skin and I write bacca. A man can never have enough bacca.

It's all just fantasy 'cos Titchy's not gonna give us a second thought once he's through those gates. Who can blame him? He won't risk his discharge. He knows that and we know that. Even so, there's a tingle of anticipation. Strange but true. It's called hope, a vain hope in a hopeless place. The list will never leave his cell. It will be ripped into little pieces, just like our hopes.

Five days later Titchy's due back at teatime. He pops his head round my cell door with that familiar cheeky grin "Whatcha Watt."

"You came back then."

"Oh believe me it was fuckin' hard mate, don't think it didn't cross my mind, more than once."

"You look different." He's had his hair cut and there's a sort of sparkle about him that only those who are nearing discharge have.

"It's all the shaggin'" his face beams at me.

We make our way to join the others for tea where Titchy proceeds to tell us, in great detail, about the things he's been up to this last week. How did he manage to cram so much into five days? The stories continue through into association. Even PJ, the gym fanatic, stays to listen. Titchy is one of those guys whose happiness rubs off and we all go to lock up laughing or smiling.

Taffy gets his 'dizzi' badge a couple of weeks later and, not surprisingly, all he can think of, or talk about, is his Home Leave, which happens to coincide with Titchy's discharge. So they leave Hawk together. Taffy will return in five days time to regale us with tales of Martha and Beth. Titchy is getting married next month, it's all been arranged. He's making a fresh start and going to live with his Grandma. His father and brother are both in prison but he doesn't want that sort of life for himself. He gives me his address but the look in his eyes tells me he's hoping I won't make contact. "All the luck in the world mate." I shake his hand knowing I'll never see him again.

Two days later there's a new arrival in Titchy's cell. As we are neighbours I pop my head round to introduce myself and find out if he smokes. His name is Phillip, Phil for short. He's from up North and seems like a right little tough nut. He asks if I've got any snout so I sort him out with a quarter and tell him the rules. I'll see how he goes for a couple of weeks and then ask if he wants to carry for me.

After showing him what's what he joins the rest of us for tea. Phil explains he was caught up in a fight between rival gangs. Says he was only walking past but got drawn into it because a flying punch happened to land on his girlfriend, so he waded in. He seems to get on with everyone.

I start to explain about the Governor seeing him tomorrow and the pro's and con's of the different jobs, just like Del did with me on my first night. God, it feels like I've been here forever. Phil had a job in a butchers shop on the outside so they might stick him in the kitchens.

At dinnertime Phil's telling me about his interview with the Governor and job in the kitchens when one of the screws shouts, "Shakedown Groom." I haven't had a shakedown in months and wonder why now. I'm very careful so I'm not too worried but there's always the possibility of a 'plant'. My goods are spread amongst carriers so there's nothing in my cell that shouldn't be there.

I walk across and into my cell. Two screws are already pulling it apart. Leaning against the wall with one foot crossed over the other and my hands behind my back, I watch as they lift and look inside everything, even the bible. Nobody speaks while this is being done.

My letter to Mom lies half written on the table. One screw lifts the piece of paper, reads it, looks underneath and places it back down. The other one moves to open my bacca tin and they just look at each other. There have been times when it's been crammed with a lot more than the 2oz allowance but these days it only ever contains about an ounce. I don't run that risk any more. 'Cover your back, think dizzi', I can hear Taffy's voice in my head. Now I've got my blue all I want is that green dizzi badge.

"Nothing?" asks the one screw.

"Nothing," confirms the other, who has been stripping my bed.

I smile at them as they leave my cell. They don't look too pleased. Still, no 'plant', thank God for that, I glance to the heavens, well to the top landing to be more precise. Sitting back down for dinner, I watch the two screws as they stand there, laughing, chatting, and all powerful. Shaking my head at Phil, "they might have control over what we fuckin' do, but not what goes on in here mate," I tap my forehead twice, and he nods.

Taffy's back, with that certain sparkle about him. His eyes could light up the whole place as he talks about Beth and how she'd sat on his lap and called him 'da da'. He's so proud you can almost touch it.

Lofty being Lofty can't help himself, "What about the shag then?"

Taffy takes it in good part, winks at me and proceeds to tell Lofty in graphic detail about a particular 'slow shag' he'd had on the sofa. The further into the story Taffy gets the more Lofty squirms on the chair and crosses his legs. Unable to control himself he dashes off to his cell.

Taffy shakes his head "If he believes that, he'll believe anything." We all laugh. I grab my bacca tin and roll one up. They've all had a bird, there's only me who ain't and I don't know what to believe.

It's not long before I'm saying goodbye to Taffy. "I'm never coming back to anything like this again" he resolves "no…I've got my Beth to think of." I wish him all the best. "You too Watt, keep yourself straight when you get out."

It's a hot summer day and sweltering in the bakehouse classroom. We did the practical last week so now it's the written exam. I put my name at the top of the sheet and turn over the question paper. Reading them through first, which is what Old Brannigan had told us to do, there don't seem to be any that will pose a problem, so I start to write.

It seems like no time at all and I've finished. Everyone else is either scrawling away or sitting with a puzzled and worried expression on their face.

Not long after it's 'pens down'. So that's it then.

"When will we get the results Sir" I ask as the papers are collected in.

"About six weeks Groom" Officer Brannigan smiles "the certificates will go straight into your property if you pass but I'll let you know, don't worry."

Six weeks later sees Lofty with his 'dizzi' badge and me with my City and Guilds 158 and 159 in Baking and Confectionary. I say it out loud as if somehow it can be something tangible if I speak it. Perhaps I can be a Baker. I quite like the sound of that. 'What do you do for a living then? I'm a Baker and Confectioner'. Wonder how much it pays.

"I dunno, Del gone, Titchy gone, Taffy gone, Lofty going soon, there's only me and you left mate," I turn towards the hand-basin.

PJ stares at the urinal. "I'm seeing the Governor tomorrow. Must be my dizzi. I'll be gone by Christmas." He does his buttons up. "When you get out you can come and stay with me for a bit of a holiday if you want. We can do the clubs, get some birds. I've got a pad in West Kensington."

"That sounds fuckin' great to me."

And so the daily round of slop out, PT, eat, sleep and work continues. Good screws and bad screws. One of the best, Officer Gregg retires. Officer Grogan gets married and comes back from honeymoon minus his moustache. Wonder what happened there then?

We have the odd ruckus now and then but nothing heavy. Hunkus goes out, which brings a sigh of relief from a lot of timid cons but, sadly, there's always another bully waiting in the wings. Lofty gets his discharge and, as we say our goodbyes, I tell him I'll never forget that he made me a smoker and he says he'll never forget the rash the curly red beard gave him! PJ goes on Home Leave and is discharged in mid December. He gives me his address and makes me promise to keep in touch. Perhaps I will.

Phil has become one of my many carriers. I knock about with him and Bones now. They both sign up for the Christmas Show and I listen to them discussing their parts and costumes. Bones, who's just got his Blue, says Tony thinks he could make it as an entertainer and is going to put him in touch with some people on the outside. Officer Grogan thinks Bones could make it as a footballer. He's got it made.

I'm pestered to join the show but my heart ain't in it. All I can think about is getting the 'dizzi' and getting Home Leave. How's that song go 'all I want for Christmas is my dizzi badge, my dizzi badge, my dizzi badge'.

A week before my 19th Birthday I am marched into the Governor's office where he gives me the coveted green badge. This means final discharge, all being well and with a following wind, by the end of February.

Christmas is a blur. The Show is excellent. What they'll do when Tony is discharged I don't know. Then it's the usual Christmas day dinner followed by a Film and now it's a new year. My Home Leave is set for 20th January. Twenty whole days to get through. I'm sitting in my cell thinking about the things I'm going to do when a screw tells me the Governor wants to see me and I'm marched straight over. What the hell. I ain't done nothing. Fuck it. If somebody's put the kaibosh on my Home Leave I'll kill 'em, there and then I'll kill 'em.

"You like football don't you Groom. You played in the winning team last year didn't you?" The Governor is looking at me and he's smiling. It's a fuckin' dream this is.

"Yes Sir."

"I am selecting some boys who are nearing discharge to come to my home and watch a football match on television. I take it you'd like that?"

It isn't really a question. "Yes Sir."

"Next Saturday. Officer Brannigan is aware. Dismiss."

Fuck me, I can't believe it. I'm not sure whether this is good or bad. Best behaviour and all that.

Saturday dawns and just after dinner I am marched out of Hawk to the courtyard. Another three boys the Governor has selected are already there and standing to attention. I see Spider and we nod a greeting. One of the Officers drives us in a posh car and for the first time I go back down that long drive to the big gated entrance. I hear the same creaks as I'd heard 2 years 7 months ago, but then I was in a Black Mariah.

It only takes about five minutes but it could have taken hours for me. Lots of rolling green countryside, the like of which I've never seen. We pull into a driveway and come to a halt outside a large detached house. A grey haired lady comes to the door and shows us through to a spacious lounge where there are glasses of lemonade and some sandwiches on a table in the middle. "I'll make a pot of tea" she says leaving the room and gesturing us to sit down. I sink into the sofa which sort of envelopes me.

"Fuckin' brilliant" I whisper to Spider who is sat beside me.

The Governor walks in and we stand to attention. It's a bit stilted but we watch the match, drink the drinks and eat the sarnies. I don't even know which teams are playing as we watch TV and I don't care much. I just make the right noises when a goal is scored. Mmm comfort. I've never sat on anything so wonderful.

The afternoon comes to an end, and, after thanking the Governor, we are transported back to Rochester. At association the cons want to know every little detail and I'm the centre of attention, telling the tale.

20th January arrives. "I'm getting out and getting laid" I tell Phil and Bones over breakfast. They both look a bit glum. "Fuckin' cheer up, your turn'll come."

I'd had the chat from Pop last night about coming back. I'm just thinking about getting out, can't think that far ahead. Five whole beautiful days. After breakfast I'm marched over to Reception where my box is waiting. The City and Guilds Certificates are rolled up on top but I push them to the bottom.

Pulling my crumpled suit from the box I feel the grin spread across my face. The sour faced screw gives me a return train ticket and some money which I sign for and then I'm outside climbing into a sort of small bus.

There are eight of us going to the Station. Glancing at the ticket I see my train leaves at 10.08am. Checking my watch it says 3am. It's been in that fuckin' box for over two years. No wonder it stopped. I ask the screw who's driving the bus for the right time, set my watch and wind it up. "Look, no handcuffs" I joke with one of the other cons. They all laugh.

It's over an hour wait at the Station but I ain't bothered. I'm outside those gates, that cell. Sitting on the platform the sights, the sounds and the smells are so different from inside. The noises are gentler. No shouting. There's always someone shouting on the inside. A couple of kids playing and laughing with their Mom, a middle age couple sitting on the next bench whispering together and looking my way now and then, a young woman with long blonde hair and even longer legs, standing near the edge of the platform, glancing at her watch every minute or so.

My train is the last to come and I've seen the other seven cons catch theirs and chuff off into the distance. There's only me, an elderly lady and the blonde bird on the platform, as my train comes into view. She shakes her head and huffs and puffs. The train is only about ten minutes late. She must be in a tearing hurry to get somewhere. I can't take my eyes off her. What a view. And she's catching my train.

I think I'll get some brownie points and help the old lady onto the train. She thanks me and takes a window seat near to the door. The blonde bird walks further up the carriage so I follow her and take the seat opposite. After a few minutes she looks across and smiles. Can't believe my luck.

"Are you going to London?" I strike up a conversation and try to talk posh.

"Yes, you?"

"I have to change trains in London. I'm going to Wolverhampton."

"Where's that?"

God. She doesn't know where Wolverhampton is! I look at her lovely blue eyes and find my thoughts wandering to her breasts. Trouble is my gaze has wandered there too and she spots it. The long blonde hair swishes around her shoulders as she shakes her head, gets up and moves further down the carriage. Oh well. I start counting hedgerows to take my mind off things as we proceed, clackety clack, to London.

Another forty five minute wait in London for the Wolverhampton train and I'm sat on the platform surrounded by birds, all shapes and sizes, not noticing me and going about their business. But I notice them alright.

One is standing quite close to where I'm sitting. She's wearing a bright blue skirt with lots of white petticoats underneath and a tight jacket with a big white belt and a little scarf at the neck. Her dark hair is tied in a pony tail and it swings back and forth as she chats to another girl.

I watch her wave goodbye to her mate and get on the train. It's my train too. Don't make the same mistake twice. Sitting opposite I open my newspaper and pretend to ignore her. I'm trying to read but can't concentrate and stare at her pretty blue and white shoes from underneath the paper.

The beautiful smell of her wafts across the carriage and I can't get enough of it. About half an hour into the journey I place the newspaper on the empty seat next to me and pull out a packet of humbugs I'd bought at the Station. Well, they'd got no liquorice. I offer her one.

"Ooh thank you" she says dipping her slim fingers into the bag. "Are you going all the way?" she giggles and unwraps the humbug. I start to laugh.

Susie is great and so easy to talk to. I think she likes me. Says she lives in Willenhall and that she's been to Islington to stay with a friend who recently moved there. I tell her I've been visiting my Grandma in Chatham. Susie pats the empty seat next to her and I waste no time in filling it.

"There's a dance at the Toc H on Saturday, I'll be there." She giggles and flashes her deep blue eyes at me.

I know the Toc H. It's a big timber building on the corner of Gypsy Lane not far from the swimming baths. I've got to be back in Rochester by Friday. Fuck it.

I smile at her. "I'll be there too, now I know you're going." Am I a smooth talker or what…

Her Dad is waiting at the Station. He glares at me as we step from the train. Roughly grabbing her hand he yanks her off towards the bus station. She manages to give me a sly wave as they turn the corner.

I want to keep what money I've got left so decide to walk the three miles to Chantry Crescent. I'm out. Breathing fresh air. Ha, that's a laugh. Fresh air, round here, who am I kidding. As the cold wind bites through my thin suit I turn up the collar and walk the familiar route home. Could do with that old fur lined coat off the back of the coalhouse door!

"Watt" Mom rushes up and hugs me "I'll put the kettle on."

"How are you Watt?" asks Pearl.

"I'm better now, good to be home." I cross to the fire and stand with my back to it. Little Barry, not so little now, sits on the sofa staring at me.

"Nice cuppa, plenty of sugar, just how you like it" Mom puts a steaming cup of tea in front of me. No sign of Dad. He must be still at work. Yes it's good to be home. Mike's out playing but Malc, Roy and Marje want to hear all about my 'adventures'. They say I look different. Well I am different.

"You got any money Pearl?"

She narrows her eyes. "How much and what for?"

"I just wanna go up town tonight. See the lads. They gave me a bit when I was released but it aint much."

Pearl pulls out her purse. "Go on then." She hands me two crisp one pound notes.

"Are you sure?"

"Make it last, you ain't getting' no more." She laughs and puts her arms round me as only an older sister can do.

I wash my shirt, iron it dry and press my suit. Combing my hair in the mirror over the fireplace I ask Pearl if Dad still locks the door at 10 o'clock.

She laughs, "Oh yes, I still have to be in and I'm getting married soon!"

"You're not! When?" checking my hair again, I give her a hug and I'm out the door as she shouts something I can't quite catch.

"Won't be back tonight" I yell, running down the entry towards the gate. Passing Dad in the street, I nod and he grunts. It's 7.30 and he's just returning, covered in brickdust, from his twelve hour shift.

A brisk five minute walk brings me to Bilston Town. I'll try the 'Trumpet'. I've never been in a pub before, was never old enough, but I do remember Bishop telling me it's where all the birds hang out. Should have known they wouldn't be ordinary birds but I'm naïve.

The pub is in sight when a familiar voice shouts me from behind.

"Hey Watt, hold on," Rob comes running up, "I went to your house… but Pearl said…you'd gone to town," he's out of breath.

"Rob mate, you need to get fit. Feel the muscle" I tense my arm and he pulls a face. Can tell he's impressed.

"Where you goin' then?"

"I thought I'd try the The Trumpet."

"You mean the 'Cunt and Trumpet'. That's what they call it you know."

"I could do with a bit of that." We both laugh.

"C'mon then, I'll come with you but I've gotta collect Maud from her Gran's and walk her home at nine o'clock." He winks at me.

"Not Maud whatsername from Hunters Close." A copper's daughter. No. Can't be true. At the bottom end of our estate there's a cul-de-sac of Police Houses, aptly named Hunters Close.

He nods. "That's the one mate. At least Mom likes her" and then, as I open the pub door and we walk in, that cheeky grin spreads across his face as he adds, "and she's a good kisser."

There ain't many people in the pub. Me and Rob get a pint of Mild and sit up the corner while he fills me in on all the local gossip. Apparently Steve was released last year but Rob hasn't seen much of him. Nobody has. Rob wants to know all about Borstal and we spend an hour or so chatting. It's like I've never been away.

The pub gradually fills up. Congenial banter and laughter drifts across the small room. Rob leaves at five minutes to nine and a couple of minutes later, as I'm contemplating one of the good looking birds stood at the bar, Johnny Bishop walks in.

"Watt mate, good to see you, heard about your bit of bother" he leans over the table and produces a wad of cash, "Drink?" I nod and he brings me a pint from the bar. He also brings over two birds. "This is Rosie, my girl" he grabs a chair and pulls it across for her, "and this is her friend Elaine."

We all say hello. "How long you been out then?" I hear Bishop asking me the question but can't take my eyes off Rosie. She's wearing a low cut dress which goes to the deepest V. I watch her breasts move as she breathes. "Today mate," I grab my pint and smile at Elaine. Rosie is Bishop's bird. Must keep that in mind.

"Cheers" Bishop raises his glass "some lucky bird's in for a good night then." The girls laugh and Elaine, who is sitting next to me, moves closer. The sweet smell of perfume wafts my way. Her hair is blonde and wavy and feels soft as it brushes against my cheek. She looks about 20ish and is wearing a fair bit of make-up. Pan Stick I think they call it. I remember the actors who stayed at my Uncle Harry's place. They used to look like that. Rosie's not wearing so much. She is dark haired with gorgeous brown eyes, as well as the fascinating V cut dress.

We chat about old times and I discover Taylor's gone off to live the other side of Birmingham and Mad Jack's doin a four stretch for stabbin' some bloke. Bishop has teamed up with Dave and they run a string of girls. "Easy money mate, the girls do the business, we look after 'em and we're coinin' it."

The bell rings for time. I put my arm around Elaine and she nestles her head into the crook of my shoulder. Looking across at Rosie I can see she is watching Bishop's every move.

Turning to Elaine "shall I walk you home?"

"You need a place tonight mate?" Bishop asks. "I owe you one." Bishop hands me a key. "Elaine knows where it is" he winks and walks off with Rosie. She looks over her shoulder at me. Oh those eyes, wish it was her.

The key is to a one bed flat above some shops on the Parade. I take off my suit jacket and hang it on one of the pegs in the hallway. Elaine goes into the bathroom and gestures me through to the lounge which is straight ahead. Streetlights shine through the pokey window and after drawing the drab brown curtains I look around. There's a big beige sofa in front of an electric fire, a couple of small wooden tables and a long sideboard, all very dull and worn.

I flop onto the threadbare sofa and Elaine, after turning off the main light and switching on two table lamps, comes to join me. She snuggles up close and nuzzles my neck…mmm…nice. Her lips make a track to mine.

We kiss, warm and tender, soft at first, but then harder. Sensing the urgency she slides from the sofa onto the rug. She's pulling her top over her head and wriggling out of her skirt.

What started as a tingle is now an uncontrollable urge. I'm trying to unbutton my trousers. She helps me. Fuckin' hell. I look down at the smooth silkiness of her belly and the next second feel it against my skin. I'm exploding. I let out a cry. Like a jackrabbit on steroids it's all over in moments. No feeling I've ever had can compare. All the adrenalin rushes in the world, nothing.

I roll onto my back and turn to look at her. She smiles at me. Still wearing her bra but little else she gets up. "Wanna cuppa?"

We drink our tea and I'm all over her again. She takes off her bra and unbuttons my shirt. When we're both completely naked she leads me into the bedroom.

The bed is unmade and crumpled as we throw ourselves on it. I stroke her breasts. She catches her breath as the back of my hand touches one of her nipples. Her murmurs fill my head as she pulls me to her.

The warmth of her body drives me crazy as we kiss. A long, hard passionate kiss. Soft lips press against mine to open. Her tongue darts inside. My thrusts are slower to start with but when she holds me tighter I just can't hold back and take my cue as she arches her back to meet me.

Just give me a fag and a cuppa every now and then; this is what heaven must be like. Eventually we fall asleep but, as usual, I'm awake early and creep out to the toilet. I climb back in and watch her sleep.

The bedcover lies across her middle and I trace a line around her breasts with my fingers. She stirs, opens her eyes and murmuring softly, guides my hand between her legs. I caress the inside of her thigh and move my hand slowly upwards.

Her eyes are closed as I lean down, kiss her breasts and playfully grab one of her nipples in my teeth. She cries out. Oh no! Have I hurt her?

We kiss and she wraps those long, silky legs around me. Moments later she pushes back my chest and places her ankles on my shoulders. With each thrust her moans of pleasure intensify. Whatever turns her on does it for me. Ain't life great!!!

Wrapped in each others arms, we doze off. It's a warm, comfy sort of feeling, even though the bed's a bit lumpy.

"Cuppa?" asks Elaine.

"Any chance of some toast?"

"I'll have a look." She makes her way into the kitchen, "wonder what time it is."

"I ain't got nowhere to go." I'm hoping she'll come back to bed.

"Promised to get some shopping for my Grandma and its afternoon already," she laughs, setting a mug of steaming tea on the bedside table.

I've only got five days home leave and I'll be gone by Friday. Perhaps the shopping trip could be cancelled. I want her with me. But no, she has to go and so do I. Promising to return the key to Bishop, she says we can meet tonight, at eight, in the 'Trumpet'.

"It's a date at eight" I tease, giving her a lingering kiss as we lock the door. "Better go else I'll be draggin' you upstairs." Her hand feels the hardness between my legs and she pulls a face as I groan and roll my eyes. She knows I'm watching her walk off and waggles her bum before a quick backward glance and wave. I turn towards the café for a bacon sarnie and another cuppa. I need it!

Doris peers at me over the counter. "Well I never."

"One bacon sarnie, well done and a cuppa with two heaped spoons."

"Yes, I remember, but how you've *changed*."

There's not many in 'cos it's the middle of the afternoon and, after eating, I head for home. Slipping out of my jacket I hang it carefully over one of the dining chairs. An unpleasant whiff from the armpits of my shirt means that it needs another wash and I'll have to press my suit again for tonight.

Wonder what's happened to all my clothes. I'd hunted around for a minute or two yesterday but was in too much of a rush to get out. Mom's probably put them in a box somewhere. Turns out they've all been pawned. Had some good gear an' all.

Come eight o'clock I make a beeline for the 'Trumpet' to meet Elaine. Bishop's in with some of his cronies and there's a lot of leg pulling, jokes and laughter. It feels good to be one of the lads again.

"You need this don't you?" Bishop hands me the key at closing time. "Keep it 'til you go back Friday."

Oh thank you sweet Jesus. Evenings are spent in the 'Trumpet' and nights at the flat with Elaine. We get up at lunchtimes, have a bite in the café and take a walk up town. It's nice to have a girl on my arm at last. She's quite a looker too, being blonde, and wears these tight tops that show the outline of her hard breasts. I see how other blokes gawp at her.

On Thursday we spend most of the day and all of the night in bed. When Elaine starts to kiss my chest and wends her way down, a tantalizing ripple of anticipation sweeps through me.

I close my eyes as her tongue flutters across my skin and she takes me in her mouth. I'd heard stories about this from other cons but didn't really believe it…'til now!

Friday comes all too soon. My train leaves Wolverhampton at ll.10am. Elaine tries to snatch the ticket from me and tears a piece off the end. "Don't go," she pleads.

I don't wanna go either. These five days have been the *best days* of my *entire life*. How can I go back to that place? Reason kicks in. If I don't they'll find me anyway, plus I'll get extra time. If I go today then at least I've only got another few weeks left to serve. There's an end in sight.

As my train pulls out, I watch Elaine's figure grow smaller as she waves and blows kisses from the platform. Sticking my head out of the window I can see her for longer until we round a bend and then she's gone.

Later that day I walk back into Hawk, a different person. It's me with that certain sparkle. It's me with that spring in my step. I'm going home. Soon. Shame Lofty's not here. Would I have a tale to tell him or what? No more baroning. I can't risk my discharge.

Next day I'm round to my carriers telling them they can keep whatever they've got of mine. Phil thinks he might take on baroning himself. "Just watch your back," I warn him.

I'm sitting in my cell after tea, contemplating whether to go to the gym or not, when it hits me. What with Elaine I'd forgotten about Susie. It's the Toc H dance tonight and she'll be there watching and waiting for me.

I remember those dark blue eyes and the lovely clean smell wafting from her hair. I find myself wondering what she'd be like, whether her breasts would be as hard as Elaine's.

Hearing the shout 'Anyone for the Gym' I think I'd better go work off some excess steam!

It seems like the longest few weeks ever but discharge day finally dawns. Yesterday Officer Brannigan had given me an easy day, wished me well and said he hoped I would make good use of the qualifications and remember all he'd taught me.

Officers like Brannigan, Gregg, Grogan and Atkins, deserved respect and, looking back, what I actually recall is their kindness and humanity in an otherwise harsh regime. The rest, hard faced and unfeeling, are just remembered as 'the screws'.

Goodbyes to fellow cons had been said last night and everyone else has gone off to work as I am marched, for the last time, over to Reception. I can feel the 2oz tin of bacca in my pocket. I'm allowed to take that out with me.

The familiar property box is lying in wait and once I'm dressed the same sour faced screw tells me I am on license for the next four months and must reside at the address shown. The Probation Service will send a letter setting out details of when and where to report.

He gives me a train ticket and I sign on the dotted line. I also have quite a bit of dosh to collect 'cos I've saved my wages for a while now and, although only a pittance per week, it's mounted up. He counts the money and begrudgingly pushes it over the counter. I look at him and shake my head. What sort of a man does this job?

The five of us being discharged literally leap into the small bus. I turn and look at the big gates being closed as we drive out. I ain't never coming back.

On the short drive to the station I reflect upon what Rochester has taught me. There are probably five things. Each one makes me smile. None of them are what the establishment wanted me to learn.

> *He who shouts loudest gets heard*
> *He who stands first in line always gets served*
> *He who shows weakness is lost*
> *He who wears the uniform is God*
> *He who has the will always finds a way*

I'm out now and what I do with the rest of my life is up to me. It's all there waiting like a giant ball. It's kicked and we follow it. All I can think about at this moment is getting back to Elaine.

Chapter 7

PORTLAND BORSTAL BLUES

Its eight o'clock and there's a spring in my step as I walk into the 'Trumpet'. Elaine is standing with her back to me. The sight of her figure and the wavy blonde hair sets my stomach churning and I sneak up behind, grab the tiny waist and spin her round.

"Watt, you're back" she squeals, throws her arms round my neck and kisses me on the cheek. Does she smell good or what?

"Want a drink?"

"Ooh yes please, I'll have my usual." She pushes her half empty glass towards the barman.

Rosie looks to the floor. "Drink Rosie?"

"No thanks Watt, I'm waiting for Johnny."

"Pint of Mild and a port and lemon then." We get our drinks and move to a table in the corner. Rosie waits by the bar, but not for long. Bishop appears within moments and heads straight for me and Elaine.

"Out for good now then mate?"

I nod. "Feels fuckin' brilliant. Couldn't wait to see my Elaine," I pull her closer and my arm tightens round her shoulders. She looks at Bishop who motions Rosie to the table and raises his hand for drinks. The barman brings them straight over.

"What's your plans then Watt?" asks Bishop.

"I ain't really thought. I'm seeing the Probation Officer on Wednesday 'cos I'm on Licence for four months."

"Some friends of mine need another crew member. Could put a word in if you're interested."

"Thanks, but I think I'll stick on my own." I raise my glass, "Cheers." In my mind's eye I can see the City and Guilds certificates Mom had carefully placed on the mantelshelf only a couple of hours ago. Sitting next to them is a letter from the Probation Officer, which was waiting for me. I might just try and get a proper job. After all, I've got qualifications now.

Dave walks in, spots us and comes over. Bishop raises his hand and another pint is brought across.

"How you doin' then Watt, I ain't seen you since…"Dave stops mid sentence 'cos he's remembering what I'm remembering. I can see him and Mad Jack walking off, their gabardine macs swaying from side to side, and I can see a pool of blood, my blood, half an inch from my face, on the rough ground.

"Bygones be bygones and all that," he says.

Standing up, I take his hand and shake it, holding and pressing hard so he can feel the power.

"Fuckin' hell" he screws up his face and looks at me "you got some fuckin' handshake there mate." Bishop and the girls laugh. Dave laughs. I laugh. We're all mates again.

Another couple of drinks and Elaine snuggles into my neck. She starts nibbling at my earlobe. It's driving me crazy so I look across at Bishop. "Any chance of that key?"

"It should be five quid for an all nighter but you can have it for one."

I'm frowning, what's he on about?

"Hey Watt, you had a fuckin' weeks worth of freebie's last time. I know what goes on in them cop shops," shaking his head and looking into his beer, "you never grassed on me and Taylor, so I owed you. But that's it mate, you want Elaine you pay."

Elaine moves off my shoulder and looks into her drink. Silence. Rosie gets up and walks towards the toilets, closely followed by her friend.

"Look Watt," Bishop leans forward, "Elaine used to be my girl, like the others, but when I'd had enough of her, you know, I asked her to fuck one of my mates. Told her she would if she really wanted me and the silly bitch went for it." Bishop takes a long swig of his pint. "A good fuck that Elaine, ain't she? Good with her mouth an' all," he winks. "Me and Dave teach 'em all the tricks of the trade mate."

"What about Rosie?"

"She's *my* girl, don't get any ideas 'bout her, but you're welcome when I've finished," he pauses to down his beer, "probably another couple of weeks, perhaps a month," he shrugs. "You'll have to pay though. It's business." Raising his hand to the barman for more drinks, "it works like a dream mate. With a bit of persuasion" he looks at Dave and laughs "they'll do anything for you, fuckin' anything. Mind you this ugly bugger," throwing a thumb towards Dave, "ain't very good at pullin'."

Dave nods, "Johnny pulls the birds, then once they're hooked I give 'em one they won't forget," he smiles to himself, "beat 'em up a bit if they don't do what we say, so they know who's boss, and that's it like."

Rosie and Elaine walk back from the toilets. Rosie glances at me and then at Bishop. Elaine catches my eye for a moment and then seems to find something fascinating on the floor all the way back to her seat.

Beat 'em up Dave had said. Has Elaine been beat up? Will Rosie be beat up? What sort of blokes are they? Sounds like more than a 'bit of persuasion' to me. Bishop's planning on doing this to Rosie. She's looking at him under those dark lashes. I watch the rise and fall of her jumper. Lifting her glass to those luscious lips she slowly sips her drink.

I finish my pint and stand up to go. Elaine looks to Bishop. "I ain't working tonight am I?"

"No" he says, "but make sure you're outside Sankeys at seven tomorrow with Mavis. Pay day, knocking off time in more ways than one," he winks at me and then speaks harshly to Elaine, "Dave will be checking."

"Oh Johnny *please*, not Sankeys, *please* Johnny."

"Getting fussy now are we. You *be* there."

She lowers her eyes and then glances at me. "Can you walk me home?"

I remember the five brilliant days she gave me. I learned a lot. The cream cakes, we had some fun with them. I've hesitated too long. Elaine hangs her head and makes for the door.

"Wait up." I manouvre myself round the table. "Night Rosie, Johnny, Dave, see you around."

"No freebies Elaine" Bishop warns, pointing a finger at her, "don't mess me around."

"Hey mate, I know the score, I'll just walk her home safe." I put my hands on his shoulders as I walk past. The likes of Bishop and Dave don't bother me any more. Not one bit.

Elaine pulls her collar up. "This way," she starts walking towards Priestfields and I fall in step alongside. Her heels click on the pavement and I put my hand out to steady her as she almost trips on a protruding kerbstone. "Thanks," she glances up at me in the moonlight and turns to carry on but I pull her back and into my arms. Stifling a cry she shrugs me off and we start walking again.

I can't get out of my head what Dave had said. "Do they beat you up?"

She looks terrified. "I just do what they say. If I don't then Dave finds me and …." she falters "well, he doesn't beat me up exactly."

"What is it then?"

"He likes to hurt me, you know" she looks at the pavement, "so I try to do what he says but sometimes he comes to find me anyway," she bursts into tears.

I ain't got a hanky so I just put my arms round her shoulders. If Bishop does this to Rosie… it doesn't bear thinking about.

"This is it" Elaine stops outside a little terrace house on the main road. "My Gran's house."

I don't know anything about Elaine. I've slept with her and know every inch of her body but I never took the time to find out about *her*. "You live with your Gran then?"

"Yes, my parents died seven years ago. Want a cuppa?"

"What about your Gran?"

"She'll be asleep by now."

I nod and Elaine unlocks the door to a very neat little house, everything in its place, and we walk through to a pretty kitchen at the back.

"Toilet's just there" she says pointing to the door. Elaine knows all my weaknesses, one being that beer goes straight through me.

"Two heaped spoons" she says, placing the teacup on the small formica top kitchen table.

Her pan-stick makeup has streaked and she catches sight of herself in the small mirror hanging over the table. "Look at me."

"I am." I pull her down onto my lap and kiss her cheek. She pushes my face away and starts to talk.

"Johnny told me to sort you out 'cos he owed you but I really liked you. Not like some of the others." I feel a shudder pass through her body.

"I thought he loved me, he told me he did. I ain't easy you know," Elaine frowns at me and I shake my head. "He said we'd get married, gave me a ring and everything. I left my job at Woolworths 'cos he didn't want me workin' six days a week. One night," she looks down and starts twisting her fingers, "we were back at the flat and I felt funny, even though I'd only had two port and lemons. I was lying on the bed and the light kept spinning, everything was spinning. Johnny was kissing me and then it was somebody else. I tried to push him off but Johnny was there and said it was alright, because if I loved him I'd do it for him."

I ease Elaine off my lap 'cos my leg's going to sleep. "Can we talk somewhere more comfy?" She leads me into the front parlour and we sit side by side on the sofa. Elaine hunches forward staring at the fireplace.

"Johnny kept me at the flat for two days. I felt woozy most of the time. I hadn't got any strength and just lay on the bed. When I woke up there would either be Johnny or his mate all over me or both of them together. Johnny told me that I'd never get another job but he'd make sure I was alright. He'd give me some money and look after me and my Gran. All I had to do was sleep with some of his mates now and then. I told him no, but next thing there's Dave, he's got a knife and he's pushing me face down on the bed. He really, *really*, hurt me. He don't like it normal." She pauses and pulls a cushion into her arms. "Afterwards Johnny said he'd send Dave to find me wherever I was if I didn't do as he said. I ain't got nobody only my Gran. I didn't know what to do." She starts to sob into the cushion.

I pull her back onto my shoulder. She looks up at me, "I really like you. We had some fun didn't we?"

I have to admit that we did. I feel sorry for Elaine. I don't know where she goes from here but I know I need a fag, a cuppa, and then some shut eye. I'm beat. Elaine puts the kettle on. "You can stay on the sofa if you like" she brings more cushions to make me comfortable, "you won't tell anyone?"

"Course not" I shake my head. "What's with the Sankeys thing?"

Elaine's shoulders slump and she hangs her head. "It means I'm on the streets. The old blokes comin' out of work, they generally want blow jobs at the back of the garages, Mavis told me, it's horrible, they ain't had a wash and it stinks. I've only ever used the flat 'til now. He must be getting it ready for somebody else."

I lie there listening to her creep up the stairs. After what she's told me I don't have the urge to creep after her. This time tomorrow. Ugh.

Streetlights weave a pattern of light through the thin curtains as I reflect on what Bishop had said. Doesn't matter where you are, bullies prey on the weak and vulnerable. I drift off to sleep and dream about Rosie.

Clatter. Clatter. I awake to the sound of cups being rattled. 'Come on Elaine, your breakfast is ready' an unfamiliar voice shouts from just outside the parlour door. Must be Grandma. I hold my breath.

Slow footsteps make a track along the tiled hallway back to the kitchen. I breathe a sigh of relief. Easing myself up quietly from the sofa I tiptoe to the door. She can't find me here. I've got to get out.

Peering through the crack I can make out a bent old lady sitting at the formica top kitchen table. She has her back to me. Elderly people are deaf aren't they? Hope so. Dreading the creak, 'cos all the doors at home creak, I open it just wide enough for me to slip through. No creak. Phew. Thank you sweet Jesus.

The front door is about five foot away and I move gradually towards it keeping my eyes firmly fixed on Grandma's back but with my left arm outstretched feeling for the latch. Panic. Did Elaine bolt the door as well?

Can't remember. The door opens with a small whine. Like lightening I shoot through and, with my tongue tracing the edge of my top teeth, pull it shut with the smallest of clunks. Aah.

Come lunchtime I'm telling Rob all about it over a bacon sarnie at the Table Mountain.

"You wanna stay away from that lot mate," he stirs his second cuppa. "Think about it, they're fuckin' trouble." He nudges me, "Cor, look at that," Rob is eyeing up two birds who've just walked in.

I can only think of one thing. "It's gonna happen to Rosie though."

"Fuck Rosie, that's her lookout. You should get yourself a decent girl, one who hasn't, you know," he shakes his head and raises his eyebrows, "been with anybody else."

Fuck Rosie, definitely, yes, that's what I want. I stare at my bacon sarnie. "What's up duck, ain't it crispy enough?" shouts Doris from the counter.

"Look, why don't you come down the Toc H tonight. There's a dance every Friday. Me and Maud are going. All the lads will be there. They'd like to see you, and there's lots of girls mate, all shapes and sizes."

Susie flashes before my eyes, soon replaced by Rosie sipping her drink with those luscious lips.

"Look, if you don't fancy the Toc H, then come to the dance at Willenhall Baths tomorrow. I gotta go now."

I roll another fag and Rob leaves me stewing over my third cuppa.

Seven o'clock sees me outside the Toc H, suited and booted. Elaine will be outside Sankeys. The thought of it turns my stomach. I can hear Rob's voice in my head 'forget her and her sort' but it's not easy to forget what she told me and the sound of her sobbing into that cushion. Wonder if Susie will be in? I turn and walk through the door.

It's a long room with a bar at one end. Lots of girls are sitting around the edge of the dancefloor. There are no tables. Heading over to the bar I notice a few old schoolmates. I must have a magnet in my suit 'cos they make a beeline for me. 'Wouldn't have recognized you' and 'how'd you get your hair like that?', 'you look like whatsisname, you know that actor on the films' are some of the comments. They don't sell draught so I get a bottle and ask the record bloke to play a slow one by Pat Boone later. Out of the corner of my eye I can see girls looking across and nudging one another.

Rob comes in with his bird, quietly spoken, she seems nice and there's a gang of us standing chatting. They want to know everything about Borstal and I'm enjoying being the centre of attention. Suppose it's a kind of notoriety. Suddenly everybody's interested so I regale them with tales of Hunkus, the Block and Carver.

I've spotted Susie dancing with a group of friends and see her glance in my direction once or twice but, as our eyes meet, she looks away. When a slow record starts to play they all sit down so I ask her for a dance.

At first the pony tail swings back and forth as she shakes her head. I ask again. She looks up smiling but says nothing, so I grab her hand and pull her onto the dance floor.

"Ooh" she giggles and then, as we sort of walk round, her deep blue eyes searching mine, "what happened to you the other week?"

I place my finger over her lips, pull her closer into my arms and breathe in the sweet smell. Her body stiffens and she pulls away slightly, but not too much. The dance finishes and I take her back to join her mates. They gather round Susie, heads together, glancing at me and giggling.

Just then I see a familiar flash of dark brown hair and turn to see Rosie walk in with a couple of other girls. No sign of Bishop. It's probably not his scene. He's older and this place is full of teenagers.

I walk over. "Hello Rosie, what you doin' here?"

Turning she looks at me full in the face for the first time. Something in my stomach does cartwheels. She is absolutely *the* most beautiful girl I have ever seen.

"Oh Johnny's picking me up later. He says I can have a last night out with my mates, a sort of one-off like, to celebrate. We ain't been out for ages have we girls?" She flashes a ring and her mates start laughing.

What flashes before me is the flat and Dave threatening her with a knife as he shags her up the arse.

"Drink then girls?" it's gonna take nearly all the money I've got to buy this lot a drink but it's the only thing I can think of to be near her. I take the orders but have forgotten by the time I get to the bar. I just buy anything and as Rosie's mates sort 'em out she tells me that Johnny asked her to marry him last night.

"It's a bit tight," she says trying to turn the ring. Probably the same one Elaine had. Don't they know? Don't they talk to each other? Then again, if you're a girl being threatened with a knife, you probably don't say nothing to no-one.

"I packed my job in today" I hear her tell the girls "Johnny wants me with him. We're gonna start a family as soon as we're married." She looks happy and twirls round, her skirt billowing out.

Maybe if I can get her to think about what happened to Elaine then the penny might drop, "Elaine was his girl before."

"That was different" she tells me. "He found out she didn't love him. She went with somebody else and, as Johnny says, if they'll go with one, they'll go with more, so he just used that and now she works for him."

"I know he's *so* much older but Johnny's *so* good looking isn't he," pipes up one of her mates "he's got the cash an' all, wish it was me."

I catch hold of Rosie's arm. The anticipation of touching her had burned within me since our first meeting and a tingle moves through my body as I pull her to one side and tell her everything Elaine had told me last night. What's the matter with her, is she deaf as well as blind? She doesn't believe it, flashes her big brown eyes, flounces her head and walks back to her mates where they gather round to admire the ring again.

Walking home with Rob and Maud, I shove my hands in my pockets and count the paving stones. When we reach the bottom of Hunters Close they walk off up the incline, hand in hand. Standing on the corner I watch them kissing in the doorway. Turning for home my thoughts are of Rosie.

I ain't got no money left so I cadge a bit off Pearl and Monday I'm up the Labour Exchange with the letter they'd given me at Rochester.

"There's a suitable job at Fryars Bakery in Darlaston" announces the friendly lady as she sets up an interview for me later today "take your certificates with you."

So I'm sitting here at Fryars, having walked the three miles. Familiar smells of the bakehouse punch my nostrils as I wait for someone to see me. "Walter, isn't it" says the grey haired bloke in his whites. A bit like Brannigan. He tells me it's a small family bakery and everyone has to be able to do everything.

He seems impressed when I tell him my experience. "Let me have a look at your certificates then Walter. Where have you worked before then?" I don't know how much it pays but at least it's a decent job. Mom will be dead chuffed and the Probation Officer will be pleased. The old guy takes a look at my certificates but the mood changes when he finds out I got them in Borstal. "Oh, I see" he says, studying me hard as he raises his head. "I'm sorry but I can't afford to take any chances." Handing them back he shows me out and I think he just locked the door!

I rip the certificates into tiny pieces and drop them down the nearest drain. Old Brannigan was wrong. They're useless to me.

The Probation Officer is a small, bald guy with round wire framed spectacles. He asks what efforts I've made to find a job and when I tell him he rustles his papers and goes red in the face. I say I've ripped the certificates up and he can't look me in the eye. Writing lots of notes he says I should try again and he can get me duplicates if I'd like.

No, I wouldn't like. I don't want that humiliating experience again. He says I should keep out of trouble, try to get work, report to him every week at the same time for the next four months, and then sends me on my way.

It's Friday night and Ian, my old schoolmate, has been round to see if I'd like to go up town with him. I don't wanna go to the 'Trumpet' any more so we decide to walk into Wolverhampton. Our route takes us past Sankeys. There she is. Elaine. I see her before she spots me. She's talking to an old bloke, about fifty odd, with a grimy rucksack slung over his shoulder. They seem to be arguing about something.

Dave appears from nowhere and slaps her so hard across the face that she falls backwards. The bloke hands him some money and walks towards the old garages. Dave drags Elaine up by her clothing. The flimsy material flutters in the wind as some buttons from her tight blouse scatter. We are close now and I hear them tinkle as they land on the ground.

Dave gestures her to follow the punter "you don't work, you don't eat, want your Grandma to starve do you?"

It's then that she spots me and Ian. "That was a good eyeful" says Ian laughing to me.

"I know her" I tell him, holding Elaine's eyes.

"Fuck me, she's a slapper."

Elaine drops her head, pulls the flapping blouse across the top of her naked breasts and hurries towards the garages. Dave gives me a wave and returns to his vantage point, the back seat of a big black car, where he watches the rest of his tarts as they proposition the workforce of Sankeys.

Quite a few blokes are hanging around at the end of the garages now. I never walk that way again and its eight months before I see Elaine again.

I've signed on and collect my money the following Friday and I'm thinking of Susie as I comb my hair in the big mirror over our fireplace. Looking good. Toc H here I come. Susie here I come. I'll be taking her home tonight. Quick swig of tea, straighten my tie and off.

Fuck it. I watch the bus disappear up the road. Maybe I can catch it at the next stop. Starting to run I just about manage to grab the pole as it starts to pull away from the next bus stop. A couple of girls, who have watched my progress from the back seat, give me the eye. I ain't even raised a sweat and, after paying the conductor, sit down coolly on the seat in front of them.

One is very pretty. Blonde, a bit like Anita Ekberg, with a figure to die for. From what I can overhear of their conversation I think she fancies me. It seems they are going to the Toc H. If Susie ain't there my luck might be in.

Susie is there and we chat. She's trying to find out more about me. I just want to feel her close to me. Later at the bar I'm talking to Rob "where do you go when you want to shag then?"

"Shag mate, did you say shag? I ain't shagged Maud yet. Not proper like. Look if you like a girl and she's decent it's gotta be worth the wait. Being first an' all."

"Suppose so," I take the drinks over to Susie. "Can I walk you home tonight then?" After the dance we make our way to Gypsy Lane. She lives in a semi-detached house, seems posh to me as we stand at the gate. I lean forward to kiss her and slide my arms under her jacket. She stops my hands but kisses me back. It's soft and warm but when I press harder with my lips to part hers so that I can use my tongue, she pulls back.

"Susie, get in" her Dad is standing in the doorway.

"I'm going to the dance at the Baths tomorrow," she whispers in my ear and then turns to flee up the path.

I've got to get some money and fast. The meager dole money and a few handouts from Pearl isn't enough. Ian has told me I can shovel coal off the boats at Tooley's Wharf for four pounds a time, so Saturday morning, bright and early, I'm one of a dozen or more blokes waiting at the Wharf.

A burly guy comes along. I'm wearing an old tight shirt and my muscles are bulging through. "You look useful" he says pointing at me and a couple of others. The rest go home.

Several barges, laden with coal, line the canal. He gives me a huge shovel and a sledgehammer. "You ain't been before, have you?"

I grab the tools, "No."

"Just pick off the big lumps and stack 'em on the side here" he points to the Wharf, "any too big to lift, break 'em with the sledge, shovel the rest, and the slack off the bottom, over the top. The big lumps stop it goin' in the cut, see. I want the boat clean mind. No coal left or you won't get paid. Four quid when you've finished if you do a good job. You can start on the 28 tonner."

Six hours later and I'm done. The others are all still at it. The bloke seems pleased with me and, after inspecting the boat, gives me my four quid. "Come again" he says, "any day."

And so I do. It's hard graft but keeps me fit and, although it's not a proper job, I get by for a few weeks. Me and Susie are 'courting', well we've been to the pictures once and I take her home from the Toc H on a Friday and from the dance at Willenhall Baths on a Saturday.

"How far you got then?" asks Rob, wanting to compare notes.

"Not far enough mate, a bit of kissing and a bit of feeling. It's been weeks now."

"Take her down the park Watt. There's that pavilion thing, you remember we used to jump up and down off the benches. I got Maud in there the other night, fuckin' great it was, not all the way mind, but we did everything else," he grins widely.

I go up town Friday to buy a box of chocolates for Susie, as a sweetener, we can eat 'em in the pavilion. I'm in the shop and there she is walking past. Rosie. I haven't seen her since that night at the Toc H. She's on her own and looks down in the dumps. I follow her for a bit just to watch the sway of her body and take in the contours of her face as she stares blankly into the shop windows now and then. I remember how happy she'd been the last time I saw her, twirling round and showing off her ring. Now she's got that beaten look. I can smell it a mile off.

"Hey Rosie, wait up."

She turns, drops her eyes to the pavement and carries on walking. "Hello Watt."

"Cheer up girl" I drop in step alongside and notice there's no ring on her finger, no sparkle about her. As we stop to cross over the road I pull her round and sink into the sadness of those big brown eyes. "I was right wasn't I?" She just nods and catches her breath, holding back the tears.

The bastard, I knew it.

"I've got to get back" she says, "he said I could have a breather for ten minutes, is all."

"A breather, what do you mean?"

Her eyes not leaving the pavement, Rosie tells me it happened a couple of nights ago, just like I'd said it would. She's been with a few of Bishop's mates but he's told her because she 'played up' Dave's visiting after dinner and there's another three coming to the flat this afternoon.

"My Dad threw me out. I ain't got nowhere to go." She starts to cry softly. "Three at once, what they gonna do to me Watt?" she sobs.

"I don't want to end up down Sankeys like Elaine." Tears are streaming down her face. She knows it's inevitable 'cos once his mates have had their fill, it's out on the streets they go. I can't let Dave get at her. I can't let it happen.

"Who's at the flat now?"

"Just Johnny but Dave's coming at half past two. The rest are coming at five," she pauses and takes a deep breath "to make a night of it."

"Right, wait for me at the Table Mountain. Give me the key." Rosie looks at me, fear in her eyes. "Just give me the key." I stand holding out my hand.

Trembling, she reaches into her pocket.

"Here hold these" I push the chocolates into her hand and sprint off to the flat.

"Be careful, he's got a knife" she yells after me.

Be fuckin' careful. I'll rip his fuckin' head off his shoulders. I insert the key into the lock and ease the door open. Feeling my face harden, the adrenalin rush sends my blood pumping and it slams against my temples. Once inside I bang the door shut.

"Fuckin' hell, leave it on its hinges" Bishop shouts from the lounge, "Hurry up, get in here and get your mouth round this."

I take off my jacket and hang it on one of the pegs. He's sitting on the sofa with his back to me. His bottom half is naked, "C'mon then bitch get to it." Impatient now I see him grab hold of his dick and sensing movement in the doorway he turns. "What the fuck…" The look on his face is priceless, his jaw drops open and he goes to stand up.

He never really knew what hit him. I smash him in the face and then punch him in the groin. He cries out in agony and I land another one to the jaw that almost knocks him out. I see a knife on the side table laid neatly next to the knuckleduster. My fingers close around the blade and for a split second I wanna plunge it into him.

Bishop's holding himself moaning, eyes half shut but when he sees the knife, his eyes widen. I grab him round the throat with one hand and raise the knife with the other. "Bastard" I shout at him "fuckin' leave Rosie alone. There's plenty of tarts out there. Fuckin' use them." He's red in the face and nods, but I know this ain't enough.

He makes a grab for the knife. I've anticipated the move and throw it over the back of the sofa. Blocking his hand, I punch him in the ribs and smash him again in the face. His head lolls back and blood spurts from his nose onto the cushion. Grabbing him by the hair I lean down to shove my face into his, "don't fuckin' mess with me you cunt, I ain't a kid anymore." Blood mingles with the blonde hair as I throw his head back onto the cushion.

"Rosie won't be wanting this." Her key lands with a ping on the side table. I smooth my hair in the mirror, dust myself down and pick up the knife. Lifting my jacket from the peg I slip the blade into the inside pocket. Might be needing it. Gotta keep my weather eye open again.

Leaving Bishop to lick his wounds I slam the door and walk briskly to the Table Mountain.

Rosie is sitting at the window seat and her face breaks into a big smile as she spots me. I give her a wave and she rushes to the door throwing her arms round my neck.

Doris raises her eyebrows and her voice. "Hey, we'll have none of that in here" she says "usual is it?"

"Make it for two Doris."

"Two bacon sarnie's and two cuppas it is then."

I smile and lead Rosie back to the window seat.

"I ate the chocolates" she says looking down at the empty box. We laugh.

Neither of us had thought any further than this moment. Where is Rosie going to go? I can't take her home 'cos I'm already sharing a room with my brothers! Then in a flash it comes to me. Old Jake, the taxi driver, three doors up, he's got a spare room he rents out. Perfect.

Laughing every step of the way we run from the Table Mountain to Chantry Crescent. That evening Rosie helps me move my stuff into the back bedroom at Jake's. His wife died a few years ago and their kids have grown up and moved away. Gladys, his new wife, at least twenty years his junior, seems pleased to have some 'young company' as she puts it.

I tell Rosie I'm getting some fish 'n chips and sprint round to Rob's house to tell him I won't be at the Toc H tonight. His mom keeps me on the step as usual.

"I ain't ready yet mate," he yells from the stairs and then when he reaches the door. "You ain't ready either by the look of you. What's up?"

He frowns when I ask him to tell Susie I won't be there tonight. "Do you want me to tell her," he pauses for a moment, not knowing how to put it, "you've got someone else?"

"Fuckin' hell, no."

He laughs at me. "You ain't gonna try and keep two of 'em going?"

"I'm nearly there with Susie mate, virgin, and all that" I wink at him and then I'm gone, shouting over my shoulder, "tell her I'm ill, you'll think of something."

I collect the fish n' chips and we sit and eat 'em on the bed. It's a nice size room, painted pink. Rosie likes that. Along one wall there's a tall fancy wardrobe with a dressing table and mirror, split into three, to match. In the corner by the window there's an old wing back chair and a radio sits on top of a small table by the side of the bed. Not a bible to be seen.

We lean on the windowledge and look over the back garden for a few moments before drawing the curtains and shutting out the rest of the world.

"I didn't think you'd want me, you know, after...." her voice trails off as she slips out of her skirt.

"I've liked you since the first time I clapped eyes on you Rosie, in the Trumpet. You were standing at the bar, before I even knew you was Bishop's girl."

Now she's lying on the bed in her bra and panties. "I liked you too. I saw you come in that first time." The fear gone, she's got that old sparkle back.

I've wanted this for so long and can't take my eyes off her as I throw my trousers over the wing back chair. I want to savour every tiny little moment. I'm naked now and kneeling astride the slender body. Pulling her towards me I trace a line along her shoulder and down her back to undo the bra. It falls onto the bed and she draws me to her breasts. Bigger than Elaine's, they're hard and soft at the same time. I kiss them one at a time and my tongue traces her nipples. She cries out and I raise my mouth to meet her lips.

On this clean, fresh smelling, bouncy bed, we kiss, a long, lingering kiss that takes my breath away. Wonderful. I lean back to look at her and when she opens those gorgeous brown eyes they're sparkling. For me.

Rosie is everything and more. I had fun with Elaine but this is intense.

I never really wanted Elaine, I've wanted Rosie forever.

Next day I'm up with the lark and down Tooley's Wharf for some extra cash. Rosie likes a top we saw in the Haberdashery shop next door but two to the café. She ain't got no clothes. The few she did have are at Bishop's place. Rosie goes to one of her mates to beg some panties and stuff.

I'm back with four quid by early afternoon. Rosie is sitting on the bed listening to the radio.

"I got some stuff off Sylvia, look" she says, opening the wardrobe door to show me.

"I'll have a quick wash and then we'll go get you that top." I quickly jump out of my work clothes.

"Really," the excitement in her voice makes me feel good.

I would buy her the world if I could. I wanna love her. Protect her. Give her everything.

She throws her arms round my neck and kisses me. I'm covered in coaldust but she don't care, laughing as some of the black stuff transfers to her face.

We walk up and buy the top. It costs £1.1s 6d. She hugs the bag to her chest all the way back and tries it on straight away.

"Looks great," I tell her but I like the view without it and make a grab for her as she takes it off. We fall onto the bed. I can't get enough.

"You wanna go round your mates tonight, catch up like, tell 'em where you're living and whatever you girls giggle about?"

Rosie seems to like the idea. "I ain't seen 'em for ages. You sure you don't mind?"

"Course not." It's good for me. She don't know it but I'm planning to go dancing at the Baths. Susie will be waiting for me. We'll leave early and I'll get her into that pavilion. I'm feeling pretty pleased with myself and pop a liquorice.

I tell Rosie that I'll probably nip round my Mom's and then my mate's house for a game of cards. "Just get yourself to bed when you come back."

She looks happy and there's a spring in her step as she walks to the gate. Giving me a wave and a big smile she turns and walks off up the road.

Doing a double dash I get changed into my suit and within half an hour I'm at the Baths. Susie runs to meet me. She looks lovely, wearing a very tight white top with a belt nipping in her waist and a swirly blue skirt. Her hair is gleaming and she smells even fresher than I remember.

"You feeling better now then?"

"Yes thanks." I take hold of her hands and twirl her round. "You look great tonight Susie."

She laughs "Do I?"

We hit the floor to rock 'n roll but I'm already watching the clock and when I suggest leaving at quarter to ten for a walk in the park she gets her coat double-quick. I steer her towards the pavilion and hope, because it's early, it won't be occupied.

Good. There's nobody about. We sit on the bench tucked out of sight in the corner. Kisses, soft and playful at first, become more urgent. Putting my hands around her, slightly above the waist, my thumbs creep towards her breasts and start to caress through the thin material. She doesn't pull back so I go a bit further.

The tight white top has buttons and I fumble to undo them. One deft move and the bra is history. Now I can feel the soft warm flesh. Her breathing is shallow. My pulse is racing. She parts her lips, my tongue darts in. She must like it 'cos she places a hand behind my head to hold me there.

I've been hard for ages and can't last much longer. Beneath the flouncy petticoats I'm reaching past the stocking tops when her body tenses.

We kiss with a crushing passion. My tongue works its magic. She clings to me and I lay her gently onto the wooden slats. The panties hit the floor. She's mine. A few minutes later it's all over.

Susie starts to cry and I put my arms around her.

"It was great" I tell her "what you crying for?"

"I ain't, you know, before. It hurt a bit," she snuggles into my shoulder as I light a fag. Doing up my buttons I notice dark stains on my underpants. I know about those. A virgin. Rob was right. It feels good, very good, to be the first. Untouched, except by me.

I walk her home and promise to be at the Toc H next Friday. Rosie, Susie, Susie, Rosie, I like both of 'em, a lot but with Susie no-one else has been there before. Means a lot, that.

Tooley's Wharf sees a great deal of me this week. I need the money. Along the towpath on my way home one afternoon I notice some old bags full of metal pieces. Looks like it might be copper an' all.

Just lying there, behind a three foot wire fence. Must come from the Refinery works. Don't look as if anyone would actually miss it. Now, who do I know with a van?

When I make my weekly visit to the Probation Officer on Wednesday he drones on about me getting a job. I visit the Labour Exchange and go for two interviews but once they know I've been in Borstal suddenly the vacancy is already filled.

Come Thursday night there are four of us parked up in a van by the bridge. "Are you sure its copper mate?" asks Matt.

Matthew is the local 'tat' merchant. He's been done for taking lead off so many roofs it's a wonder the whole of Bilston don't take a shower when it rains!

We walk along the towpath to reccie the gear. I'll get paid according to how many bags of copper he manages to get away. The full moon casts an eerie glow over everything as we reach the wire fence.

Matt and his cronies hop over to check the merchandise. Apparently there's a bit of everything so they're pleased. Now all we need to do is shift the stuff. It's much too heavy and cumbersome to carry a quarter mile.

An empty barge lies on the opposite bank. Shimmering canal water laps gently against her sides. "You swim for it" says Matt looking at me.

"Fuck off mate."

"Let's draw matches then," suggests one of the others.

Matt pulls a box from his inside pocket and breaks one in half. He holds 'em out towards the three of us. Lucky for me I don't draw the short straw.

The one who ends up with it is named Gavin. He strips to his underpants and with much trepidation lowers himself into the water, which must be cold, 'cos it takes him ages to get in. Muttering obscenities he swims to the other side, unties the barge and pulls it across.

In the meantime, me and the other chap tear down a short stretch of wire fencing and drag some of the heavy bags forward towards the canal.

Matt peers into the empty barge. There's water in the bottom. "Well, we ain't got far to go have we lads, load up."

The barge groans under the weight and sinks lower and lower in the water as bag after bag is hauled aboard. "How much then Matt?"

"Thirty do you?"

Shoving the dosh into my pocket I stand on the towpath as Matt orders his cronies to grab the ropes and start pulling. All goes well for a couple of hundred yards. The bridge is in sight, spirits are high.

That's it for me. "I'm off then mate, see you around."

I make my way to the bridge and stand on the brow watching as the barge slips lower and lower into the water. There's much commotion as it sinks sedately to the bottom with some bags of 'tat' jutting out of the water for a moment or two before slowly sliding sideways into the murky depths.

Matt looks towards the bridge and shouts but I'm gone. I can hear 'em splashing around trying to salvage some of the gear. Can't help a sly grin which quickly turns into a laugh as I hear the cry, "ugh, dead dog, dead dog."

Friday comes round. Rosie has got herself done up. "Shall we go to the Toc H tonight?" she asks.

My heart sort of stops for a moment or two. Susie will be there. "Let's go to the pictures. There's a John Wayne on." Rosie looks disappointed. It's easier for me to stay with her. Why complicate things? We're shacked up together. A shag on tap when I feel like it.

I try not to think about Susie and push the guilt to the back of my mind. Me and Rosie don't go to the Toc H that night or any other night. For the next couple of weeks we mostly stay in the bedroom, have some fun and listen to the radio before dozing off.

"Can we go to the fair tonight Watt, everybody else is going?"

The fair had come to town a couple of days ago and this is the second time Rosie has asked me. So here we are. Music, rides, lots of flashing coloured lights, and a boxing booth.

Some champion boxer or other is appearing for a demonstration with his two brothers. They do a few rounds with local hopefuls. Our best is Sammy Reynolds and he puts up a good show but the pro wins on points.

The Champ comes on and the crowd goes mad. Glad I came now. He does a bit of sparring. Rosie isn't too interested and keeps pulling on my jacket 'cos we've been standing here for ages. She wants to go on the dodgems so we wander off for a bit, eat some candyfloss, win a teddy on the shooting range and enjoy a couple of rides, before heading back to the boxing booth.

They are advertising a five pound note for anyone who can stay three rounds of three minutes with the resident boxer. He looks useful but I'm really fit. Besides, I need the money.

Lots of my mates are here, all crowded round watching the contenders get bashed. Not one of the three blokes who have just been in the ring have lasted more than two rounds, let alone three!

The resident boxer stands in the centre of the ring, bashing his gloves together and calling for 'anyone else?' He's twice as big as me and twice as ugly. I take off my suit jacket and hand it to Rosie.

"No, you'll get hurt," her dark eyes flash and she tries to pull me back.

I step up to the ring and raise my hand. A sidekick shoves some gloves on me. Now I'm in the corner and hear the bell ring. Ugly boy catches me with one or two good body punches but I manage to protect my face and don't go down. The round seems to last a lot longer than three minutes though.

Five pound note, five pound note, I keep telling myself during the second round. I'm fast but he lands a couple to my jaw as I dart all over the ring to stay out of his reach. Can't understand the boo's from the crowd but then I spot one of my mates having words with the man who is supposed to be ringing the bell for time.

The third and final round seems never ending and it's obvious to everyone what's happening. Don't think the resident boxer was expecting anyone as fit and determined. He catches me with my guard down momentarily and his fist connects with my face. To great roars from the crowd I rally with a good body punch followed by a couple of fast jabs and an upper cut.

I ain't trying to prove anything here. I just want the dosh. This round lasts almost as long as two put together but eventually the bell rings. Grudgingly I'm handed the crisp five pound note. My eye feels puffy and ouch, my jaw hurts when I move it, but apart from that, I'm on top of the world. Did it. *Yes.* I kiss the fiver, leap up and punch the air.

Rosie rushes over, closely followed by my mates and we head off for a well deserved drink.

Old Jake has taken to giving me the odd driving lesson in his taxi, just around the Crescent. It's great and I get the hang of it quite quickly. He tells me I'm a natural. Perhaps I can be a taxi driver. Rosie's gone to see if she can get her old job back at the flower shop. I'm a bit bored and Jake's in bed after a late shift last night. I'll just take the taxi for a spin on my own.

Judgement flies out of the window. There it goes. Gone. I've only just set off when fuck me, a copper, and he's stepped into the middle of the road. There's nowhere to go because it's so narrow. Only one pavement and that's dotted with lamp-posts. Do I run him over? I jam on the brakes.

"I know you" he says walking to the side window.

And that's it. No driving licence, no insurance, no nothing. I'm hauled up to the cop shop, a night in the cell and then in front of the Magistrates next day. My Probation Officer comes to Court and gives his report. As I'm on Licence, they say there's no alternative but for six months Borstal Recall.Back to Winson Green for assessment and allocation. I've been before so I know the system. After a month I'm relieved to be sent to Portland which is close to Portsmouth. Anywhere out of Winson Green will do.

It's a closed Borstal like Rochester and run along the same lines. I'm not too happy about having to share a cell. I'm two'd up with a guy called Tezz. He's doing a two stretch for assault. Being from the Black Country we have something in common, even if it's only our accent.

Tezz works in the kitchens and I'm allocated to the Bakery because of my qualifications. I soon settle into the routine again. PT, work, exercise. It's a bit harder to build up wages to start baroning this time because of smoking myself, but I manage to do it over the course of a couple of weeks.

There are a few faces I recognize from Rochester on recall, including Spider and Amos. Tales of Hunkus and the Block circulate round Portsmouth and apart from the odd ruck, I don't have much trouble.

Tezz plays the mouth organ, mainly Country and Western tunes. He goes on at me to get a guitar and lends me his 'Musical Instrument Catalogue' to browse through. I find a nice acoustic and with money from my property, eight pounds which I had on me when I was arrested, I send for it together with a chord book and some strings.

A week later the guitar arrives. "Shut the fuck up," "Stop that fuckin' racket" and "I'll wrap it round your sodding head in a minute" are some of the nicer comments emanating from the rest of the cons as me and Tezz tune it up. There are no radio's allowed so I rely on the sounds Tezz plays on his mouth organ and try to marry up the chords.

I learn a blues riff first and then decide to try my hand at songwriting. I call it 'Portland Borstal Blues'

"Hey, you're a good singer Watt, we're a regular duet." Tezz is pleased 'cos he loves music.

For me it relieves the boredom. Something different to keep my mind occupied. Like everything else, I give it my all.

I write to Rosie and the odd letter to Rob. I feel bad because Rosie was relying on me. Turns out she got her old job back and is renting a room at one of her mates. She says that she'll wait for me. The thought of her keeps me going and I count the days.

I find myself thinking more and more about Susie. Out of the blue, two months into my recall, I get a letter from her. She'd been to Rob's for the address and says she had to write to tell me she's getting married next week, on the 25th.

'I'm having a baby. My Dad has fixed me up to marry one of his friends before I show too much because I'm already three months gone' she writes. 'Duncan is 40. His wife died. He says he'll bring the baby up as his own.'

I'm stunned. Can't believe it. Don't wanna believe it. The baby must be mine. I know Susie and how long it took to get her into that pavilion. At the end she signs her name and underneath, 'I'll always be yours. I'll never forget you. Please, don't write back.'

I don't want Rosie. I want Susie. Fresh, innocent, Susie. I want to look after her. To cradle her in my arms. No.No.No...I punch the wall 'til my knuckles bleed. Fuck this place. Fuck everything. Next week the letter says. It's the 25th tomorrow.

It seems like the longest night but dawn finally breaks. It's a grey, cloudy day. Just like my life. The seagulls cry but I can't see them.

Later, work over, me and Tezz sit down to play our tunes. "Portland Borstal Blues" shouts one of the cons.

Tezz, mouth organ at the ready, looks across. I shake my head. No. I can't. Not tonight. The hurt inside is ripping me apart. She is lying in someone else's arms; his hands all over her, his lips on hers. I can't bear it. Fists clench and unclench. What have I done? The barred window mocks me as I sink into the chair and hold my head in my hands. I close my eyes but there is no escape. No escape from my thoughts, no escape from the pain, no escape from these four fuckin' walls...

Chapter 8

THE SHAPE, THE BODY AND THE GRIP

I get my discharge just in time for my 20th Birthday and Christmas. It's 1955.

Me and Tezz have learned some great tunes on the guitar and I lay it carefully against the empty seat next to me on the train home. Home? Where's that?

As always, I head for Chantry Crescent, walking the three miles from Wolverhampton Station with my guitar slung over my back. Several girls give me the eye. Tezz had told me that any musical instrument is like a magnet for the birds. Think he's right.

It's dark and cold but as I turn into the Crescent I see Jake's taxi parked outside and his front parlour light is on so I give him a knock. What reception will I get?

"Oh, it's you is it you bugger," Jake answers the door. He's chuckling. I'm relieved. "Come on, you look perished," he steps aside to let me in and then shouts over his shoulder, "Gladys, put the kettle on duck."

We have a cuppa and then I ask the burning question. "Have you still got that room?"

He looks at Gladys.

"I'm gonna get a job. I can pay for a couple of weeks, I got some wages from Borstal…look," pulling out the earnings I'd saved. Gladys smiles at me. It's not a motherly sort of smile.

"I reckon so" says Jake, "but no driving my taxi when I'm not looking." We all laugh. Jake goes off to his shed where the stuff I'd left upstairs has been stored. Gladys leans forward, a bit too close for my liking, to pick up my cup and smiles at me again. "You remind me of someone, a handsome actor, whatshisname in the westerns. Another cuppa?" I'm pleased when Jake gets back with the big brown cardboard box.

Gladys is a lot younger than Jake. She'd be about thirty, a good looking woman with shoulder length dark wavy hair and green eyes. Nice trim figure and always dressed very smart.

"Ooh, you play the guitar," Gladys spies it in the hallway as she follows me up the stairs. "I'll just settle him in, fresh sheets 'n that" she says, turning her head towards the parlour where Jake sits in front of the fire reading his paper.

Placing my stuff on the wing back chair in the familiar pink room, I turn and take the bedding from her arms. "I can do it Gladys, had to make my own bed every day in Borstal."

"You sure? I don't mind. *Anything* you need, just shout."

I close the door. This might be a mistake. Who is this actor guy everyone says I look like. Studying my image in the mirror I ain't bad looking, even if I say it myself. A mop of thick jet black hair, brown eyes, a good physique and I'm fit, oh yes, and I'm full as a butchers dog! I do a bit of shadow boxing at myself in the mirror. Better nip down the road and tell Mom I'm home. She might be worried.

Later, when I'm unpacking the box, I notice a little slip of paper with PJ's address on it. Pushing it into one of the drawers I think I might just write to him and fix something up.

For now, I want to see Rob and get all the news, specially about Susie. He'd written a few times. The censors didn't like his letters much 'cos they always had lines blacked out. In one of them it said Maud had seen Susie once after the wedding to this Duncan bloke and they live somewhere the other side of town. "He's out" Rob's mother tells me, "at his girlfriend's house, and he won't be back until ten o'clock."

I walk round to the address Rosie had given me, her mate Sylvia's house, which is on the main Bilston Road. Rosie's letters were regular at the start but I haven't heard from her for over a month. Sylvia's Mom answers the door. When I say I'm looking for Rosie she frowns at me. "But you're not her young man are you and anyway she's out."

So that's it then. Rosie's got another bloke and everybody's fuckin' out, except me. I'm beat anyway so head back to Jake's and get to bed. Keeps a nice house, does Gladys, everything always clean and smells fresh.

Next day is Saturday and I'm up the Table Mountain. Rob's always in on a Saturday morning. Sure enough, there he is at the Juke Box. His face lights up when he sees me. "Mom said you'd called but I was invited for tea last night, at Maud's. I've been promoted and, wait for it, I've asked her to marry me. What do you think of that then?"

"Fucking hell mate. You don't mean to say she said yes." We laugh. I'm pleased for him. He's got his life on track.

I order some toast and sit down. "You might need a fag mate," his face changes. "It's Susie. She had the baby premature a couple of months ago and ….." He stops and looks at me.

"And what?"

"It died mate, the baby died."

It takes a while to sink in. He's right I do need a fag. "Was mine, you know that don't you?"

"I guessed."

We sit in silence for a minute or two eating our toast and drinking our tea. "Don't know what to say mate, but there's something else as well."

"If it's about Rosie, I know. She's got another bloke."

Rob seems relieved I already know. All the bad stuff out of the way we chat and I tell him about my guitar. He seems impressed and can't wait to hear me sing. He tells me Bishop and Dave have been done for living off immoral earnings and are banged up on a three stretch. Steve's back in circulation and Ian's got a girlfriend, at last.

"We're all going to the dance at the Baths tonight if you wanna come."

"I'll give it a miss this week. I got shopping to do and stuff to sort out. See you next Friday at the Toc H mate. Say hello to Maud for me."

I've made some decisions while we've been chatting. No Susie, no baby, no Rosie, just me. I'm gonna get me some money and have a good time. Saturday night is the best night. People go out, get drunk, and most important of all, sleep soundly. I learned that much from the likes of Mad Jack 'n Dave.

After collecting my bit of shopping I walk back along the main road and weigh up the market trader's house. Word is, or used to be, that on a Saturday, after a good day, there could be a lot of cash in there. I'm not gonna bother with anything, only cash. Nothing to sell, no bulky stuff to carry and store, no bother of trying to sell it on. All I gotta do is spend it.

In my darkest clothing I creep out of Jake's at about 2.30am. I've lain on the bed fully clothed for the last two hours and 'cos these walls are very thin I listened to Jake and Gladys have their Saturday night shag. Poor Gladys. Didn't take Jake long! I smile to myself.

A dark figure on a dark night, I walk along the gulley and climb over the rickety fence into a back garden. The house is a few gardens down so I climb over each fence until I'm standing at the back kitchen window and pull on my gloves. I check my pocket for the meat and chocolate bar.

Can't see any open windows, so taking a small towel I'd nicked from Jake's bathroom, I wrap it round a small bar and jab at the window. It shatters but not too noisily. I lean in and turn the back door key. No bolts. Good.

There's a growl and a scurry of feet as I walk through the door. Biggish dog, Alsatian I think, with a deep throaty bark. Just once it barks. Quick as a flash I throw the meat and chocolate from my pocket. All dogs like one or the other. This dog likes both and snaffles everything. It then proceeds to lick me to death as I roam around looking for cash.

Under the stairs there is a small cupboard which I have to really bend down to get into. With my torch I can see a dark coloured holdall. Looking good. The sound of padding footsteps comes from upstairs. I freeze. My heart is thumping. It's so loud they might hear it!

A toilet flushes. More padding footsteps. I don't move a muscle and hardly breathe for the next five minutes. Snoring. Two different lots. Sounds like a pig farm up there. Perfect.

The Alsatian wags its tail as I pull out the holdall and quietly open the zip. There it is. The wages of sin. Looks a lot. I'm excited but try to keep calm as I close the bag and loose myself out of the back door.

Legging it over the gardens I get to the bottom of the gulley, almost home and dry now. It's about 3.30 am and there's nobody about. The stillness of the night is only broken by the pounding in my head.

In the safety of my bedroom I turn on the small bedside lamp and slip out of my gear. Turning the holdall upside down several bundles of cash scatter all over the bed. The most I ever had was a couple of hundred. It takes me ages to count and I can hardly contain myself. There's almost a thousand quid. Fuck me. I'm rich.

Sunday. No shops open so I can't splash the cash. It's very frustrating to have to wait until Monday. Gladys say's she'll cook dinner for me. Jake asks if I want to come to the pub for a pint with him while it's cooking. Instead I decide to nip round home.

"Thanks for lending me when I didn't have any." Pearl's face lights up when I count out sixty quid.

"No need Watt, you know I'd never see you go without."

It's true. Pearl is always there for me.

"Anything the kids need?"

"Where you had this money from?" Pearl is suspicious now, "you been up to no good?"

"Never you mind. What do they need?"

"Marje could do with some new shoes and Barry needs a coat."

"Here, see to it," I give her a wad of notes. "Get some grub and a bit of coal with what's left. And sort out anyone in the street as needs anything. Don't let Dad get his hands on it."

"Don't worry Watt."

Mom comes in from the kitchen with a pot of tea. "Cuppa?"

"No thanks. Gotta go now, Gladys is cooking a Sunday roast."

I leave her and Mom laying out the money on the table. It'll be away in their purses before Dad gets back from the pub.

Monday morning and I'm up town waiting for the shops to open. By ten o'clock I'm suited and booted with several extra changes of clothes and shoes.

A quick trim for the old hair, Brylcream, some nice scented soap and I'm back to Jake's by lunchtime. Can't wait for a bath, get changed and then off up the Table Mountain. See who's about so I can show off my new gear.

"God luva duck" exclaims Doris. "You look like a tailor's dummy. Toast is it or bacon sarnie?"

"Give us the bacon Doris, and lots of it."

She laughs. "Comin' up."

I'm just rolling a fag and waiting for the sarnie when a familiar voice says "Hello Watt."

"Elaine!" She looks a whole lot different from when I last saw her. Hair done up, nice clothes and smiling, a big bright smile. "Want something and a cuppa?" She nods.

"Another bacon sarnie and a cuppa over here Doris please."

"How long you been out?"

"Not long. But look at you. What you up to these days?"

She puts her shopping bag on the empty seat, slips her coat off and sits opposite me. "My Gran died a few months back. I've took over the house now."

"I heard about Bishop and Dave going down."

"Yes, and I heard about what you did to Bishop. Rosie's got a lot to thank you for."

I feel bad. I could have done something to help Elaine, that night at her Gran's, but I didn't feel the same about her as I did about Rosie. She knows what I'm thinking and puts her hand across the table to rest on top of mine.

"If I speak the truth Watt, by the time you came along, I'd probably gone too far with it. After Bishop and Dave went down, me and a couple of the girls got together. We pick our punters. All regular guys. There are three bedrooms at my Grans old house."

Doris brings our sarnie's and I order another cuppa.

"I charge the girls rent, see, for use of the rooms. I make a few bob, well more than a few bob," she laughs.

"You're looking good Elaine, I mean really good."

She leans over. "Give us two's on that will you. I ain't got none."

I give her the rest of my fag.

"Susie, you were sweet on her," Elaine holds my eyes. At the mention of her name my heart jolts. "*Somebody* got her up the duff and she had to marry an old drunk."

I study the bottom of my teacup. Oh Susie.

"She lost the…."

Raising my hand, "I know, I know."

"Everybody thinks the baby was yours. She'd never been out with anyone else." Elaine bends her head down under mine and looks into my eyes. "It was, wasn't it? By all accounts she's got a right life with that Duncan bloke. Rosie saw her up town the other day. She told me. Face all bruised." Elaine seems to be enjoying telling me this stuff.

"You see Rosie then, do you?" I'm trying to change the subject.

"Now and then. She works in the flower shop, you know, next door to the Bank. She's courting an office type. He's got a bit of money."

Elaine prattles on, as only a woman can, but I ain't listening. Eventually she gets up to go. "If ever you need anything you know where I am." She leans over and whispers in my ear "but a good looking guy like you, you'll never have to pay." Her lips brush my cheek. "See you around."

It isn't long before Steve and some of the lads come in. We laugh about old times, scrumping and school days; the others listen as me and Steve recount our Borstal experiences. In lighter mood I head back to Jake's.

Can't wait until Friday and the dance. My Birthday is mid-week and Gladys makes a fuss, does me a special tea an' that. "Twenty today," she remarks, "not a teenager any more."

Jake harks back to when he was twenty and how times have changed. It don't sound all that different to me.

The Toc H is full when I walk in. I want to make an entrance and it works. Lots of girls are staring as I saunter over to the bar. Rob admires my sharp Italian suit and Maud tells him in no uncertain terms he's not having one!

I notice a blonde bird, the Anita Ekberg look alike, watching me. "Who is she?" I ask Rob, casting a glance in her direction.

"Ian knows her. Wasting your time there though mate. Won't even dance with anybody. Ian…here a mo" Rob waves him over.

Ian introduces me to Carol who happens to live by him. What a stunner. She seems to give me the eye but won't dance. "We call her the Shape" he tells me. I can see why an' all.

"We got nicknames for some of 'em" Ian informs me. "See her over there, that's Lizzie, we call her the Body and the big fat 'un in the corner, she's the Grip. The Shape, The Body and The Grip." He laughs.

"The Grip?" I frown at him.

"We reckon them folds of fat 'ud grip you like a … Ssh, here comes Sybil."

Ian protests but is dragged onto the floor. Rob and Maud are smooching over the other side. I want to feel a woman in my arms so decide to ask Carol again but she refuses. I walk along and ask a couple more but they all say no so I pop to the toilets and look in the mirror. Is there something wrong with me?

Better get a bottle and take the weight off. No sooner have I sat down than this dark headed girl plonks herself on my lap.

"My name's Jean," she says.

Fuckin' hell, what big tits. "I'm Watt."

"I know," smiling at me she grabs my hand and pulls me onto the dance floor. Rob looks over and winks. Nice enough girl but a bit forward. She tells me I'm walking her home and parades me past the other girls on the way out.

Nobody else seems interested so I'll take what's on offer. She lives roughly a mile away and we chat, mainly about me, as we make our way through the cold streets. I have my arm round her shoulders and she slips her hand underneath my coat and holds me round the waist. Jean tells me that she works in Willenhall and lives with her Mom. Her Dad's dead. "I saw you months ago at the dance, before you went away again, but you never noticed me did you?" she asks as we stand in the shelter of the arched porch.

"I saw a lot of girls."

Jean catches hold of my head and pulls me down to kiss her. This girl knows what she wants alright. She's all over me like a rash and unbuttons my shirt as I undo her blouse. I'm getting a bit hot and breathless and feel like climbing the walls of this tiny porch when she calls a halt to proceedings, straightens her skirt and buttons up her blouse. "See you tomorrow then at the Baths." It's not a question.

Saturday night and it's almost Christmas. The Baths are decked out with streamers, the mood is light and everyone is in good spirits. No sign of Jean yet so I think I'll try my luck and ask some of the other girls. One by one they refuse. Can't understand it.

I drown my sorrows until Jean arrives. We dance the night away and I walk her home. In this tiny porch I have my first shag standing up.

"You're mine" she murmurs.

Afterwards at the gate I turn and she blows me a kiss, "Come for Sunday dinner…bring your guitar."

Jean's Mom takes to me straight away. Roast beef and Yorkshire pud with apple pie and custard for afters. Smashing. They love listening to my songs and when Jean's Mom goes for an afternoon lie down there's just me and Jean on the sofa. I serenade her. We kiss and then she tells me.

"You'll never get another girl, not now." She kisses me again and starts to unbutton my trousers.

What's she on about?

"I've warned them off, everybody. I told them you're mine."

And so it was. I'm flattered. I fill the coalhouse and pantry. Jean invites me for Christmas. Might as well. It's the first Christmas dinner I've had out of nick in three years. The house is all prettied up and there's a tree with baubles and coloured fairy lights. Her Mom's a good cook, what a lovely day.

For a few months I court Jean. We go to the Toc H on a Fridays, occasionally the pictures and sometimes the Baths on a Saturday. We have long chats and even longer shags in her Mom's front parlour. Life's great.

I've got plenty of money left but I'm a bit bored. One day I'm on the bus from Wolverhampton when a shiny motorbike goes whizzing by. The guy looks good, his hair and white scarf blowing in the wind.

Next day I'm at the dealers and buy an Aerial Square Four. It's a beauty. In my best suit and Italian shoes I arrive early for the Toc H dance. Lots of girls are queuing to get in and they gather round my big shiny bike, including Carol.

"You gonna dance with me tonight then?" I ask.

"I can't," she says looking uncomfortable.

"You don't like me then, is that it?" I flash an especially nice smile.

"Oh no," she glances up at me "it's not that."

"Look, I know Jean warned everybody off, she told me, but what's she gonna do? I'll dance with who I want."

"She said she'd beat us up. She fights like a bloke."

"I'll take care of Jean. You'll dance with me tonight then?"

Carol smiles and I know I've cracked it.

Jean makes a scene and throws a few punches at me. I dodge 'em and catch hold of her hands. It makes me laugh but it makes her madder and she storms out of the Toc H.

"The Shape, you ain't taking the Shape home, you lucky bugger," Rob seems jealous as we stand at the urinal, just before the last dance.

I take Carol home on my motorbike. She squeals with delight at the sound of the engine. She's happy, I'm happy. Especially when she climbs aboard and wraps her arms around me. We don't have a care in the world and the wind takes our breath away as we roar along the roads.

We go lots of places on the motorbike. I take her to Bridgnorth on a Sunday. There's a big hill, called the Hermitage, and zooming down it is wonderful. Carol's on the back shrieking all the way. We sit by the river, romantic like, and kiss.

Carol is a bit like Susie was. She won't let me have much more than a kiss and a fondle. I'm getting a bit impatient. Two months pass.

We're on her front doorstep. I've walked her home from the Toc H. "A mans got needs" I tell her "and I need you. You'd really like my room, its pink."

She blushes and pushes my hands away.

As I turn the motor bike at the end of her road my mind is already focused on other things. Money is running out. I need to pull another job, and fast.

A couple of days later I'm sitting in the Table Mountain and meet Spike. We get chatting over a cuppa and a fag. He tells me he went to Borstal at Hull when he was eighteen. "Learnt everything I know in there." We have a laugh. He drops it out he's a safe-breaker with a crew in Stoke. I'm impressed.

Spike's older that me, late twenties, dressed smartish with short back and sides, about 5'10". LOVE and HATE are tattooed on his hands. He leans over the table and lowers his voice, "I don't get over this way much but I've been casing a joint."

I prick up my ears. "You ain't looking for another crew member are you?" From what he'd told me, safe-breaking sounded very lucrative. I'm thinking 'Banks'.

"No. I'm doing it on my own. It's a factory."

I must look disappointed. "Thousands in there mate, thousands."

Sharp intake of breath. "We could do it the two of us. I've done factories before."

"Dunno," he ponders over his empty teacup.

"Another two teas over here Doris," turning back to Spike, "look mate, ask around, I ain't no fuckin' pussycat, know what I mean." Perhaps he thinks I ain't up to the job. "Where's this place then?"

"There's only me knows about it. Thought I'd do it on my own but suppose it's better with a lookout."

"Fifty, fifty?"

He nods.

"I'm in."

After our tea we take a walk around town. In hushed voices we discuss the plan and arrange to meet tomorrow outside the Alhambra at ten o'clock.

That night, hands behind my head, I lie staring at the ceiling, there's a damp patch on the right hand corner that always catches my eye. Perhaps if I buy Carol something really nice she'll come back to my room. I drift off and dream about a big safe bursting with money and Carol in my bed.

Next morning I'm up with the lark. Gotta get to the shops for a bit of steak and a bar of chocolate. From past experience I know that some factories have guard dogs. I ain't taking no chances. I'll get a new pair of gloves while I'm on.

Jake's already gone to work. Coming out of the bathroom, I can't hear Gladys downstairs. That's funny. I turn towards their bedroom and the door is wide open. It wasn't open when I went in the bathroom that's for sure 'cos I would have seen her lying there.

She's propped up on lots of pillows, her dark hair splayed out against the pretty green of the bed linen. It matches her eyes. She's naked, smiling at me and patting the empty space on the bed next to her. Fuck it. She's got a really good figure an' all. Careful now. My brain is racing. I wrench my eyes from her body and lodge them firmly on the landscape picture above the bed.

I'm stood on the landing with just a towel wrapped round me. It would be so easy to slip in there…in more ways than one. She laughs as the towel moves of it's own volition. Jesus! This might be the hardest thing I've ever had to do. I move slowly towards the doorway.

"I can see you want me" she says eyeing the roving towel.

"Look Gladys." I have to put my hand over the towel and push it down. "I like you a lot but you're Jake's wife. He's been good to me. I'd feel bad." She rolls across the bed towards me, her legs slightly open. She sees my line of sight and opens them a bit further. I grab hold of the door handle and turn to walk into my room. My towel slips and she squeals. "Ooh please Watt. He won't know."

I've heard Jake's grunts. They're only in bed about two minutes and he's done it and snoring! I could show her a good time. Just this once. I'm talking myself into it. No, it's no good. "I'm sorry Gladys. I really want to but it ain't right."

She covers herself with the sheet as I close the door. Should I find somewhere else to live? It's a shame 'cos I like it here. This time tomorrow I'll have the cash to splash. I rub my hands together. I'll think about it then.

Half past nine and I walk up town towards the Alhambra. All dressed in black, gloves and small torch in one pocket, meat and chocs in the other. Spike's already there and nods as I fall into step with him. We make our way along the Wolverhampton Road and then onto one of the side streets.

"That's it." Spike stops to light a fag and inclines his head in the direction of a large brick building. "There's an alleyway next to it, see, leads to the canal. Down there, over the fence and we're in through the back door."

Walking and chatting we make our way slowly along the pavement and then quick as a flash into the alleyway. On with the gloves! I give Spike a leg up over the fence but he rips his trousers on a loose piece of wire.

"Bollocks. These was new last week," he hisses under his breath.

The back door to the factory is just behind a cycle shed. Spike pulls out a glass cutter and small suction pad. Nice. Pressing the pad onto the glass he noiselessly cuts a small circle and pulls the glass out. He hands it to me and I place it quietly on the ground. I step back and look up at the factory windows. No lights showing anywhere. I dart across to the wire fencing. No-one about in the alleyway. I give Spike the thumbs up.

Putting the cutter and pad back into his pocket he reaches into the hole and pulls the latch on the door. From his trouser leg he produces a long piece of bent wire with which he hooks the top and bottom bolts and draws them across. Gets better.

I follow Spike inside and close the door noiselessly. We tiptoe along the passageways and finally reach our destination. The sign on the door reads 'Cashiers'.

It's locked. Spike pulls out a small jemmy bar from his other trouser leg. He must have pockets specially sewn into 'em. Amazing. I'm at the end of the corridor keeping an eye out for the Nightwatchman. He must be fuckin' deaf if he can't hear the noise of that splintering timber. I shine my torch on my watch.

According to form rounds are made every two hours, so by Spike's reckoning we've got about one hour thirty eight minutes left. Piece of cake he'd said.

A flickering light. I hold up my hand. Spike has opened the door and is just about to walk into the room. We both freeze. The searching flash disappears. I drop my hand. Spike disappears.

What seems like a week later but is actually only a matter of three quarters of an hour Spike re-appears with two large canvas bags. He hands me one of the bags. It feels heavy. I'm smiling. We move along the myriad of corridors. A loud bang followed by coughing. Not far away. A wavering light throws patterns on the wall. It's coming our way.

"Shit" whispers Spike, "he must have changed his route."

"Fuckin' piece of cake you said." Adrenalin is already high. I ain't gettin' caught.

Quick as a flash I've backed into the toilets, three doors down. I'd spotted 'em as we passed. Spike creeps in behind me but trips over his own feet.

"Bollocks."

"Sshh." I close the door quietly.

There's bound to be cubicles in a Ladies and turning round I can make out a row of 'em at the far end. We tiptoe past the basins, each sit on a toilet and close the doors. Fuckin' comical this, sitting on the shithouse with thousands in our laps and nowhere to go. Coughing gets louder. My heart beats faster. I stop breathing as the main door to the Ladies creaks open. A flickering light shines momentarily above the cubicles. The door bangs shut. Heavy boots clomp into the distance. The coughing gets fainter.

"Fuckin hell, let's go." I'm up, off and down the stairs to the back door. We race past the cycle shed and throw the bags over the fence.

"C'mon." I cup my hands to give Spike a leg up. I've just got him over when sirens and claxons start ringing in my ears. Bright lights shine from every window in the factory. Spike grabs the two bags and starts to leg it.

Leaping over the fence I race after him. "Are you stupid or what?" grabbing one of the bags I turn and run in the opposite direction. Spike's heading straight for the main road. Get to the canal. I know this place like the back of my hand. Plenty of gulleys and alleys. Keep off the roads when you can. Mad Jack's words come back to me.

Spike's following me now. I can hear his heavy breathing and wait for him under the bridge. "You was gonna go without me you bastard."

"No, mate, no" he gasps.

"Split it now. This my half?" I hold up the bag.

He nods. I'm gone.

One thousand three hundred pounds in notes, fifty pounds ten shillings and six pence in coins and a bundle of postage stamps. It's a fuckin' fortune. I leave it laid out on the bed for a while and sit staring at it from the wing back chair.

I can buy a car. Carol would like that. Opening the top drawer I pull out my bacca tin and a slip of paper floats to the floor. Picking it up I see PJ's address in London. "Yes." I pop a liquorice. Reckon I've earned it.

I write to PJ and get a reply straight back. 'Come on the train,' he writes, 'see you Thursday then mate. Looking forward to it.' PJ had always gone on about the birds down London. Bet it won't take two bloody months to get into *their* panties.

"I'm visiting a friend. Don't know when I'll be back" I tell Carol. Her face drops and she frowns at me. We're sitting in the kitchen with her Mom.

After a bit of thought she says, "I do like pink you know."

I know exactly what she means. It's bait to try and get me to stay. Maybe when I get back I'll show her the pink room and she'll give me a bit more than a kiss.

The only time I've been on trains is back and forth to Borstal so this journey is a bit of a novelty and enjoyable. I take a taxi to PJ's from the station. The money is stashed in a box at home. Roy's looking after it for me. I've got a hundred pounds with me.

PJ's flat in West Kensington is very posh. It's a two bed place so I've got my own room. We do a bit of reminiscing and then hit the town. He takes me to the 51 Club; very lively and full of birds. "They like champagne" he tells me as we get the fourth bottle. They sure do. I ain't used to it and the bubbles seem to go straight through me.

I don't remember much about it but wake up next morning with a stunner by my side and a stinking headache. I stagger to the kitchen where PJ's making coffee. He's not a big fan of tea. I gulp it down and, after the aspirin he gives me, feel better. Wandering back to the bedroom the stunner has woken up.

"Hello you" she yawns and stretches her arms in the air.

"Hello yourself," I throw myself back onto the bed. Being as I can't remember last night, what about now. I go to kiss her.

"Ooh" she runs off naked towards the toilet and I watch her bum as she goes. Not bad. She runs back and leaps onto the bed, her breasts still bouncing up and down. Does it for me. "Do what you did to me last night" she giggles.

I can't remember! We surface at lunch time and she goes to take a shower. Strikes me I don't even know her name.

"You coming in or what," she shouts. This feels good, real good. We soap each other down and hit the bed wet and laughing. Her name is Lynda.

We hit the shops in the afternoon. I buy myself some stylish gear and Lynda wants a nice top, so I get two, one for Carol as well. PJ's got some business to attend to so we have the flat to ourselves tonight.

All in all it's a great few days in London and on Monday, promising to visit again soon, I head home.

Leaping on my motorbike at teatime I roar round to Carol's. She's just walking back from her job at the Co-op and runs across to kiss me. She's real excited with the present, dashing in to show her Mom.

I don't usually see her on Mondays but ask if it's alright to take Carol for some fish and chips, seein' as how I've been away all weekend. Her mother says she's got to be home by ten. We roar off to the chippie and then to Jake's.

After the meal we sit on the bed chatting. I want to rip the clothes off her back, but need her to make the first move. She starts to nuzzle my neck. We kiss, but nothing heavy. Slim fingers flirt with the folds of my shirt. I raise my eyebrows and undo the top two buttons. She does the rest. Her touch sends a ripple through my whole body. Outwardly I don't stir.

Carol raises her beautiful blue eyes to mine. "You do love me don't you?"

"Course I do." I kiss her tenderly and sit up to take control.

She raises a shoulder to help as I slip off her blouse. So far so good. I suggest it might be best to remove her skirt to stop it getting crumpled. A few nervous giggles later it sits neatly folded on the wingback chair. Our lips meet as I fumble with the bra hook. Damn thing. Eventually it gives. My mouth finds the hardness of her nipples. She catches her breath. We kiss again. Fingernails dig deep into my flesh. Soft skin presses hard against me.

She stiffens slightly as I caress her inner thighs and move to her tummy.

Sliding my hand lower I gently ease down her panties. My trousers quickly follow. Now we're both naked. Her sweet perfume, the warm body...I'm kissing her mouth, neck, breasts. At this moment there's nothing else in the whole wide world. Just me and Carol. An explosion of breathless passion. She clings to me. At last, she's mine.

We lie facing each other and I stroke her hair. The girl of my dreams smiles and snuggles into my shoulder. I need a fag but don't want this feeling to end.

She looks up suddenly, panic in her voice, "What's the time?"

Jesus! Its half past ten. We can't find her panties and pull back the sheets to find 'em. A small red stain catches my eye. I'm chuffed. Always nice to be first! Gladys won't be too pleased though.

Carol's Dad isn't pleased either as we roar to a halt outside. She's three quarters of an hour late. "Get in our Carol," he shouts, "and you" pointing at me "don't come here again."

At a loose end, bored, I nip round home next morning. Mom, as usual, makes the brew. "Here, our Watt, can you take this coat back to your Aunty Lil, I borrowed it for old man Tyler's funeral last week."

"I'll come with you," pipes up Roy. Any excuse for a ride on my bike.

Mom rolls up the black coat and places it into a shopping bag which she hands to Roy. It isn't far to Aunty Lil's house, about three miles. My bike roars into life and off we go. Nice day, wind in our hair and I can lean into the corners with a bit more speed than when the girls are riding pillion.

We whiz along laughing and Roy is busy giving a busty blonde the eye, well, we both are, when something hits my front wheel. The bike stops dead, a mass of clothing with arms and legs flies over my head. No control. I loose my grip of the handlebars and my face meets the rough, stony ground with a deafening thud.

The engine is still running as I slowly raise my head, look to the bike and then scan for Roy. The busty blonde is crouched by his side. He's sitting up looking a bit dazed.

My face feels sort of wet. I can see blood gathering on the stones. It's dripping from somewhere. My head!

Gingerly I pull myself to a sitting position, phew, is my neck sore or what? The busty blonde walks across with a hankie to stem the bleeding from a cut above my right eye. What the fuck...where are we? Sitting in the middle of a new island, that's where we are. It wasn't here last week, this circular row of kerbstones with rough ground in the middle.

Miraculously we are both just walking wounded. The bike is laying on its side, half on the road and half on the island. There are a couple of scratches here and there, nothing much. The coat has flown out of the bag and landed in something unmentionable, it's covered in dust and stuff.

We finish the errand and listen to Aunty Lil going on about ruffians on motorbikes while she cleans us up. Then I drop Roy off home before heading to Jake's for a long soak in the bath. Funny old day.

I'm laying in bed a couple of days later contemplating the damp patch which is getting darker. After a while I see Susie's face, staring at me with those deep blue eyes. 'I'm yours forever' she'd written. It's my fault she's with some old drunk who beats her up. I'll ask round at the dance, somebody must know where's she's living. I need to see her, make things right.

Looking at the empty pillow next to me, I picture Carol and wonder if she'll be at the dance on Friday. Ouch, that hurt, I rub my gum through my cheek and then the twinge has gone. Rolling towards the radio I turn it on.

'POLICE, OPEN UP' Thunderous banging, shouting and a right old commotion going on downstairs sees me leaping out of bed and reaching for my trousers. I'm half way through the window when they burst in.

A uniform smirks as he slaps me in handcuffs. It's a short trip to the cop shop and in jig time I'm sitting in an interview room with two detectives.

I recognize one of the C.I D.blokes from last time. He's the one that beat me up but I was a kid then. "You again Groom, your sort never learn do they?"

The other cop opens the questioning. "Do you know a chap by the name of Samuel Evans?"

"Never heard of him," which is true, I only know him as Spike.

"Well he says you were with him when he stole over six thousand pounds from a factory last week."

They study my reaction. I try to keep stoney faced but six thousand pounds!

The bastard. I didn't get fifty fifty.

"Where were you on the night of the 15th?"

Best not to enter into any conversation with 'em. They're gonna beat the crap out of me in a minute whatever I say.

"Where's the money?"

I just stare at the wall. There's a black speck, a fly or something. I keep my eye on it. One cop nods to the other and he leaves the room. I know what's comin' and brace myself.

"Stand up" he says.

I look at him, the big bully. I can't fight back because if I do I'll get done for assaulting a copper and that's bad. Carries a big sentence. They've got *all* the power and know how to abuse it. Slowly I push the chair back and stand up.

He launches into me, punch after punch, only to the body and legs mind. Nothing that will show in Court. But I'm still toned and fit. I can take it. It's hard but I just have to stand there like a punch bag 'til he's exhausted himself.

The other cop comes in with a cuppa. Same old routine. Bad cop, good cop. I never say a word.How can they convict me without any evidence? There ain't no fingerprints this time, I made sure of that. Fuckin' grass.

A couple of days later, surprise, surprise, I'm refused bail. The grass is in Court. I spit at him. He knows the score.

The grass gives evidence against me. The cops found eighty two pounds in my room at Jakes and nothing at Mom's. Good old Roy. Turns out the grass was picked up in a car and he had the canvas bag from the factory in the boot!

Dickhead or what?

There's a code. He who gets caught takes the wrap but whatever happens you never grass. The Judge gives the grass 'a chance' with Probation because 'he has co-operated' and 'been out of trouble for almost nine years.' If I ever get my hands on the cunt I'll swing for him.

I am sentenced to four years and sent to the Dana Prison in Shrewsbury. I wonder what its like. Can't be worse than Winson Green, can it?

The Black Mariah stops and I can hear the heavy gates creaking. With time off for good behaviour it'll be 2 years and 8 months before I see this side of the prison walls again.

Setting my face hard, there's only one way to get through it. Show no emotion. The bastards will control everything physical for the immediate future, but what goes on in my mind, oh no, that's mine.

We move forward and the gates clank shut. I trusted Spike and he grassed me up. Susie trusted me and I let her down. Stepping into the air I look to the heavens…payback time is it?

Chapter 9

MY FEATHERED FRIEND

Shrewsbury is a high security prison with one main block, called A Wing and a small block for young prisoners, B Wing. Following the usual reception rigmarole, I'm led to a cell on the second landing in A Wing. A rank smell hits my nostrils and I move quickly to open the small slider for a breath of fresh air.

A set of bunk beds line the one wall and opposite is a single. The bottom bunk is obviously vacant, it has no bale of bedding, so I plonk myself down and have a bit of shut eye for five minutes.

I guess it's about half past four in the afternoon. My watch is now in a box with the rest of my property. Apart from the number of beds, this cell is much the same as the others I've been in. Don't fancy sharing though. Three pisspots stand in a line underneath the window.

My two cell mates aren't bad. When they come back from work we sit and have a chat. Foster, nickname Fuzz, a ginger haired bloke with a beard, in his mid 40's, is doing a four stretch for embezzlement. He's only been here a couple of days. The other guy, in his mid thirties, name of Les, is from a place called Dawley, which he says is not far from here. He's half way through a two stretch for shop-breaking. Les is a laugh, stands about 6ft tall and already going bald. "The cause of too much wanking," he says. "Suppose I'll be going blind next."

Les has been in and out of prison since he was twenty two and works in the engineering shop.

At teatime I follow Fuzz and Les. We have to walk three feet behind each other and there's no talking. In fact we're only allowed to speak to each other in the cells, during exercise or on association. This is gonna be tough.

The layout is much the same as Rochester with cells lining a central area. There are four landings with two steel safety nets stretching from side to side. At the middle of each landing is a recess with two toilets, a long deep trough for slopping out and a cold tap for filling the jugs. We only get to use proper toilets during work or association. The rest of the time we are locked up and have to use pots. I can see a dartboard and billiard table in the central area together with a few tables and chairs.

Meals are collected from the kitchen servery which is located along a corridor off the Wing. A screw in each corner stands watching as we proceed along the counter with our trays. Food smells good, don't look half bad either. Meals are eaten locked in the cells.

After tea the cell doors remain open until end of association. Fuzz doesn't mix much and settles down to read. Me and Les go for a game of darts. As soon as we reach the board I feel a tap on my shoulder. I know that face.

"You must remember me."

"Yes mate, course, Rochester." Truth to tell I'm struggling with his name.

"How are you then Watt?"

Grimacing, "well, I'm doin' a four, so I ain't good." It's coming back to me now. Milburn. He was on the top landing in a cell next to the Brummie kid but we never hung round together.

"What about you and that Hunkus?" He turns to Les, "down the Block four time, *four times,* he was" then turning back to me "Everybody thought you was a nutter."

"Suits me," I shrug. Well it does in one way 'cos most cons won't bother a nutter but on the other hand there's always someone with something to prove. Perhaps if Milburn puts it about that I'm a nutter my weather eye can have a bit of time off!

Another bloke, name of Southall, joins us for a game of doubles. Others are waiting to get on the dartboard so we move to the tables. A couple of cons are shuffling cards and one of them looks up as we sit down.

"Watt!"

I do a double take. It's Rusty. I know him, lives by me. Turns out he's doing a two stretch for safe blowing.

"Where you workin' then Watt?" asks Milburn.

"Mailbag shop mate."

"I'm in the kitchens. Butchery," he grins, "plenty of steak."

"Me an' all,"says Rusty, "pity you sewing them fuckin' mailbags all day."

Association over, me and Les nip to the recess. "Hope Fuzz has been to the 'john'," says Les.

Back in the cell we grab our tin mugs and stand at the door. An orderly comes round and fills 'em with cocoa from a huge jug. Then it's lock up. One hour later the lights go out.

Fuzz hadn't been to the 'john' as Les puts it and gets up in the middle of the night. He's on the top bunk and I get his foot in my face as he clambers down. That's not the worst of it.

"Fucking hell Fuzz mate, you got a dead rat up your arse?" Les turns away from the smell.

"Light a match and we'd fuckin' blast our way out." I get up and slide the window open. I'd sooner be cold than gassed in my sleep.

A bell rings. It's daylight. Fuzz's foot looms over the side of the bunk and I roll towards the wall. Les is already at the wash stand. "Seven thirty mate, rise and shine."

I hear the familiar sound of the spyhole being flicked. Les shouts at the door. "Yes we're all still here, more's the fuckin' pity."

A few minute later screws can be heard shouting. "A1, all correct Sir, A2, all correct Sir, A3, all correct Sir, A4, all correct Sir." Then there's a command from the Principal Officer, PO for short, to open up. Two screws on each landing open the doors followed by another handing out razor blades.

I take a leak in the pisspot and make up my bunk. Quick wash and shave in cold water and get dressed before joining an orderly procession to slop out. Back in the cell a screw comes along to collect our blades.

It's about eight o'clock now and on command we fetch our breakfast. Not enough sugar, there's never enough sugar for a decent cuppa. I need to get working in the Bakery, plenty of sugar there. Why have they allocated me to the mailbag shop? Can't understand it. Don't they know I've got qualifications?

After breakfast the doors are opened for another slop out, then it's off to work. I'm wearing a blue bib and brace type overall. Sewing mailbags! Me? Never done any sewing in my life. I will, however, become proficient at it. The more you sew, the more you earn. Out there, in here, it's what makes the world go round.

Fuzz is in the mailbag shop as well. He's new to it and shows me lots of scratches on his fingers where the needles have caught him. It's a large room and immediately I notice a raised podium where one screw sits observing everybody else. Another two move around watching all the time.

A few cons cut the canvas into shape with sharp knives. The pieces are sewn together to form a bag. That's where I come in. I'm told there must be eight stitches to the inch. Rope is then sewn in around the tops to make them stronger and rope handles are sewn on the sides. Finally the Post Office logo is stenciled on with ink. We work in silence.

When I've finished one I take it to a screw. He checks the bag over and makes a mark against my name in a ledger. Towards dinnertime we get half an hour exercise. Milburn makes a beeline for me. "Been telling everyone about you and the Block in Rochester," and then, out of the side of his mouth so the screw doesn't hear, "got any bacca?"

"Only got here yesterday mate," I start laughing.

Les looks at me. "You a baron then?"

I just nod. A man's gotta do what a man's gotta do. It's called survival and that's what I do.

We get another half hour exercise late afternoon and then its back to the cell, change out of our work clothes, wash, tea and association.

That's the routine, day in and day out. Once a week I can take a tepid bath in three inches of water and get a change of clothes. I could go to Church on a Sunday but don't bother. Fuzz goes but not because of any religious calling. He likes the change of scenery. I'm allowed one letter a week and one visit a month. I write home and send a VO.

It's cramped sharing a cell. No space, privacy or time to myself. The stink Fuzz creates every night is doin' my head in. I've got to get a single. Perhaps they don't know about my 158 and 159. If I can get into the bakehouse I'll probably get a single 'cos of the unsocial hours.

Next morning I mention it to Officer Pugh, one of the nicer screws, as he unlocks us for work. Just as I'm telling him about my baking qualifications there's a scream. We turn to see a con plummeting in thin air, legs and arms flailing, blood running down his face. A resounding clunk echoes around the landing as he lands in the netting. A commotion starts above. Shrill whistles, shouts from the cons and the dull thud of handrails being thumped.

The order comes from the PO for lock up and we're back in our cells while they get things under control.

"Gotta keep that old weather eye open." I remark to Fuzz. He's never heard of the saying. "Means the eye you need in the back of your head." He mutters agreement and goes back to writing his letter.

I sew mailbags for about two months and become quite fast. Although the pay is a pittance I earn enough to save towards the old baroning and keep me in the bit of bacca I need.

The news finally comes that I'm being transferred to the Bakery. I'll be able to take a bath and change clothes three times a week now. That's the regulation. Once a week for cons unless working with food. Officer Pugh tells me there isn't a single cell available yet but I'm next on the list.

Les and Fuzz don't take kindly to my new job 'cos it means me getting up very early but they brighten at the mention of extra sugar for our cocoa.

A screw fetches me at 6.30am, takes me to the bakery and locks me in. There are just two of us, me and a Red Band called Charlie. (Trusted cons wear a red band around the top of their arm.) I'm the number one Baker but he's got the key to the pantry.

I start working, making mental notes of the routines. During the day a steady procession of screws pass through, unlocking and locking the doors as they go. Les and Fuzz will be expecting their sugar tonight but I need to get the lie of the land first.

Two days later I'm clearing away and thinking about putting a small bag of sugar in my sock, when a blood curdling scream and loud clattering stops me in my tracks. It's coming from the adjacent butchery.

Me and Charlie run to the door. Three screws are bending over a con who's slumped at the foot of a big, wooden chopping table. A long knife protrudes from his stomach and blood is gushing everywhere.

"Stand back," orders the screw as one of the other cons tries to get to the bloke. He ain't screaming any more but his leg is shaking and his one arm reaches for the knife and then flops to the floor. His blood has stopped spurting and is now a steady flow.

Milburn and Rusty sidle over to the door. "Looks bad mate," says Rusty.

"You see anything?" I ask.

Rusty shakes his head.

Milburn rolls his eyes. "Me mate? No nothing. Best way in here. See no evil, hear no evil, speak no evil."

It was never discovered whether he took his own life or if someone stuck it to him. I heard on the grapevine that the poor guy had a dear john from his wife. Perhaps he thought if he injured himself and was in hospital she might come and see him. Desperate times call for desperate measures. On the other hand, according to form, he'd been moaning and groaning about it for weeks. Perhaps some other con thought 'shut the fuck up' and shoved the knife in.

Not long after that the butchery cons had to wear chain mail vests to prevent something similar happening again.

Finally the news I've been waiting for is delivered by Officer Pugh. A single cell is available from tomorrow. It's like winning a big prize 'cos it's something everybody wants. My grin spreads from ear to ear.

"That sorry to be leaving us then eh?" remarks Les.

The cell is on the ground floor. I like it better down here. It's closer to the billiards and dartboard. During association I scrub it out, getting rid of the body odour and stains.

Feel sorry for Les stuck with Fuzz. I'm looking forward to a methane free night and lie on the bed contemplating my new 'home'. As ever Susie creeps into my thoughts. What's she doin' now, right this very minute?

Association is almost finished so it's too late to join the lads. I roll over and grab my book. Can't beat a good Western. Hearing a flutter, I glance at the window. A pigeon lands on the tiny ledge. It pecks at the glass but flies off at the first sign of movement. It's free.

Cocoa. Mmmm, with extra sugar, I reach for my stash once the door is locked. Ouch, that bloody tooth again.

Pearl visits with Tom. I'd looked forward to it for weeks. At least it's not so far to travel as Rochester. Les tells me the Dana is almost in the centre of Shrewsbury and less than five minutes walk from the Station.

Pearl and Tom are married now and living in a small village called Pelsall, near Walsall.

"You'd like it our Watt," she tells me, "lots of greenery an' that. You can come and stay with us when you get out," turning to her new husband, "he can, can't he?" Tom nods. "I'll make sure you don't come back here again." She smiles and gives me a big hug on the way out.

I'm baroning again. Les and Milburn are carryin' for me plus three others. Fuzz isn't into that sort of thing. His choice. My empire is building slowly.

Now I have my own cell I start exercising at night after lights out; shadow boxing, pressing the bed and my usual routine. Thank you Officer Atkins. What he taught me in Rochester keeps me fit for many a year to come.

Most associations are spent around the dartboard or billiards. Everyone seems to be occupied and, fancying a game of cards, I wander over to one of the tables. There's a huge guy, name of Henry, sitting shuffling a pack. Nobody seems to want to play with him. "Game?" I ask.

"Five card brag?"

I nod and take the empty seat opposite. Henry looks to be in his late thirties, about 18 stone and standing over 6ft he looks useful. I ain't chatted to him before but I've heard tell he's serving a one stretch for some kind of fraud. Scarpered to Mexico but came back when a family member died and that's when they got him. Sounds interesting.

In the middle of a game he starts telling me about his wife. He glances at the screws. "They don't give me my letters, I don't know why, but they just don't." Cleary agitated he scrunches the cards.

I'd actually noticed when other cons had their letters he would always hang round but never seemed to get one. It never bothered me. I didn't expect any but he'd call the screws names and bang the cell door with his fists.

I want to say 'well maybe she ain't written any' but think better of it.

A week or so later I'm getting ready for work. It's very early. Most of the nick is still asleep. The spyhole has just flicked and I'm about to be unlocked when, Bang. BANG. BANG. It's getting louder and faster. The spyhole is stuck open and peering through I can just make out a group of screws gathered outside Henry's cell, which happens to be opposite mine. BANG, SMASH, BANG, CLATTER. Don't know what's going in there but it's woke everybody up and cons are knocking their tin mugs against the doors, yelling and shouting.

A giant roar can be heard echoing round the place. Perplexed screws stand outside his cell door for what seems like an age. Amid this deafening racket the Governor appears and tries to calm him down.

It ain't doin' no good. The roaring, smashing and bashing continues and now there's a scraping sound. All the time the Governor, who is standing directly outside Henry's cell, is saying he will look into the letters.

A screeching sound and WHAM, a sort of spear comes at the Governor through the spyhole. It misses his eye by inches. The screws take a step back and the Governor exits left.

I'm riveted. I can only see straight ahead through the tiniest of holes and my eye is literally aching, along with my tooth!

Ten screws appear. Two are holding the water-hose. Another two have a mattress held in front of them. The rest draw their truncheons.

Bastards. One screw inserts a key into the lock and looks at the others. They give the nod and when the door opens Henry is blasted by a powerful jet of water. He's a big bloke but it pins him against the far wall. With the mattress in front of them two screws rush into the cell closely followed by others wielding their truncheons. He puts up a good fight but eventually goes down under a rain of blows to the head. Henry is carried out bloodstained and unconscious. Bread was late that day.

"This fuckin' tooth" I'm nursing my cheek and telling the night screw in the hospital wing. I've been sent to get some aspro water, the cure for everything in here. "Can't you take it out Sir?"

He frowns. "I'm not fully qualified."

"I didn't ask to see your papers. I'm in agony here Sir." It's true my toothache has grown steadily worse. Been eating 'on the other side' for months now. The pain is shooting through my head and seems to be taking over my whole body.

"If anything happened…" he trails off.

"I'll say I did it with a piece of string or something. Honest." I'm screwing up my face. "I won't blame you Sir."

"Come with me then," he leads me to a chair and fetches some sort of pliers. "Can't give you anything, brace yourself, this is going to hurt."

Seconds later the bad tooth is down the sluice and I'm bleeding like a stuffed pig but, oh yes, the sheer relief washes over me. He shoves a sort of cotton thing in the hole and tells me to rinse with salt water for the next day or two. "You work in the bakery, don't you. It won't be too hard to get hold of some salt then." He gives me the aspro water. "That's all you've had off me," he nods, and calls a screw to take me back to my cell.

Pearl and Tom visit me again. It's nice to have visitors in one way but very hard when they go. Roy is with them. Somehow I hadn't noticed him grow up. He tells me all the news from the Toc H. I'm itching to ask him about my stash of dosh but daren't in case we are overheard. I've thought of some sort of code but he might not catch on. I give it a try.

"You know them toy soldiers I gave you when you was a nipper. Still got 'em ain't you?"

Pearl looks puzzled, Tom takes no notice, but Roy catches the intense way I'm looking at him. We're brothers, we've shared a bed, shared our lives.

"Course I have," he laughs. "I knew you'd be wanting 'em back. They'll be waiting for you, don't worry Watt." We've never owned a toy in our lives, let alone any soldiers. I can rest easy now.

Rob writes to tell me about his marriage to Maud. Roy had already told me. 'All the women were on the gates as she came down from Hunters Close. Big posh cars and everything' he'd said.

There's something not right about Rob's letter. I think he found it hard to write. We've been mates since school, done everything together, highs and lows, dreams and failures, seen it all and shared it all. 'Now I'm married' he writes, 'and you know Maud is a policeman's daughter.' I look up at the window. The pigeon is back. I throw a few crumbs out of the tiny slider and turn back to the letter. It's Policeman now is it. Not copper any more. Our Rob is getting posh. 'She says I shouldn't be writing to you... where you are.'

He never writes again.

Over the next few months I have some tattoo's done. There's a bloke on No.3 landing who's a bit of an artist with the old ink. It's just something to do really, relieves the boredom. First I have LOVE and HATE just below the knuckles. Most of the cons have got those. Then I decide on some family names. A bigger project, the snake up my arm takes a while longer. It's a source of regret and forty three years later I have the ones on my hands removed.

Thanks to Milburn's 'tales of Rochester' my reputation serves me well.

I don't get much trouble. My baroning ticks along nicely and I earn a few quid. Just keeping my nose clean, doin' my time. Les goes out saying he's never coming back. The screws shout "see you next year then Les." He laughs.

It's December 1958. I'll be 23 years old next week. Eight months left to serve and another bleak Christmas in nick to get through. Rusty, lucky sod, has just gone home.

I'm coming back from work, thinking about what I'm missing, and happen to glance across the Wing at some new prisoners. I look again. It's him, Spike the bastard. I can tell him a mile off. The grass is being led to a cell on the first landing.

Spike spots me when we collect our tea trays. I see him speak to one of the screws. He might be asking to go on protection so there can be no waiting and there's not much time for planning. I reckon during association is as good a time as any.

It don't take long to spread the word. Cons hate grasses. Next to nonces (blokes who interfere with children) it's the number one sin in prison.

Distractions are planned to keep the screws busy.

One of his cellmates has been told to keep him chatting in the cell while everyone gets organized. On the nod from Milburn I head up the stairs.

"Hello Spike, nice to see you." The other con fucks off quick and I close the door.

He backs up to the wall. Wrong move. "Look mate, they beat the shit out of me. They said they'd go…"

Spike never manages to finish the sentence 'cos I smash him in the face. I don't wanna hear it. Truth be told he ain't much of a fighter. His head bangs against the wall and he cries out. Big baby. I belt him in the stomach and as he doubles up, I bring my knee to meet his face and bash him on the back of the head for a double hit. He goes down.

"Get up."

Spike lies there groaning and holding his head.

I haul him up and throw him against the wall. He tries to defend his face but I go for the body and as his hands drop to clutch his stomach I give him a right-hook to remember. Going down again, he doesn't know which part of his body to hold now.

"Fuckin' grass, it don't end here," I growl at him. "All the nick knows what you are," grabbing him by the hair. "And don't even think about it. Protection's for nonce's and you get worse for being one of them."

I throw his head back and it cracks against the wall. "You slipped on the soap, remember?"

He just nods and stares into the pool of blood that has gathered on the floor from his nosebleed.

Feeling better I make my way down the stairs to join Milburn at the billiard table. "Give us two's on that will you mate, left mine in my cell."

He grins and passes me the rest of his fag. "I've been telling the new intake about Hunkus and the Block."

It's a bright, sunny morning with a bit of a nip in the air as I step through the gates into Howard Street in late August 1959. The walls seem even bigger from here as I turn to look at the prison. Raising my face towards the sunlight and the sky, I take a deep breath of free air and walk away. No, I ain't never comin' back.

A short train journey to Wolverhampton and I'm soon knocking on Jake's back door. I press my face against the thick obscure glass and can see Gladys in her green stripey pinafore. Wears a lot of green, does Gladys. Last time I saw her she was standing in the hallway looking frightened as the cops dragged me downstairs and away. I'm not expecting to get my old room back but I could do with my stuff, if they've still got it.

"Ooh Watt, you're out. C'mon in, let's have a cuppa."

I'm pleased at this 'cos it might mean I can stay! Jake was in bed but he comes trundling down the stairs when he hears voices.

"You're looking well you bugger," he greets me, "come for your stuff have you?"

"I can get the box if you like." I'm thinking I had a lot of clothes and the box might be heavy. There's the guitar and I wonder what he's done with my motor bike?

He smiles at me. "Never had a son of my own, you know."

I smile back at him. Yes I know. He was blessed with daughters.

"Come with me."

I follow him upstairs to the pink room. My stuff is still hanging in the wardrobe, all my shoes are polished and laid out neatly underneath and my guitar is lying on the bed. He moves to the window and I follow him. We look out on something standing by his shed, all trussed up under a tarpauline.

I'm a bit overcome. "I don't know what to say. Thanks. She's my pride and joy." Had some real good times on that bike and gave the local kids a quid to clean her of a Sunday, knowing it would help their Moms.

"I kept it oiled and such" Jake looks well pleased with himself, "and Gladys put all your stuff back when the cops had finished. We ain't touched it."

"Can I leave the bike here for a bit? I'll just take my stuff and get out of your way."

"You got somewhere else to go then?"

"Not exactly, but I thought…"

"You're welcome to stay for as long as you want. Gladys likes you and that's the main thing. Can't have anyone in the room she don't like," he shouts down the stairs, "ain't that right Gladys?"

She's carrying a tray of tea through to the front parlour. "He's welcome if he wants."

"I'll see you right Jake."

"C'mon now, have a cuppa. I'll get Gladys to do you some crispy bacon."

After a long bath, nice breakfast and change of clothes I nip round home to see Roy. Dad's at work and Mom's in the scullery. She's pleased to see me and once I've given her a big hug she puts the kettle on. I race upstairs takin' 'em two at a time.

Leaping on the bed I wake 'em all up. There's Roy, Mike, Malcolm and young Barry, who's coughing his little heart out. After a few minutes of rib prodding and laughing, I pull Roy onto the landing.

"Give us a hoist" he says glancing towards the ceiling. I cup my hands and he heads into the dusty loft. Ten seconds later I'm holding my shoebox.

"It's all there." He laughs and we hug on the landing. "Good to have you back."

"Fuckin' good to be back."

Roy tells me he saw the cops at Jakes and knew they'd be round to search here. "I just legged it out back and through the gulleys. Kept it at my mates house for six months."

"You ain't so daft as you look" I ruffle his hair like I used to do when he was a nipper.

"Geroff."

With the loot safely stashed in the bottom of my wardrobe at Jake's I head towards the shed. The tarpauline falls to the ground revealing my gleaming black beauty. Jake has looked after her alright and she roars into life first time.

Gladys comes running out. "Jake says I'm not to let you go off on it, you need insurance and stuff," she sees the looks on my face, "he's only trying to watch out for you."

"I'll just take her round the block," ain't gonna be told by no woman what not to do, so I roar off. At the bottom of the Crescent I turn round and come back. Jake's right. What am I doing? Gladys seems pleased and as I replace the tarpauline she brings me a cuppa.

"Looks like rain."

We look to the heavens, which promptly open and drown us as we run laughing into the house. I've spilt my tea and she makes me another. While I'm drying my hair in the kitchen an idea comes to me. "Think I'll get a car."

Gladys looks very impressed. If she's impressed, the girls will be too. When Jake comes back I run the idea past him. If I get a car will he get it insured and drive me up town when I wanna go? It keeps me happy and out of trouble. He's got a licence, the insurance and everything's legal. "I can give you a few bob, like driving the taxi."

Jake agrees provided it doesn't interfere with his work so next day I head for the bike dealers. According to Jake it should be pushed there. In fact I get to the corner of the Crescent and start her up. One last ride won't hurt. The wind rushes through my hair and my jacket flaps open but I know I'm making the right decision when it starts to rain again.

Bike sold I make my way to the car dealership. There's a sleek blue Jaguar sitting in the showroom. It's a Mark 11, what a looker, got a running board and everything. The gorgeous smell of leather hits me as I open the driver's door and slide behind the wheel. The long bonnet has a leaping Jaguar. This is the one for me. I sit in the middle of the back seat stretching out my hands…yes…plenty of room in here.

I stand back, viewing the car from all angles, trying to contain the big grin that's bursting to be free. The dealer asks me if I'd like to see the engine and opens up the bonnet. Never pay the asking price. I knock him down a bit and the big cat is mine.

When I say I'll fetch the cash the dealer is astounded. I think he's even more astonished when I actually turn up with it fifteen minutes later. Jake drives her home.

Causes quite a stir in the Crescent. Everyone who ain't at work comes out to look and have a sit inside. The kids queue up for a ride and want to know how much I'm gonna pay for cleaning it!

Friday night. Toc H is for teenagers. I'm 23 now so I hit the clubs in town. Well, to be more precise, I have a few drinks with Jake first and then he drives me round. The Jag purrs along and when we stop outside the clubs, I wind down the window. All the girls come rushing over wanting a ride so I pick two. I'm in the middle of the back seat and choose which one gets dropped off first, a sort of selection process. Good game this. When there's one left we park up and Jake takes a walk!

Oh yes, plenty of money, plenty of fags, plenty of liquorice, plenty of birds, but not necessarily in that order. It don't get much better than this!

But, every now and then, a niggle pushes forward from the back of my mind, Susie. I need to do something. She used to work in a dress shop in Bilston, trouble is, which one? There are several.

After a bacon sarnie in the Table Mountain I decide to set about finding her and several blanks later, end up chatting to a very smart lady in Brett's, right at the top of the town. She tells me Susie left Brett's under a bit of a cloud. I can imagine. But, thank you sweet Jesus, she saw Susie only last week working at Harpers, the haberdashery shop in Victoria Street, Wolverhampton.

Half day closing today, so bright and early next morning Jake drops me in town. There she is. I stand looking at her through the window. More mature, but her hair is still lovely and figure as trim as I remember.

Better not walk into the shop. She might be embarrassed. I'll do a bit of shopping myself and come back towards closing time. It's a long wait but worth it. Susie steps out with an older lady. Oh no, please don't start walking off together. I'm in luck. The older lady locks up and turns in the opposite direction.

I follow Susie for a little while. She hasn't spotted me yet but when she pauses to glance into a shop window my reflection stares back at her. There's a squeal of delight as she turns and throws her arms round me.

Wasn't expecting that. Wonderful. Her hair smells as fresh as it used to and I nuzzle into it. "Is there a café round here?" I ask.

She grabs my hand, pulls me along the road and into an alleyway. "This one's open 'til six."

I order the tea and we take a seat holding hands across the table. It's like we've never been apart. She's happy. I'm happy.

"I'm glad you came. I'd hoped you would but to be honest…" her eyes drop, "a lot has happened. I didn't think you'd come after all this time."

"I heard about the baby." I gently squeeze the slim fingers. She snatches back her hand.

"Was for the best…oh Watt…I didn't mean…"

"I know what you mean."

There's a moment of silence while we contemplate our teacups.

"I heard this Duncan bloke hits you. Is it true?" I'm not sure where this is leading. I haven't thought it through. Am I going to sweep her off her feet and carry her into the sunset like they do in the films?

"He did at the beginning, because I wouldn't…" she lowers her eyes again. "He said it was a husband's right and when I didn't want to…I think that's why I lost her."

It hits me like a bolt. A little girl. A baby girl. My baby girl. Guilt, anger and frustration do battle inside my head.

"I didn't know what to do when I heard you'd gone back to Borstal. Told my Dad you'd marry me when you came out but he wouldn't listen. Shame on the family he said. A child out of wedlock. No daughter of his was marrying no jailbird. Said he wouldn't give permission anyway."

"I would have looked after you, you know that."

Her deep blue eyes begin to water and her bottom lip is trembling. "Duncan worked with my Dad. He'd watched me grow up. Next thing I know everything's arranged. It was horrible Watt. On the wedding night he was drunk, slobbering all over me," her body stiffens at the thought of it.

"You still with him then?"

"Yes," she sighs and then hastily adds "but we don't share a bed, not now. He's been taken very bad with liver disease. He's dying Watt, he's dying."

I don't know what to say. She looks like she could do with a cuddle so I move round the table and put my arms round her. The café is closing and we have to leave.

"It drove me mad when you wrote me that letter," I tell her as we stand on the step.

Susie fumbles with her gloves. "Seems like a lifetime ago. I heard as you went away again," she raises her eyes to mine for a second, smiling now.

I take hold of her shoulders and pull her towards me. The pavement suddenly holds an attraction all of its own and her voice is hardly audible.

"I wish I could leave but there's no-one else to care for him apart from the old dear from next door who comes in when I'm at work."

"I've thought about you a lot."

"Me too, and it's *really* good to see you. Still as handsome as ever," she runs her fingers slowly through my hair. "I've got to go else I'll miss my bus. Perhaps we can do this again if you're passing."

"I'm sorry." It sounds lame but she nods and I stand there watching her walk away. Stopping at the corner she turns and glances back, tears streaming down her face. Then she's gone. In a blur I can see us, in the pavilion, that one single defining moment that shaped her path, forever.

****

Our Barry is poorly. His chest has been very bad and now he's recovering the Doctor sends him for convalescence to a place in Barnstaple, Devon.

Me and Roy want to go see him. It'll be a bit of a holiday as well. I ask Jake if he'll drive us down but he says it will take too much of his taxi time.

So it is that we go on the train. Dad decides to come with us and I give him the money to buy the tickets.

Barnstaple is a lovely place with quaint cottages and we stay overnight in a nice Bed and Breakfast just down the road from the convalescent home. Barry is excited to see us and we have a smashing time. Probably the only smashing time I ever spent with my Dad.

"Why didn't you get return tickets?" I ask him as we stand on the platform. "I gave you enough money." Can't fuckin' well believe this. We gather odd bits of change from our pockets to send Dad back on the train. Me and Roy will have to make our own way with the small amount of money left over.

"Take the cases with you then," I start to put them onto the train.

They drop with a thud back onto the platform. "No, I can't carry them." With that Dad shuts the carriage door and waves us goodbye.

We've got hardly any dosh, about 200 miles to walk and a suitcase each. Roy looks to me 'cos I'm his hero. "C'mon, let's go to the cop shop." Never thought I'd hear myself say that in a million years.

We find the local Police Station and tell the Officer our plight. I ask if it's possible for him to get two tickets and we pay at the other end. He keeps looking at my hands, LOVE and HATE tattoos, a sort of trademark for a tearaway. He says he can't help but, to his credit, gives us a cup of tea before sending us on our way.

And what a way it was. Day and night we walk and trot, trying to hitch a lift. Hot, sticky and out of breath, I buy some bottles of pop along the way and stop for some chips on the first night. We sleep in the hedgerows, usually near to a garage, so we can use the cold tap or the water can for a bit of a drink and a swill in the mornings.

A lorry driver stops on the road just past Bristol but he has to turn off for Stroud soon after. Still, every little helps. Eventually we get to Kidderminster where a kindly old gent in a big black Humber gives us a lift into Wolverhampton. The last three miles to Bilston are the longest. My feet are killing me 'cos I ain't exactly got walking shoes on!

Never have I been so glad to see Chantry Crescent. My socks have sort of melted into the soles of my feet which are just one massive blister.

"There's one thing I've learned," I say to Roy as we sit with our feet soaking in a bowl of warm water.

"What's that?"

"I ain't never goin' on another train journey with Dad." And I never do.

****

Money runs out, as it does. I fill up a few coalhouses and stock a few pantry's along the way, especially for old Mrs.Clegg on the corner who has nine youngsters. I'd noticed two of 'em begging for scraps and cast off's at the big houses on the main road, like I used to do.

My car is the cleanest one for miles 'cos I never say no if a kid comes round offering. They get paid a good whack and there's a lot less of 'em running about with no shoes.

In the back of my mind I want to get a decent job and go straight but the cops are always on my back lately. Seems like every week they haul me in for '*questioning*' even though I ain't done nothing.

The cop on the desk, Flanagan, takes pity on me, bringing cups of tea through to the cells when he's on night duty. Seeing as how there's nothing to tell and they really don't have anything on me, I'm released without charge every time.

All this hassle makes me feel like going back to my old ways. If I'm gonna get pummelled anyway...

Usually I keep my mouth firmly shut but today something builds inside.

As the detective brings his fist back to hit me in the stomach for the third time it just sort of bursts out, "if that's the best you got mate I'd give it neck if I were you."

He don't like it that's for sure, stops him in his tracks. For a split second I think he's going to break the golden rule and smash me in the head. His face contorts. The next punch doubles me up. Spitting obscenities, he walks behind and lands a vicious kick on my back. Fuckin' hell it hurts. Something seems to snap as I hit the deck.

I'm taken back to the cells. Needing the toilet bad, I ring the bell. Nobody about, must be on their break so I resort to using the pisspot. Glancing down I can't believe it. What's this? I'm passing blood. The bastard. I've got terrible pains where he kicked me and my finger stays on the bell.

The young copper takes one look and fetches Flanagan. He sends for the Police Surgeon who examines me and my urine. I'm released and told to visit the Hospital. I don't bother. The middle of my back is very sore but I've been through worse. Perhaps they'll leave me alone for a bit now.

On one of her visits to Mom, Pearl gets wind money is tight. "You ought to sell that car and come live with me." She's more like a mother than a sister. "You don't wanna end up back inside."

It's true, I don't. If I stay round here temptation is ever present. There's always somebody asking whether 'I want in' on a job.

Decision made, I sell the Jag, pack my stuff, and with my guitar slung over my shoulder make a track to Pelsall. Pearl wants to keep me out of trouble and I stay put for a few months. No-one knows about my past so I relax, make new friends, date a few girls and generally have a good time.

Pearl and Tom's pre-fab is a short stroll from the village which has plenty of pubs, a good chip shop and wide open spaces with trees and greenery they call the common. Everything is within walking distance but if I fancy a change a short bus ride takes me into Walsall town.

On one such trip I bump into Bernie Watkins. "Hey Watt, Shrewsbury wasn't it? Good to see you."

I remember him. Reputation for being a hard case. Was in for armed robbery. He'd kept out of my way and I'd kept out of his. "What you doin' over here then Bernie?"

"Bit of shopping with my Ma," he turns to the striking lady standing just behind him, 'meet Josie. Just goin' for a cuppa, got time?"

I'm at a loose end so why not?

Josie seems to take to me 'like another son' she says and one cuppa leads to another. Bernie's tales of safe-breaking and robberies make me feel alive again.

Before long he says they could do with another crew member and I've agreed to go and stay with them. "Plenty of room," he tells me.

Pearl is not happy but I go anyway. Haven't felt this good in ages. Bernie comes to pick me up in a shiny black Roadster. He looks great in his teddy boy gear. "Had this made" he says. "You want one?"

Within two weeks I'm wearing my first made to measure suit. The three quarter length jacket is bright blue with black piping. Drainpipe trousers, a bootlace tie and the old blue suede shoes complete the look.

At the local dances we cut a dash. Bernie is about the same age as me, not quite as good lookin' but we pull the birds alright. He can dance an' all and shows me the best moves. I can bop with the best of 'em now, throwing the girls up and over, pullin' em through my legs and rolling 'em over my back. We have a great time.

The Watkins family consists of Bert and Josie and their two lads, Bernie and Stan. Home is a big four bed house close to Dudley centre. My room is at the back, similar size to the one at Jakes, painted a soft blue colour.

I'm in the swing of things again, in more ways than one and the adrenalin rushes are back. We're at a dance one night and word goes round there's a new stunner in the corner. I take a wander past to have a look see. Fuckin' hell, it's 'the Shape'.

Carol tells me she'd heard on the grapevine I was living round here and has been to lots of dances in the area to see if she could find me.

"Well you found me now," I take her in my arms for the last dance, "what you gonna do about it?"

"I'm over 21" she nuzzles my neck. It tickles and makes me laugh.

When Carol meets Bernie, I can see he's well impressed. Still as beautiful as ever. "What'd you think Josie would say?"

Next day Carol leaves her job at the Co-op and Bernie fetches some of her stuff across. It's like nothing has changed between us as we chat about old times and old friends.

Most evenings we gather round the big kitchen table for a slap up dinner. She's a good cook is Josie. Me and Bernie take turns recounting Borstal and Prison tales, smoking and drinking tea 'til the early hours.

Bernie's got a job lined up for tonight. "Sit tight 'til I get back" I tell Carol, "shouldn't be more than a couple of hours."

It's 1.30 a.m. and Bernie is standing in the kitchen looking a bit worried.

"Stan's gone fuckin' missing. I'll shoot the cunt when he gets back."

Stan is our lookout.

"Oh well, let's do it tomorrow then" I'm thinking about my nice warm bed.

"Can't mate. Money's there tonight. Where the fuck is he?" shouts Bernie. Josie rushes downstairs. "Why don't me and Carol lookout?" she asks.

The clock is ticking and we need to get going. I ain't happy about it. No bird of mine is coming on a job. Josie nips upstairs to talk to Carol and in a jiffy she's standing at the kitchen table.

"No way." I shake my head. "And that's final."

Bernie throws out his arms. "Well what we gonna do? You tell me."

"Stan might turn up. Let's wait."

Josie makes tea and we watch the clock. Another half hour goes by. I push back my chair. "We'll do it without a lookout."

Carol follows me to the door. She runs her fingers through my hair and we kiss. A long, passionate, lingering kiss. It's the last one we'll ever have. When we meet again, many years later, our lives have changed completely.

The job is a big warehouse a little way out of town. Lots of dosh ready for wages is stashed in a safe and Bernie knows how to crack it. We park two streets away and walk briskly to the gates. One hop and we're over. A couple of wrenches with the jemmy and we're in.

In a matter of minutes, as me and Bernie are making our way to the offices, all hell breaks loose outside. Sirens, flashing blue lights, shouting and the sound of clomping boots coming our way. Must have been one of them silent alarm jobbies.

Bernie dashes for the side door. I ain't got a clue which way to run and duck behind some racking as the uniforms charge in. They pass me by and I crawl unseen to the outside.

As I make a run for it the cops give chase. Two of 'em grab my arms but they can't hold me as I sling 'em round the lamp-posts. One looses when his head bashes against the cast-iron but I ain't got no chance when reinforcements arrive. They've got me bang to rights.

At the first hearing my Uncle Harry steps forward to say I can live with him and my bail application is granted. Couple of months later I'm stood in the dock at Stafford Quarter Sessions.

27th September 1961. My Uncle Harry, God bless him, gives a wonderful speech on my behalf saying as how I'm like the local 'Robin Hood' robbing the rich to feed the poor but the Judge sends me down for three years.

I'm 25 years old and Shrewsbury Prison is becoming my second home. With time off for good behaviour I'll serve two years and it seems to stretch in front of me like an eternity.

Like an old shoe, the routine slips on with little effort. Why am I not surprised to see Les again? I'm straight into the bakehouse this time. Officer Pugh likes my bread, best ever, he says. Within two days I'm into a single cell on the ground floor. It's close to the dartboard and looks out over the woodyard. Well, it does if you stand on your chair.

A week into my sentence I'm playing darts and have just tripped over the fuckin' manhole cover again. There's a coconut mat on top which keeps slipping. Les comes over with a con I've seen around but don't know. He's younger than me, 5'6"ish and slim built with a scar on his left cheek, lots of tattoos and light curly hair. His eyes dart everywhere. Does he want some bacca? Perhaps sugar? As it happens that's the furthest thing from his mind.

I nod a greeting and Les waves me away from the crowd. The little guy can't wait. "I've just started a stretch for affray. One of the cops is in a bad way. He's still in hospital."

I look at Les and raise my eyebrows. "What's this got to do with me?"

"If he pegs it I'm a gonner" continues the little guy. "I knew the bloke who was topped a few months ago, right here in this prison."

I still don't know what he wants me to do about it.

Les puts his hand on the other guys shoulder. "Let me talk to Watt." He motions us to an empty table and pulls out a pack of cards. "This is Tonker. He's just come over from B Wing." Les sidles closer and whispers into my left ear "and he wants out."

To say I am speechless is an understatement but I soon rally with "don't we all mate?"

"I thought you might be able to think of something." Les has a blinding sort of faith. "You know this place like the back of your hand."

Now I am stunned. "But you've been in and out of here since you was twenty two years old!"

"I know, but I can't think what to do."

"Pity Fuzz ain't here." We burst out laughing.

Tonker frowns but then again he don't know the power of the Fuzz fart!

Les tells me Tonker is a local lad which means he knows the lie of the land if we can get over the wall. Useful. Les will help, but he's almost at the end of his sentence so needs to tread careful.

Tonker's eyes are pleading with me. "I'm desperate mate. You gotta help me."

"You'll have to give me a few days to think. Can't promise anything."

Association ends and we go our separate ways. I want my freedom too but it seems an impossible task. A shiver of excitement ripples through me. Can I pull if off? The odds are against me but I'll sure as hell give it a go. A steely determination takes hold. Where there's a will and all that...

Back in my cell I stare out of the window at the towering walls which take on a menacing darkness in the glow of the shadows as night draws in.

Flutter. The pigeon's back. Wonder where you've been today then?

I reach into my pocket for a few crumbs and chuck 'em out of the tiny slider.

My feathered friend dives for his tit-bits and I lean forward to watch him peck at them. It's then that I see it. A dirty great grid.

I laugh out loud. It's been there all along, the way out.

The pigeon, having finished his feed, hops onto the wheelbarrow and walks sedately across a few planks in the woodyard. Another flutter and he's up, up and away, soaring over those walls. It a good omen.

Chapter 10

THE SILENT CLOCK

I'm first at the dartboard the following evening and casually bend down to straighten the coconut matting. It's here alright. I've cursed this manhole to high heaven on more than one occasion. Must lead somewhere and if my guess is right....

I'd been up most of the night, my mind racing ahead, making mental lists and notes of the who, the what, the when and the how. But first things first, I need to have a look see down this manhole.

Tonker and Les dash over to the dartboard. My grin must be contagious 'cos they're both wearing beaming smiles by the time they reach me.

"You got something?" Les looks excited and turns to his mate, "told you didn't I?"

I kick at the coconut matting so the edge of the manhole is clearly visible. Their eyes follow me as I lift the mat before straightening it. Me and Les have a very quick game of darts so as not to arouse suspicion and then the three of us move towards my cell.

Tonker is impatient. "Can you get me out, like, down there?"

I raise my hand. "Maybe" and nod towards the barred window.

Les and Tonker jump onto my chair and peer out.

Les turns round. "Can't see nothing."

I'm sitting on the bed. "Look again mate, down and to the right."

"A wheelbarrow and some planks," volunteers Tonker.

"I see it, a big steel grid thing," Les is laughing now.

"If, and it's a big if, they're connected, it just might be our way out."

Tonker shoves his hands in his pockets and looks to the floor but Les still has the faith.

"We're gonna need a load of stuff and some mates we can trust, but first we need to go down the manhole and see if it leads to that grid in the woodyard."

"It must do. They're too close not to be connected." Les ain't coming with us but the excitement in his voice is obvious. Suddenly we've got a purpose in life.

Tonker blows out his cheeks. "Even if we get that far, we've still got to get over the wall."

"You want out don't you?"

He nods.

"Then have faith. We gotta take it step at a time. First we need mates we can trust to watch the screws and grasses. Let's get going."

We move out of my cell and head to one of the empty tables. Les lays out some dominoes. Tonker brings his mate Billy, and I motion Gordon over, lives local to me in Bilston and I've known him for years.

We quietly play dominoes. I lean towards Billy and Gordon and nod at Tonker, "we're getting out."

"Bollocks" is Gordon's response, "you've only been in a fuckin' week."

"You're off your trolley mate." Billy looks at Tonker who nods vigorously. His mop of curls do a jig of their own.

"Watt's gonna get us out." He's grinning from ear to ear.

Billy, Les and Gordon will help. We'll have to bung 'em some bacca or sugar, or both. Nobody does something for nothing in nick. Although I've only been in for a week I'm already rationing my own bacca consumption so as to start baroning. Tonker will have to put some of his into the pot.

Now we've got three helpers but we're gonna need more as time goes on.

"We could do with something to get that manhole lifted." I look at Tonker, "'cos tomorrow night I want me and you down there."

Les, who works in the engineering shop, says he'll scout round for some sort of tool to lift the manhole but it may take a couple of days.

"Do your best mate." I turn to Tonker, "bring some utensil, fork or a spoon, shove it down your sock. We can bend 'em up if Les ain't got nothing. Were do you work?"

"Mailbag shop."

Good news. He also has at least three reliable mates working alongside him. Music to my ears.

"What about your cellmates?"

"What do you mean, where they work like?"

"No, I mean can they be trusted?"

"Both local lads, know 'em well. No worries."

A regular symphony playing in my ears now. Tonker don't know it yet but if all goes to plan he's gonna be busy in there after lock up in a day or two. Mental note. Another two cons to be added to the list. Worth a bit of bacca to keep the old mouths shut.

Next evening, here we are, assembled by the dartboard. Me, Gordon, Les, Billy, Tonker and three of his mates. Tension is high. Act normal. It's hard.

Les has got his eye on something to lift the manhole but ain't managed to get it out yet.

"Stand in a line together at the end of the matting" I whisper.

They move into position, me and Tonker drop to our knees and lift the matting. I produce a sturdy pudding spoon from my sock and Tonker pulls one from the side of his boot. We bend them to form a sort of hooked lever. Placing our spoons at opposite ends of the manhole cover, we try to lift it. Not only doesn't it budge but the spoons break in two. Fuck it.

"Relying on you now Les." Gutted, I shove the two bits of spoon in my pocket.

The next day I go through the motions until association. I'm totally focused and even old Smith, the singing screw who sometimes moulds the bread alongside me, with his 'I love you for homosexual reasons' tune, is unable to interrupt my thoughts.

I've got one thing on my mind. Freedom. And how to get it. I'm kneading the dough but all the time the army of information in my head grows and reassembles as pieces slot into place.

Now the plan is formulated I've just got to make it happen. My nerve ends tingle with anticipation. Even before he reaches the dartboard I can tell Les ain't been able to get anything. My stomach sinks.

We move to one of the tables and start a game of cards. Getting down that manhole is crucial.

A con wanders over as I'm dealing. "I want in" he says pulling up a chair.

I'm thinking he's meaning a game of cards. Inconvenient. "Not tonight eh. Got a bit of business."

"I don't mean ace of spades Watt. Word has it you're planning a breakout."

Word has it. Fuck me. I can't believe it. Need to get moving. The longer we take, the more likely it is we'll be grassed.

"I'm Dennis. You can trust me. Used to run with Bernie Watkins before I got this," he taps his left leg.

I study him hard. He's tall, dark haired, carries some weight and walks with a limp. Not good. He ain't fit and that's a worry to me but any friend of Bernie's is a friend of mine and vice versa. That's how it works.

"Glad to have you on board" I say, shaking his hand.

"You'll have to put an ounce each week into the pot" I warn him as Tonker and the others introduce themselves.

Reluctantly Bernie's mate agrees. There's always a price for freedom.

Sugar is the other highly coveted substance in nick. The allocation is two spoons per day per con. Certainly not enough for anyone who likes two heaped spoons in everything.

The Redband in the bakery is named Chris and he holds the key to where it's at. The pantry. He likes his smokes and so I put my proposition to him. I'll give one eighth of an ounce of bacca for every one pound of sugar. The look on his face tells me we're in business.

Sugar is kept in half hundredweight sacks. Quantities are weighed out for many different uses so it's virtually impossible for the screws to check and it's not missed.

Chris puts it into small cloth bags with drawstring tops. I take one in each sock back to my cell from where it can be exchanged for whatever we need, and we need plenty. I reckon I can smuggle ten pounds of sugar a week. That should buy us a fair few favours.

I'm pinning all my hopes on Les bringing something to lift that manhole cover tonight. He walks over nonchalantly, hands in his pockets, but his beaming face tells a story. At the dartboard he slips me two pieces of hardened steel and winks "don't think these will break."

My mates, including the Welsh Crusher, are watching known grasses.

Nobody messes with him 'cos he's got serious connections down London. A real hard nut, 14 stone, stands a shade under 6ft with mousey brown hair combed forward.

Gordon, Billy, Les and Dennis keep an eye on the screws as well as making a sort of screen. Me and Tonker hold each others eyes for a moment before dropping to our knees. This time the manhole cover gives. We're in. Les takes the makeshift levers 'cos someone has to lift the cover when we return.

A thin steel ladder leads into the blackness. I swing myself onto it and Tonker follows. At the bottom we find ourselves crouched in a narrow, walled tunnel. The darkness envelopes us as the manhole cover is replaced above.

With barely room to stand and my heart beating like a trip-hammer, the silent count begins. There is no way of keeping track of time, except in my head. Every sixty is one minute. I'm allowing thirty minutes. Any longer is too risky. It's not as if I'm an anonymous type of con. The screws know me well.

Tiny shafts of light penetrate the tunnel at regular intervals. I knew it! Daylight is coming from somewhere. It must be outside. The first one is about twelve feet away and, as we approach, I can see the rays emanate from a long, low, grille.

I motion Tonker to stay where he is and creep past. We drop onto our bellies and, with heads almost touching, look through. The steel grille is two foot high and about three foot wide. It seems to be the entrance to some kind of lengthy ventilation shaft. There looks to be another grille at the other end.

Tonker grabs one side and I put my fingers through holes on the other as we try to wrench it free. No matter how hard we push and pull it won't budge. I feel around the perimeter. No screws or bolts. It seems to be cemented in....fuck it.

We make our way back to the ladder and Tonker goes up first. Two taps, light floods in, I'm blinking and we're out. Les replaces the manhole cover and Billy kicks the coconut matting over the top. Phew. Wave of relief. Tinge of disappointment.

Fuckin' hell, our shirts and trousers are covered in black dust and grime.

The lads form a screen as we walk the twenty feet to my cell, chatting and laughing. Gordon and another two guys who are in the know stay round the dartboard and finish a game.

One of Tonker's mates works in the Laundry which is useful. He's brought us a change of clothing concealed under his shirt. The clean gear has been deposited in my cell during our excursion underground.

We give the dirty gear to Tonker's mate who came in looking 9 stone wringing wet and goes out a well padded 12 stone with half ounce of bacca in his pocket.

To business. "We need something sharp. Fuckin' grill is cemented in," I turn to Les, "and something to knock it with."

"You'll have to stash these. I can't take the risk."

Taking the two pieces of steel from him, I strap them under the corner table with some sticky tape which had walked from the First Aid box in the bakehouse.

"We *can* pull this off." I look up and they're both grinning. Tonker has the faith now, I can tell.

It's a dead cert that the grilles I saw down there lead through to the rusty grid outside my window. Other facets of the plan can now be put in motion.

Back in the central area we sit with the cards. Gordon shuffles. I grab 'em and deal. Me and Tonker find it hard to sit still.

"Had a letter from the trouble and strife today," says Les. "She's bringing Mom and Dad next week for a visit."

My own thoughts drift to Carol. I'd had a letter from her today saying she'll wait for me and that.

A despondent mood engulfs the table as everyone gets lost in thoughts of home, wives, girlfriends and kids. Tonker breaks the silence and starts to chat about the local bloke who was topped in February "right here in Shrewsbury" he reminds us.

According to Tonker a woman was robbed and murdered. "George was well known to the cops, being a bit of a lad like, but everybody who knew him didn't think he'd done it."

We murmur our agreement to the concept that as long as the bastards get *somebody* they don't much care *who* it is.

"Big demonstrations and everything outside the prison gates on the day of the hanging," Tonker tells us, "hundreds of people chanting and waving placards but it made no difference."

We stop playing cards and consider the awful thought of being sent to the gallows. The tightening of rope…

I lean towards Tonker, "rope, we're gonna need rope and lots of it."

They all look up and Tonker seems a bit alarmed. "How....?"

Before he finishes, "Mailbag shop, lots of rope. Shove some up your shirt or wherever you can, wrap it round your body. If you got any mates that will do it, well, we need 'em. Tell 'em a quarter ounce or some sugar."

"But where we gonna stash it?"

"Tomorrow morning make a slit in your mattress with the razor, put the rope in at night and sew the mattress back up. You work in the mailbag shop so you can get a needle and thread."

Tonker nods.

"Each night unpick the mattress and shove the rope in. Plait it together with the other length, get it? Then sew the mattress back up."

"Yes, but what we gonna use for a hook? Rope's no good on its own."

"I'm onto it. Don't worry. Just do your part. It's a fuckin' big wall. You need to start getting the rope."

"Got legbreakers the other side."

Yes, I'd noticed them when I walked out at the end of my last sentence. The time I said I wasn't ever coming back. I lie awake thinking about the wall. Looks high but I've got an idea for a hook, simple really, but whether it will work is another matter. Only time will tell.

I need a contingency plan, just in case we make it out of the Block but can't get over the wall. Its Saturday 7th October 1961 today. Now... who do I know that comes from London and is going out soon?

Next night Me and Tonker go down the manhole again but this time, compliments of Les, we're armed with a sharp chisel and a small heavy bar to knock it with. Gordon's given me a piece of old towelling to deaden the noise.

Starting my silent clock we head for the shaft of light. Crouching or working on our bellies, we take it in turns to knock and chip away at the cement surrounding the grille.

The mortar is old but solid and a thudding noise reverberates round the enclosed space as makeshift hammer meets makeshift chisel, deadened only by the old towel. Gauging how much we've done tonight I reckon it will take us another three days to get through.

"Time's up" I whisper to Tonker when my silent clock gets to forty five minutes. The longer we're down the hole the more chance of being missed. Shall I leave the tools here? No, best not. Just my luck for some sort of maintenance check.

Back at the ladder Tonker climbs up to tap the manhole. A heavy thud comes back. This is the signal to say we can't exit safely.

"What the fuck's goin' on up there?" I'm impatient to get out.

"Can hear Officer Shaw, he's laughing about something."

I'd stopped my silent clock but start it up again. Forty five minutes, add ten minutes before we'd started and another five for good measure. A further twenty minutes pass with me and Tonker hardly daring to breath. A good kicking from the screws waits for us if we get caught, plus loss of remission.

Its almost end of Association. We're gonna get trapped down here. Can't believe it. Fuckin' screw. What's he fuckin' doing?

The ladder is finally flooded with light and we're released. The relief is intense. Association has ended and cons are all but back in their cells. Good job the screws are busy.

We head to my cell. No time for anything but a quick brush down. Tonker combs the dust out of his hair to calls of "WILSON" coming from the landing above. I shove a book towards him as he exits my cell. Two screws are now shouting his name. Tonker sprints up the steel stairs.

"Sorry Sir, just borrowing a book."

"Where you been for it Wilson, down a coalmine?" The screws laugh.

Next night, as we're standing at the dartboard waiting until its safe to go down, Tonker says that between him and two others, he's managed to get some rope out of the mailbag shop.

"Keep up the good work. " I turn to Les, "Did you hear anything last night, any clonking?"

"Not a thing mate."

"Let's hope old Shaw doesn't want another game of darts tonight, bit of a close shave that," remarks Gordon.

Down we go again, chiselling and chopping and, as predicted it takes us until 10th October to remove the first grille. Shoving it clear brings a huge grin to my face. At last.

On our bellies we peer through. The other grille stares back at us. I roll on my back. "It's probably cemented in, same as this fucker."

We brush the bits of cement and mortar into the hole. Must keep it tidy just in case, and replace the grille, carefully propping it so that at first glance there wouldn't appear to be anything wrong. Can't get further tonight but tomorrow…second grille here we come.

Excitement builds as we crawl into the hole on our bellies, commando style, and shuffle along to reach the other end. This second grille is much, much harder. Not only is it cemented in but the working space is a lot more cramped. I can't seem to get any force behind my chiselling because of the angle and now I've got a painful crick in my neck as well as a mouthful of dust and an eyeful of grit.

"If I take a drink of water with all this cement stuff inside me I'll turn into a fuckin' statue," I whisper to Tonker as we wait for the manhole to be lifted.

He's chuckling as light floods the darkness. Billy and Gordon usher us into my cell. Something's up. Can tell by the body language and the look in their eyes. Mister Laundry Man lurks outside. Dennis goes to commandeer a table and set up some dominoes.

Tonker's having a wash. "Think there's rats down there Watt? This smells like shit," he's screwing up his nose and pointing to some brown stains on his shirt. After ditching the dirty gear and paying the bacca, I turn to Billy and raise my eyebrows.

"There might be rats up here an' all."

"Who?" I'm combing my hair.

Gordon's sitting on my bed. "Crusher said to tell you, him with the pointed head, you know, whatsisname, works in the laundry, must have heard something, says he's gonna split to get in the screws good books." Gordon gets up. "We need to move, been in here too long. You ain't played darts for ages Watt."

Tonker goes with Billy to play dominoes. Me, Les and Gordon hang round the dartboard waiting for it to become free.

I'm scouring the scenery to see if I can spot mister pointy head. Need to nip this in the bud right now. Our eyes meet, he's leaning over the rail on the first landing. He shifts immediately and walks into a cell. Wrong move.

"You play darts, I've got business."

I saunter to my cell and collect a book. Cons are always up and down swapping paperbacks with each other. Look natural. I swing the book and whistle a tune as I stroll towards the steel steps.

Out of the corner of my eye I notice some raised eyebrows from the domino players and make a sign with my hands for them to turn up the volume. As the banter gets louder I take the steps two at a time.

Inside I'm taut and ready. Nobody, but nobody, is gonna get in my way. I set my face and stride through the half closed door. The bastard is sitting writing a letter. I throw my book onto the top bunk. His cell mate, who is lounging underneath, takes one look at me and legs it.

Pointy head turns and I smash him straight in the face. Reeling backwards, he grabs the chair as it topples and he falls awkwardly, tangled in the legs.

"Fuckin' grass" I growl at him.

He gets to his feet and makes a fist but I jump up and put the nut on him. There's a strangled cry and he clutches his face. His body undefended I punch him in the stomach and ribs. Reflexes bring his hands down towards the fresh pain and he feels the weight of my fist on his jaw.

Backed against the wall, I pin him there with my arm across his throat. "Grass on me you cunt and it'll be the last thing you ever do." I tighten my hold, "Understand?"

He's clearly choking. Sweat is pouring from him as he nods. I loosen my grip and he grasps his neck.

"Know something 'bout me you wanna share with the screws then?"

"No, no, not me."

"Keep it that way, eh, stay healthy," collecting my book, I smooth my hair and leave the grass licking his wounds.

Before we go down the manhole the following night I ask Tonker if he's heard anything about the cop he'd beat up. "Nothing good mate, had word its touch and go like."

"C'mon then, let's get at it."

Taking turns, sweating and cursing, we hack away at the hard mortar around the second grille. "How long you think?" whispers Tonker.

"Another two, maybe three days mate."

Ouch, a short sharp pain in my neck. I stop, lowering my head for a moment. There it is. Through the grille I can see the dirty great grid. So close. With renewed vigor I lift my arms in this cramped, claustrophobic space and chip away.

When my silent clock reaches forty five minutes we edge backwards, heads down, pushing with our arms and scrabbling with our knees. It's harder to get out. I bang my head. Fuckin' hell.

Ten minutes later we're sitting playing cards.

"How's the rope coming then Tonker?"

"Good, got about 25 feet tripled up and plaited like you said."

Here comes the geezer from London. I turn to the lads and fold my cards. "Sorry, I've got a bit of business to sort."

The cockney is due for discharge tomorrow and I need a big favour.

No-one will know of my contingency plan unless I have to put it into action.

We're almost there. Next night I let my silent clock tick along to fifty minutes in the hope we can shift the bloody thing. It's a big risk and in the end doesn't pay off anyway.

No amount of pulling and pushing will shift it. One side is free but we're gonna need the whole thing out to crawl through. "Just one more night," I whisper to Tonker on our way to the ladder.

He climbs up and taps the manhole. It lifts, Tonker gets out. I'm hot on his heels when WHAM the cover slams shut. "What the ....?" I rub my head where it hit, virtually forcing me back down.

I stand on the ladder for what seems like an eternity. Indistinct voices grow louder. The game of darts degenerates into an argument. What the fuck are they doing? Mates? They're supposed to be keeping a lid on things by the dartboard. It's the last place to have a ruck.

The screws will be round now. The clock is ticking. Can't be long left.

It goes quiet. A few minutes pass before light floods the hole. Thank you sweet Jesus.

Les pulls me out and the others crowd round as we walk swiftly to my cell. "You almost brained me," I'm feeling my head, parting my hair and looking in the mirror for signs of a lump.

"We never noticed him 'til he was on top of us," Billy looks apologetic, "you know, him as likes a game darts."

"Fuckin' close that was mate," Tonker is smiling, "I just got out and nearly come face to face with Officer Shaw."

"We started an argument to take his attention so Tonker could get clear," explains Les "see you lot tomorrow then, I'm gone."

He leaves closely followed by Tonker and Billy. Only a few minutes of association left anyway so I lie on the bed, nursing my bruised head. Flutter, pigeon's back. Ignoring his pecks at the glass I pick up my book, could do with a fag but pop a liquorice instead. This time tomorrow…

Sunday 15th October and it absolutely drags. I'm on the servery as well as baking today which is good for my mates, 'cos given half a chance I slip 'em an extra cob or pastry.

I drift into thoughts of the main plan but also the contingency. In my own mind I'd set a date for the escape. My mate from London went out yesterday. Wonder if he's made contact. If we can't get over the wall…

Chapter 11

COME TO DADDY

I'm looking out of my window at the dirty great grid. Association is just about to start and we need to get through the second grille and underneath that grid. Tonight.

There's a sort of big rusty bolt on the one edge. It's an old grid. My eyes flick across the woodyard to the towering prison walls beyond. No time for doubts. Not now. We *can* do it.

Laughing inwardly I collect my 'tools' and head for the dartboard. Me and the lads have a game 'cos the screws are hanging round, too close for comfort. I'm usually pretty good with the old arrows but can't hit the fuckin' board tonight!

Eventually the screws attention is taken by a ruck on the second landing. Me and Tonker scramble down the ladder and crawl into the shaft. I can hear the pitter patter of rain as it falls through the dirty great grid.

One last section of cement holding the grille is taking an age. The chisel doesn't seem to be making inroads. Sheer brute force with the makeshift hammer brings cracks and then clumps as it breaks away. The noise echoes. It must be making a racket outside.

We give the hammering a rest and try pulling at the edges. No good, can't get any purchase on it from this position. No choice but to carry on.

"Let's come at it feet first and try booting it out" I suggest.

We scrabble out of the shaft and I go in again, belly up and feet first. Not being able to raise my knees very far, I can't get enough power behind the kicks. I try hard but it's useless so push myself backwards until Tonker can grab hold and pull me out.

Back in we go and after thirty minutes I prod Tonker but he shakes his head. "Just a few more minutes." With frantic energy he makes one final flurry of hits. "C'mon you bastard," he's talking to it now. I'm pulling with all my might. It gives. I sink my head into my hands.

Later, gathered round the table playing dominoes, we give a progress report. None of them really thought we'd get this far.

"Don't want to be a killjoy, but there's no way you're getting over that wall," Gordon places his hand face down on the table and smiles smugly.

Must have a double blank.

"I'll be waving at you from the other side of Watt's window soon," Tonker tells the lads. They start laughing at him.

"Words out now, bigtime an' all," Les interjects as he places a three onto the ever growing chain of dominoes.

It worries me. The chance of getting caught, either by nosey screws, an untimely shakedown or the ever present grasses, is always at the back of my mind. My turn next, I've got a three.

"My bed's lumpy as fuck," Tonker complains pulling a face. He leans forward, "how much do we need?"

"Just keep getting it, much as you can. Need at least thirty five foot."

Tonker nods, looks at his hand of dominoes, screws up his face and taps the table.

"Where we gonna go then?" Dennis taps the table and looks at me, "you know..."

This sounds like he thinks he's coming with me. I'd thought we'd split up but I ain't telling them that, not yet. "Let's get the grid sorted. Like I said at the beginning, one step at a time."

Monday 16th October dawns. Before work I take another look at the dirty great grid. I can't see all of it from my cell window but I can just make out some long hinges. Perhaps it'll just lift up once the nuts are undone.

All day my mind's whirring about the grid, the wall, the rope, the hook, and now, it looks like Dennis and Tonker think they're coming with *me* once we're out. Need to have a chat. Tonight after our little excursion.

Can almost taste freedom now. London, I'd liked it there. A big place, big enough to get lost in. Met quite a few cons from down 'The

Smoke' during my last sentence. Milburn had regaled everybody with the 'Tales of Rochester' so there was a lot of mutual respect an' all that. Smiling to myself, I knead the dough.

"You look happy," remarks Officer Smith. "Shall I sing you my tune?" he winks. Always a kindly word, can't help but like him, even though we think he 'bats for the other side.'

"No thanks Sir, but I can tell you a good joke if you like."

He nods and so I tell him the comedy sketch from Rochester that me and Lofty did. Smith finds it hilarious and goes off into the kitchens. I can hear bursts of laughter as he tells it to the other screws.

Association finally arrives. This is the big one, the final grid. If we can get through then I know we can get out, over the wall or not. My body tingles with anticipation as we make our way down the ladder.

I remove the first grille and pass it to Tonker. We share a moment of eye contact before dropping to our bellies and scrambling into the shaft. He pulls the second grille, turns it round and thrusts it forward.

Crawling through the hole we drop into a sort of small chamber. The grid is directly above and looks to be about 5ft by 3ft. Crouched almost double, my fingers reach through the slats to find the bolt. Motioning Tonker to do the same on the other side, we try everything to loosen to fuckin' thing.

First one hand, then the other, then both. I'm covered in scratches and cuts. The nut and bolt are rusty and totally seized. Even with some sort of tool I don't believe we can get the bolt undone from this side. I signal Tonker to go back, follow him up the shaft and we're out in jig time.

The lads are surprised to see us so soon and when we've cleaned up, gather round a vacant table.

Dennis is shuffling cards and looks up frowning. "What's wrong?"

"Can't get the bolt undone mate." Turning to the assembled group, "any of you lot know a con who has access to the woodyard?"

Les works in the engineering shop and can get spanners, oil and suchlike. Now all we need is somebody on board from the woodyard party to take the spanner and oil, undo the bolt and return the gear without getting copped. Sounds easy?

"I know a chap," says Les, "but don't know if he'll risk it. Gets out in a couple of months."

"Tell him one ounce. If he can do it, I'll throw in a bag of sugar."

Tonker hangs his head. He's lost the faith.

"This time next week Tonker me old mate, you'll be shaggin' some bird somewhere." It lightens the mood and everybody laughs.

"Do your best Les." He shrugs his shoulders but I know he'll use all his powers of persuasion. The bacca and sugar on offer will help too.

The following day, **Tuesday 17th**, drags like a week in hell. As soon as I hit my cell after work, I'm at the window. The rusty old bolt stares back at me. Untouched and unoiled.

Tonight I'll tell 'em about my idea for a hook and sort out plans for once we hit the other side of that wall. One way or another we'll get there.

"Who is this woodyard bloke?" I ask Les as soon as we sit down, "he ain't done nothing yet."

"Redband, say's he'll think about it."

"How long for?" asks Tonker, panic in his voice.

"Well I don't fuckin' well know, do I," Les is getting a bit aggravated, "did my best."

"I know, I know," I shoot Tonker a glance. We need everybody on side. "You offered him one ounce and a bag of sugar?"

Les nods. I ain't got time for this Redband to *consider* it.

"Up it to two ounce and a bag of sugar if he can get it done by Thursday at the latest. One ounce Thursday and the rest Friday."

Sharp intake of breath from everyone. Two ounce of bacca in nick is a fortune. Tonker and Dennis don't seem happy, they know what's coming and they're both frowning at me when I say, "without this Redband we ain't goin' nowhere. I need one ounce from each of you."

With a bit of muttering they hand over their bacca.

"Watch it" warns Billy as a screw approaches.

The uniform walks past slowly and we revert to normal chit chat about home. Les starts to talk about his upcoming visit. The screw looses interest and moves off.

"Now, the hook."

"You won't be needing no hook Watt," laughs Gordon.

"Oh ye of little faith." I think I read that somewhere, probably in one of them bibles. Most of the cons gathered round this table, although they're keeping watch and helping in return for sugar and bacca, do not believe we'll get out. It doesn't take much to knock Tonker's faith and he's got that hangdog expression again.

I set my face. Everyone shuts up. "The hook; we're gonna make it from handles off buckets from the recess. I need two buckets brought to my cell."

"I'll get 'em" Dennis volunteers "but when?"

I raise my hand, "let me finish eh. When I tell you, is when."

"Are you sue it'll work like?" asks Tonker.

"Course I am. We'll need a bit of rope that's not tripled up to tie 'em together to form the hook."

Tonker nods as he lays some bacca into a paper. Then, licking the end and rolling it to form a fag, he looks across at me. We both need to believe.

"Like I said, this time next week, we *will* be out. I know where I'm going, what about you two?"

Tonker and Dennis look even more worried now.

"With you," says Dennis. Tonker nods in agreement.

"What about we stick together for a couple of days and then split up?"

It strikes me that although they want out, neither of them have thought any further. If they ain't got a plan by now then I need to keep 'em with me 'til we're safe.

Later I'm lying on my bed, hands clasped behind my head, staring at the ceiling until lights out. Got a few more things sorted. Good moon tonight and it shines into my cell. Don't want a good moon on Friday. Hope the Redband does his stuff tomorrow. Me and Tonker can shoot down and give the grid a trial run. I drift into a fitful sleep, dreaming about cowboys, shootouts and guns.

Wednesday 18th and it's a bright day. Can't believe the rusty bolt is still untouched. A drop of oil is all that stands between me and freedom. I'm rooted to the spot with my palms against the glass of the window.

Wrenching my eyes away from the bolt I stare at my boots. Fuckin' Redband. Maybe Les can't get him to do it, but I might. Stepping out of my cell, I glance towards the dartboard. Lots of activity over there. Too much for my liking.

Tonker and Billy are standing on the coconut matting. Les, Gordon and a few others are also gathered round. There's some sort of argument. Officer Pugh is getting interested. Need to keep screws away from the dartboard as much as possible. There are marks and deep scratches on the manhole cover from so much lifting and replacing.

I zoom over and head him off. "How was the bread today then Sir?"

He stops and looks at me, "very good Groom, as usual, I was meaning to ask…those Rock cakes…couldn't do me an extra half dozen could you. I'll nip down tomorrow afternoon." He looks over his shoulder, there's some shouting coming from one of the tables.

I smile at him, "course, anything for you Sir."

It's quiet at the dartboard now and Officer Pugh walks towards a ruck started by Tonker's mates over at the tables.

"What's going on then lads? Let's get a game going." I grab some arrows.

There's another guy standing there, wearing a redband, face familiar, I can sort of guess who he is but I'm not sure.

Les goes to introduce the guy to me, "This is…" but I stop him, don't need to know names.

I nod at the Redband. "You can get into the woodyard?"

"I want 4oz" he's staring at me. Normally I'd just knock his teeth down his throat.

"Play fuckin' darts," I hiss at Gordon and Les. Turning to the Redband, "you're on, do it tomorrow, now fuck off." He hurries towards the billiard table, puffing his fag ten to the dozen.

Me and Tonker watch Les and Gordon finish their game and then casually stroll over to where the lads have got some domino's going.

There are screws around so I join in the general banter until it's safe to talk. The Redband is sorted and I'm in high spirits 'cos I know in two days time we'll be gone.

"I'll be going to the Smoke when we get out. All arranged." I'd received word, in a coded letter today. "We get there, couple of days, then split, agreed?"

Tonker and Dennis murmur their agreement.

"You know the local area Tonker so once we're over the wall I'm relying on you to get us away and we're gonna need a car."

"Can't drive."

"Nor me, got a gammy leg."

I shake my head. "I ain't asking you to drive. I'm gonna drive. You just get me to where we can nick a decent car."

"Leave it to me Watt," Tonker taps his nose.

"Still don't think you'll make the wall" smirks Gordon, ever the pessimist, "I'm gonna enjoy watching from your cell window though," he starts laughing.

"Call yourself a mate," I dig him in the ribs.

He winces, "might even have a bet on it."

I'd heard there was a book running on whether we'd make the wall or not. As long as we get through the grid, that's all I'm bothered about. The bolt better be eased by tomorrow else I'll swing for that Redband.

Thursday 19th and Officer Pugh comes for his rock-cakes in the afternoon. Trouble is, with everything else on my mind, I'd clean forgot. He looks disappointed so I promise to make an extra special batch on Friday.

I close my cell door and sprint across to the window. One shiny, oily bolt stares up at me. You beauty.

As soon as association starts I'm out of my cell looking for Tonker. My grin tells him what he wanted to know. "We'll do a reccie tonight just to make sure it's loosened enough."

Pretty soon we're crouching in the pit with our fingers stretching through the grid slats. Difficult to reach but at last the nut and bolt are in my grip. "Got 'em."

The grease makes our hands slippery and progress is slow as we ease 'em round, bit by bit. The thought goes through my mind to loosen 'em right the way off, but then again, some sharp eyed screw or grass might notice. Bad enough the nut and bolt being freshly oiled. We leave 'em hand tight.

Back up top, once we've washed the oil off our hands, we head for the tables. "Tomorrow night," I say dealing the cards, "we go tomorrow night."

Tonker's face lights up.

"Here give the Redband this 2oz," I slip Les the bacca. "Give him the rest and the sugar after I'm gone."

"Screw" warns Gordon. Billy tells a joke and we all laugh, even though we've heard it a million times before. I think better of telling my hillbilly joke 'cos of the hanging, probably be a bit too near the mark for Tonker.

The screw moves past.

"Split whatever stuff is left in my cell between you lot and Tonker's mates." They look hopeful so I add, "there ain't much. Cost a bomb this lot."

I tell Dennis to bring the buckets as soon as association starts. The rope is more problematic because there's lots of it. Tonker and his mates need to get it to my cell where we can finish the plaiting, make a hook and tie it on.

"I'm allowing half an hour. We need to be down the manhole by then. That'll give us an hour and a half 'til headcount."

"We'll be well away by then mate," says Tonker, his blue eyes sparkling under the dancing mop of curls. He's laughing, I'm laughing, we're all laughing.

"Let's split," I nod at Gordon and Les, leaving Tonker with his mate Billy and the others.

We turn towards my cell. I need to show Les where my stash is.

"Think you're fuckin' hard..." a voice comes from nowhere and I spin round fast, just dodging a punch. Oh no, I don't need this. Not tonight, of all nights.

I know that face. Rochester. It's Jonah. A mate of Hunkus. Another punch comes my way. I manage to sidestep but almost push Les over. I can't afford to be involved in a fight. Could mean a spell on bread and water in the punishment cells.

Gordon steps forward and I can see by his stance he's gonna put the nut in so I push him away. I can handle it. Believe in a fair fight, me. No gangs, just one on one. If this guy's got some grievance...

I'd deck him if we weren't in full sight of the screws. I'm hoping the screws can see me trying to avoid a fight. My reactions are razor sharp and I dart out of reach as the bastard comes after me with another right hander. He's a big guy, crew cut with tattoos on his earlobes.

Officer Pugh and another three screws come across. They've seen what's gone on. Jonah is carted off. I never struck a blow, lucky for me and even luckier for him.

Friday 20th October 1961, D day, tonight's the night! Up with the lark and whistling all day in the bakehouse, I make Officer Pugh a dozen rock cakes and eat a couple myself for good measure.

"You got a visit soon or something?" asks Officer Smith.

"No Sir," better take this Cheshire cat grin off my face.

The screws think I'll be here tomorrow but I know different. Gives me a sort of glow inside.

"These mine?" Officer Pugh licks his lips as he comes to collect the cakes.

"Hope you enjoy them Sir," I really mean that. He's one of the good guys and it's a pleasure baking for him 'cos he always shows his appreciation.

Every nerve in my body is on fire as association approaches. My senses are on high alert and I can hear the clanking of buckets before they've left the recess.

Tonker and his two cellmates appear at my door, wearing outsize shirts borrowed from other cons. Stripping off they reveal three long lengths of rope wound round their bodies. Tonker laughs. "Feel like the fuckin' Michelin Man!"

I pass him a bag of sugar which he gives to his mates. They will share it with the three cons who loaned the large shirts.

Within minutes the five of us are working away like beavers. Me and Tonker are plaiting the last of the rope together and Gordon is making a hook with help from Dennis and Billy.

Les is on lookout, lurking around outside. Crusher and other cons in the know are ready to make a ruckus at his signal to create a diversion.

Gordon has unhooked two bucket handles and crossed 'em. He's holding the 'hook' while Billy binds it together with rope. "Needs to be really strong lads." Seemed a good idea at the time but now it looks flimsy.

Fifteen minutes later, rope plaiting complete, we're ready. We've just got to get this lot to the dartboard and down the manhole. There will be no time for goodbyes later, so we say 'em here.

After some joshing and lots of 'see you later' and 'sure you don't wanna come', 'thank you's' and backslapping, the mood changes and we get set.

Billy pops his head round the door, Les gives the signal for a diversion and shouting fills the air as a ruckus begins. Walking in tight formation, carrying the rope with hook attached, we reach the coconut matting. Les lifts the manhole and we throw the rope down. Tonker scrambles onto the ladder, followed by Dennis, then me.

I came in the front gates on 27th September. On 4th October I was approached about the possibility of an escape. Here I am, just sixteen days later, getting out.

This is it. Deep breath. Heart thumping, I take a last look at the faces peering down at me before the cover is replaced, then darkness.

We drag the rope towards the shaft of light and rip off the first grille. "You wait here until I call for you" I tell Dennis "then push the rope in front of you. Tonker will pull it from the other end."

Me and Tonker drop to our bellies and crawl into the shaft. We get to the second grille, turn it and push it through the hole. Now we're into the cramped space of the pit beneath the grid. I call softly for Dennis to make his move. Tonker turns and goes head first back into the shaft to pull the rope through while I start undoing the bolts.

Dennis, who isn't used to the claustrophobic atmosphere, and hampered by his gammy leg, must be finding it difficult. I can hear him huffing and puffing his way towards me.

By the time Tonker gets back into the pit with the rope behind him and Dennis lying prone in the shaft, I've loosened the nut and bolts right off.

"Here we go then." Me and Tonker try to push the dirty great grid open with our arms and hands. We don't have much leverage 'cos we're bent double. It creaks and groans but it ain't goin' nowhere. Panic. What's holding it? "We'll have to put our backs to it."

We manouvre ourselves into position. Taking a firm stance we line our backs against the slats and on the count of three, push. It's either stuck or too heavy for us. Hadn't banked on this.

A bit more of a creak. "I think it moved, 'bout an inch," says Tonker.

An inch…a fuckin' inch! "Try again."

I turn to Dennis who is lying with his head sticking out of the shaft. He looks petrified. "You count."

Looking at Tonker, "deep breath."

"One, two…threeeee"

"Heave." I'm red in the face and Tonker looks like his blood vessels are gonna burst out of his neck.

"Think it moved more than an inch then," says Dennis "try again."

The clock is ticking. We've gotta get over the wall yet. "Everything you got" I tell Tonker. "Try and relax. Like lifting weights. Deep breaths."

We get our backs to it again. Don't know how much the grid weighs, but it's heavy, real heavy. To get out we've gotta raise it. We are crouched in this pit not much more than 3ft high. With every fibre of my being, I will the thing to lift and with every muscle in my body, I push my back against the slats. I'm gonna stand up at all costs. This grid ain't gonna beat me. Nothing is gonna beat me.

"One, two...threeeee," counts Dennis

With supreme effort and great strain, gritting our teeth and letting out muffled roars, we slowly stand. There's an enormous thunderous groan as the grid opens, the hinges creak and it thuds onto the ground

Utter elation floods my body. Out of the pit and into the cold night we step, pulling the rope and Dennis after us. I punch the air. *Yes*.

Gordon and Les are at my cell window giving us the thumbs up. Moving closer, I tell Les to send anyone else through who wants to come. He shoots out of my cell door and comes back a minute or so later making a slit throat signal, meaning no. Can't believe it. They all bottled out. I shake my head. To think, this could have been Shrewsbury's version of the Great Escape!

We gather the rope and clamber over the woodyard gate. "Go back of the topping shed" I tell the other two, "get the rope untangled and ready to throw. I need a leak."

The 'topping shed' as it's known is actually a brick building almost opposite the woodyard. The perimeter walls stand about ten foot behind it and the gap between gives perfect cover.

Tonker and Dennis start unravelling the rope. Dark, very dark, can't see anything. I step past them and walk the length of the topping shed, scouring the ground as I go.

Dropping to my knees I search the damp ground with my hands. There it is. My contingency plan. Feeling the cold steel against the edge of my hand, I pick it up. Come to Daddy.

Chapter 12

HE WHO HAS THE WILL ALWAYS FINDS A WAY

I push the gun into the back of my waistband. Walking towards the end of the building I can hear Tonker and Dennis talking in hushed whispers about the best way to throw the rope. They have no need to know about the gun, not yet, at any rate.

Tonker tries first. The hook clanks against the stone and falls, almost hitting Dennis on the head. I study him. He ain't never gonna pull himself up that rope even if we can get it hooked on. I'm superfit, Tonker's young and wiry but Dennis…well…he's podgy, unfit, and he's got a gammy leg. What was I thinking of?

Seizing the hook in one hand and the rope, with plenty of slack in the other, I chuck them bucket handles skywards. They clank straight back down again.

"Lads was right, we ain't never getting over this wall," Dennis sounds despondent.

"Wanna have a go?" I offer him the rope but he shakes his head.

Me and Tonker try again but the hook's not catching anything.

"C'mon lads, back to the woodyard, got an idea, we ain't done yet." I must try everything else before resorting to the contingency.

"Bring the wheelbarrow and anything that'll give us some extra height." We pile some heavy sacks into the barrow and I move towards a short plank that's propped under my cell window. Gordon's standing there grinning at me from inside and points to an imaginary wristwatch. Gotta get a move on.

Tonker wheels the barrow alongside the perimeter wall and I place the plank on top of the bags. It won't give us much extra height but every inch counts. We huddle together, heads down, like a rugby scrum.

"Dennis" I whisper "you're the biggest so you stand on the plank. I'll get on your shoulders. Tonker, tie the rope around your waist and climb up the two of us."

Dennis has no agility and it takes him forever to get into position. A bit precarious, he's wobbling all over the show. I clamber onto his shoulders. Don't think he can carry my weight.

"C'mon Tonker," I put out my hand. He starts to climb. Dennis shifts his weight as his legs buckle. Tonker leaps away, I jump down and Dennis lands in a heap at the side of the barrow.

"I ain't strong enough," he whines.

Running out of options here. "We'll try again, quicker this time." Dennis looks towards the woodyard. I know what he's thinking. "We ain't goin' back." He looks doubtful but gets to his feet and struggles onto the plank. "This time lads, this time." It's gotta be, 'cos time is running out.

"Hold onto the wall Dennis" I tell him, almost flying to the lofty height of his shoulders. Tonker's feet don't seem to touch anywhere and in jig time I'm holding his ankles as he reaches for the top of the wall.

"Can't quite reach, need another few inches." I move my hands to form two cups. He puts one foot in first and then the other.

"Brace yourself Dennis, don't let us down." The tension runs through his shoulders and into my legs as he shakes beneath me.

"One chance Tonker." I push him skywards with all my might. His feet leave my hands as Dennis's legs give out and I jump to earth landing with a forward roll.

Tonker is lying flat on top of the wall. The rope dangles in front of us. "Up you go then Dennis. Tonker's the hook now." Don't think he's done a day in the gym in his life and his progress is painfully slow. Every minute seems like an hour as he claws his way upwards. Almost there. I hold my breath.

"Can't make it" he cries, loosening his grip and falling to the ground.

"Let me go. Me and Tonker will pull you up," I grab the rope and quickly hoist myself almost to the top. Now I know why Dennis couldn't make it. The wall becomes rounded and the rope is taut, laying flat against the stone. There's no grip, nowhere to put my hands.

"What that in your waistband?" shouts Dennis from below. He's spotted the gun. Ignoring him, my eyes meet Tonker's.

"Can you….reach down mate….give me a hand?"

Tonker is already taking the strain, but inch by inch, and with supreme effort, he manages to stretch further and I grasp his arm. I'm scrabbling for a foothold and he's pulling with all his might. A giant wave of relief washes over me when I find myself sitting on the wall. "Down" hisses Tonker and I throw myself flat. We watch with baited breath as a screw walks beneath us to his car, which is parked just a few feet away. I close my eyes. Please God, don't let Dennis shout anything, not now.

Somebody up there's looking after me 'cos the screw is driving off when Dennis cries out "what about me then?"

"Tie the end of the rope round your waist."

Dennis does as I ask

"We'll take the strain, you climb up….ready."

He's about half way when a commotion breaks out in A Wing. I hear the shout. 'RE-COUNT'. Cons are banging their tins mugs against the doors. A sort of warning.

"C'mon Dennis, make an effort."

He's clinging to the rope, "Can't do it."

I turn to Tonker, "we can't leave him, you pull from the bottom and I'll pull from here, hurry up."

Tonker nods and I take the strain as he lowers himself to the ground on the outside of the wall. We start to pull. A bit knackered now I whisper some encouragement, "almost there mate, almost there, another foot to go."

I reach over to catch his arm, which one minute is outstretched and the next is receding at speed. He lands with a dull thud and a muffled cry. The rope has come apart at one of the joints. Plaiting not strong enough.

"Dennis, are you alright?" peering down I can see him lying in a heap, clutching his leg.

"I can't move…think it's broke…you go."

The screws are shouting our names. A Wing is in uproar as cons cheer and bang everything in their cells.

Tonker is staring at me from the screws car park. "Mind the legbreakers," he warns.

"Here, catch this." I grab the gun and lob it to him. He breaks into a grin as it lands in his hands.

I lower my body over the side of the wall. It's a long drop. Please don't break; I'm talking to all my bones. One glance to the heavens. I let go and push myself out. The solid ground of the screws car park makes contact.

A bolt of pain shoots through my feet, legs, spine, into my neck and out through the top of my head. Although I'd bent my knees and done a backward roll on landing, it wasn't enough. I sit against the wall. The pain had taken my breath away. My feet are on fire. I'm in agony.

Slowly I move my joints. Nothing seems to be broken. Oh thank you Sweet Jesus.

"C'mon Watt, we've got to make it to the tracks." Tonker hands me the gun.

The screws are shouting our names. Heavy boots are running along the perimeter wall.

Tonker runs and I hobble behind him towards the railroad track which is just a few metres away. We scramble down the bank. Need to put as much distance as we can between us and Shrewsbury.

After about two miles there's a whistle blowing in the distance. A train coming. We dive into the hedgerow. Once its gone Tonker goes to get up but I pull him back down.

"My feet need a rest mate." They don't feel like part of my body any more. All pins and needles and I've still got shooting pains in my legs and back.

We sit on the grassy bank engulfed in a leafy enclosure. Tonker reaches into his top pocket and produces a fag. Seeing my face he pulls out another and we lay back for five minutes.

"You did it mate, you got me out."

"Got me out an' all! Anyway, couldn't see you with a rope round your neck."

"Think he'll grass?"

"Hard to tell. He seemed to be in a bad way. If his leg's broke and they give him a kickin'…"

Poor Dennis. He'll try not to but he'll talk alright.

"We can't go to London, not now. Need to head somewhere else."

I'm trying to think of contacts made during my last sentence. There was a guy from Moss-side in Manchester. At least it's in the opposite direction to London.

"What's with the gun Watt?"

"That was my contingency plan mate, if we couldn't get over the wall we were goin' out the front gates."

Tonker's eyes widen. "You mean it an' all."

"Once I start something…what can I say…I *never* give up."

We finish our fags and get to our feet ready to move on. "We was always gonna get out once I set my mind to it."

"If we get caught with the gun though…" Tonker's voice trails off.

True. Dennis had seen the gun so he'll probably tell the screws, but it's just his word with no proof. Extra time? Who needs it? I throw the pistol into the hedgerow, shove my hands deep into my pockets and set off again along the tracks.

"We can get a car in Wellington Watt."

Good job one of us knows the lie of the land round here. "How far is it?"

"I've never walked it before mate," he jokes.

It takes us hours to reach Wellington, dodging in and out of bushes to avoid passing trains, smoking the odd fag and sharing jokes. I'm getting to like Tonker. Funny to think that less than a month ago I'd never set eyes on him and here we are sharing this experience of a lifetime. Good to be out. Good to be alive. I breathe it in deeply, this smell of freedom.

We climb some steep steps at the side of the station and find the streets of Wellington deserted. The odd car drives past. Turning left we walk up an incline. Not many lights on. Must be late.

"What about that one?" Tonker points to a neat looking house with a timber garage at the side.

"It'll do me." We need a few bob and a car to get to Manchester. All we've got between us is a few ounce of bacca, fag papers, matches and some liquorice.

The small chisel tool I'd brought with me makes short work of the garage doors. A lovely Wolseley car sits inside. It's not locked! There are a few coats hanging at the side and we rifle the pockets for odd bits of change.

Tonker sits in the car. After showing him the brake pedal and telling him to hit it hard when he hears me bang on the boot, I open the garage doors wide. Lucky for me it's on a slight downward slope, so pushing the car out, along the drive and away from the house is easy. Tonker steers a zig zag for fifty yards and when I bang on the boot and the car stops dead.

Lifting the bonnet, I cross the fuses, which bypass the ignition system. A quick press of the cellanoid and the engine roars into life. Tonker's beaming as he moves over and I slide behind the wheel.

"Where'd you learn to do that Watt?"

"Oh, I had many good teachers, don't worry 'bout that."

Tonker gives directions to the A5 avoiding main roads and it isn't long before we see a sign to Wolverhampton.

Rifling through the glovebox, Tonker finds a few mints and then messes with some knobs. The radio splutters into life. It's a police radio. Can't believe it. A fuckin' coppers car.

We listen to 'em. Hilarious. One step ahead or what? They seem to be keeping watch around Tonker's house at Meole Brace in Shrewsbury.

A tinge of disappointment. Life in 'the Smoke' would have been good. For the time being, I'm officially on the run and headed home. If the cops are watching Tonker's then they're bound to be outside my Mom's too. I need to keep the old weather eye open.

As we approach Bilston I have a thought. "We'll park up in the old garages. No good leaving a car like this outside a council house."

Tonker nods, "good thinkin'."

In the early hours of the morning we creep through gulleys and clamber over garden fences. I've used this route many times. Never been caught before. It's nerve-racking as we inch closer to the back door.

I motion Tonker to stay put while I make a dash for it. Not locked. I quietly step through and listen. No voices. Good.

In the parlour Roy is dozing on the sofa and Mom smiles at me from Dad's chair by the fire. I put my finger to my lips, creep back out and signal Tonker to come in.

Mom puts the kettle on and we gather round the fire. In a hushed voice she tells me the Police have been to check the house and there is a big black car parked at the top of the Crescent.

The tea is hot and steaming, with two heaped spoons, just the way I like it. Funny. We're sitting in here and the cops are sitting at the top of the road. Only difference is, we *know* where they are!

We wolf down some bread and cheese. Another cuppa and we must be on our way.

"Thanks Mrs.G." says Tonker giving my Mom a big hug.

"What do you need Watt?" asks Roy.

"I don't like to ask but we could do with a bit of money."

Roy hands me £15 and some change. It's all he's got in the world. He creeps upstairs so as not to wake the others and fetches two jackets. "Here, have these over the top, like."

I feel exhausted but we can't stay here. Jake and Gladys? No, too risky. It comes to me. A couple of streets away there's a bird who fancies me. Linda.

Lives on her own with a kid.

Mom gives me a lecture saying I should give myself up. Rolling my eyes, I take her by the shoulders, kiss her on the cheek and tell her not to worry. She strokes my hair. "Take care son."

With that we're gone, back the way we came, across the fences and over the gardens. Linda is about thirty, nice looker, she'd always come on to me but she's got a kid. Last time I saw her Dodger was 'visiting' now and then.

I knock three or four times before a light goes on upstairs and she appears at the window. "Need some help," I whisper. Next thing she's at the door. Tonker hovers behind me in the shadows and Linda seems a bit frightened.

"This is my mate, can we come in?" I give her one of my extra special smiles. She melts and stands to the side.

"Everybody knows 'bout the escape Watt."

"Better lock that back door. Look, can we get a bit of shut eye here? It's too hot at Mom's."

"Just for a couple of hours then. You can sleep down here. I'll fetch you a couple of pillows," she goes off upstairs and Tonker winks at me.

I'm comfy now. Me on the sofa and Tonker in the big armchair when the back door opens and in walks Dodger. He likes to think of himself as a bit of a 'jack the lad', has a few women he 'visits'.

He don't seem surprised or put out to see us but now we have to chat to him.

My eyes are dropping as he drones on. Probably came for a shag but goes off after about half an hour saying he'll get us some fags and booze from his house. Looking at the clock on the mantelshelf it's 2.30 a.m. I snuggle back into the pillow. Nice pillow this, smells good.

BANG. BANG. Like a shot we are awake and at the front window. I draw back the net curtain slightly. My Uncle Harry is at the front door. There seems to be a regiment of cops out there. Some are armed and a few are holding dogs. Linda comes rushing down the stairs, crying and shouting that she'll be in trouble.

Firmly I take hold and push her towards the stairs. "Go back up and stay there," don't need hysterical women round me right now.

BANG. BANG. BANG. Uncle Harry is shouting through the letterbox. "Let me in Watt. The Police know you're here. They want me to talk to you. Just me on my own. Let me in."

I signal Tonker into the back kitchen. "It's alright. Uncle Harry's OK. I'm gonna let him in." My mind is racing now. Need to buy us some time.

"I'M OPENING THE FRONT DOOR," shouting as loudly as I can.

Grabbing the latch I pull the door open and stand behind it. Uncle Harry walks in and I slam it shut. "Let's have a cuppa Tonker," I shout through to the kitchen.

"Give me the gun and give yourselves up," pleads Uncle Harry.

"Was it Dodger who went to the cops?"

"No. He came to me and I went to the Police. You've got a gun. I told the Police I could get you to give yourself up without the use of guns."

"I ain't got no gun."

"That isn't what the Police say. They're armed out there and they'll shoot you," he turns and takes the cup of tea off Tonker, "and your mate."

I need a fag. Gotta think fast here. Uncle Harry is trying to protect me in his own way but I ain't never givin' myself up. Dennis must have grassed about the gun. Nobody else knew.

"I'm to get the gun off you and take you outside. I'll walk in front so they won't shoot."

I nod at my Uncle. "Look, I ain't got no gun, you gotta tell 'em that. You go first and say we're coming out with our hands up but we ain't got no gun so not to shoot."

Tonker is looking at me panic struck. As my Uncle makes his way towards the front door I motion Tonker towards the back. He cottons on and moves off into the kitchen.

Uncle Harry walks out the front door and I close it behind him. I can hear him talking to the cops as me and Tonker leg it over the back fences and away.

We keep running over the gardens and end up almost opposite the Police Station in Bilston. The safest place to be.

It's raining heavy and we're wet and exhausted when I spot a big bunker. Lifting the lid I can see a small amount of coal in the bottom. Good. We climb in and curl up. Sleep overtakes us.

I'm awoken by the sound of dogs barking. Tonker nudges me. "Think they followed our scent?"

We can hear the cops talking to each other and the clump, clump of their heavy boots as they search the area. The dogs must have lost the scent in this downpour.

Hardly daring to breathe, we stay in the coal bunker until it's been quiet for a long time. Dawn is breaking as we lift the lid and make our way to the car. The old garages are in sight now as we scramble over the last fence. I can see the car is still there and there's nobody about.

This Wolseley is very comfortable. Shall we just have a kip here? No, too dangerous. Need to get a wash and a change of clothes. My sister Pearl. We'll hotfoot it there. Lifting the bonnet I do the business and it roars into life. Pretty soon we're on our way to Pelsall.

Ditching the car in a side road Tonker follows me across the cemetery and into my sister's back garden. No sign of cops anywhere. We must look a state.

Bedraggled, exhausted, hungry, tired and covered in coal dust, we fall through her back door into the kitchen.

Pearl cooks us some bacon and eggs. The grubby prison clothes lie strewn on the bathroom floor and I take a long, leisurely soak while she finds us some clean stuff. Lucky for me I'd left an old suit and a couple of shirts here when I moved out. Tonker is about the same build as Tom.

"Better get these dyed or something. I'll put 'em in my boiler," says Pearl as I hand her the prison garb.

Tom thinks it won't be long before the cops pay a visit and says we should move on. I'd made some friends round and about when I lived with Pearl and ask Tom to get a message to one of 'em. He goes to Walsall while we relax on the sofa. Pearl wants to chat so we don't get any kip.

Tom returns soon enough with my mate in his builders van. He says we can stay with him for a couple of nights until things die down. Pearl wishes us luck and away we go.

All I want to do is lie on a bed and go to sleep. There's only one spare room but the bed is enormous. It's high and looks really, really comfortable with lots of blankets and pillows.

Me and Tonker jump onto it. BANG. It's the sound of our backs breaking as we hit the board. It's like a fuckin' rock. "Worse than being in prison," says Tonker and we burst out laughing.

Notwithstanding the hard mattress we drop off to sleep and it's almost night time when we finally emerge.

"Here, look at the papers. You're in 'em". Several newspapers are spread out on the kitchen table. We read about the escape and stay up 'til the early hours chatting, smoking and drinking.

My mate says he can get us a job on the building site, casual like. "You could disguise yourselves." He fetches a woolly hat to cover Tonker's hair and a dab of make up to hide his scar. To be fair it has made a difference.

"You're dark haired Watt so you could pose as a black. Here, I've got some potash."

It's not realistic but he gets me to try, "to see if it'll work." Amidst lots of joking I smear the stuff on my face. Within ten minutes my skin feels tight and starts to tingle. The tingling turns into a sort of burn. Tonker can hardly stand up for laughing. I scramble into the bathroom. Where's the soap? Over an hour it takes for my skin to feel normal. What a relief.

As we pull the eiderdown under our chins I tell Tonker we'll stay another night, nick a car and head to Moss-side. I know people there.

Tonker shoots me a glance as he turns over, "hope they've got a better bed!"

Chapter 13

MOST WANTED

"That was lovely Annie," I flop onto the sofa after Sunday lunch.

She ain't too pleased to have us here. I'd heard them talking in the back kitchen. Can't blame her. The escape is headline news, front page in all the papers, on the radio and TV. Our faces are everywhere.

I lean across to pick up my cuppa from the side table. "We'll be gone tomorrow morning, it's good of you to put us up and we appreciate it."

"Best dinner we've had in ages, eh Watt." Tonker smiles at Annie, who seems to relax now she knows we're not planning to stay much longer.

Me and Tonker groan when a game of cards is suggested, but play anyway, and spend a pleasant evening before wending our way to bed.

I'm in the bathroom taking a leak and through the open door I can see Tonker lying on the bed staring at the ceiling. He turns towards me. "Should we dye our hair Watt?"

I glance into the mirror at my jet black hair, washed, combed and looking good. I run my fingers through it. No, can't say I'm mad on the idea. "Fancy yourself as a brunette then do you?"

Tonker laughs and rolls over. "Oh mate, my back's killing me. Think I'll take a blanket and sleep on the floor."

Next morning Annie cooks us a nice breakfast and finds me an old watch that belonged to her Dad. I don't really want to take it but there's no denying a timepiece will be useful. She goes to visit her mother and, having said our thanks and goodbyes, we leave at mid-day.

As Tonker locks up and places the key under the mat I make a mental note of this address. I'll return the watch as soon as I'm able. It's fifteen minutes past one and I'm not sure how far it is to Manchester. One thing I do know is that we need a car.

"At the end, cross over and keep about fifty yards behind me. Any problems, you just make a run for it."

Tonker nods and we walk past three or four houses to the street corner where I carry on and he crosses the road. I'm heading for a block of old garages I'd noticed on the way here. We're not far out of town and with every person that passes I put my head down to light a fag, or grab a liquorice.

The clouds are gathering, a dismal day, already a slight drizzle in the air. Hope I ain't got lost. Thought the garages were round this corner. Must be the next one. Cop car. Momentary freeze, look away, turn up the nearest path. I'm standing at this green door pretending to look in my pocket for a key. Out of the corner of my eye I see Tonker drop to his knees and tie his laces. The car passes.

Down the path, a smile at Tonker, and a brisk walk round the next corner brings me to the safety of the garages. Pulling out the small chisel tool, I briefly think of Les and the others who took risks for us. Tonker keeps a lookout at the end of the block. The tool does its job. I'm soon lifting the bonnet of a big old Rover and doing the business.

Tonker jumps in, throwing the rucksack full of sandwiches and pop Annie had given us, onto the back seat. "That was a close 'un" he lights up two fags and passes one over. "We're laughin' now mate."

Looking at the fuel gauge I'm not too sure about that. "Is there a map anywhere?" We need to take the back roads but I ain't never been up North before.

"Here we go," Tonker pulls a road atlas from under the seat. I vaguely know we have to head towards Stafford first. There ain't much petrol in this car. Need to find a garage. Risky, but gotta be done.

Just through Stafford I see a Shell sign up ahead. "You get out and wait in this lay-by." I pass the watch to Tonker. "If I'm not back in ten or you see anything suspicious…"

What does this Rover do to the gallon? Remember Jake said the Jag was a guzzler. How far is it to Manchester? Ain't gonna waste too much money. Don't usually like rain but right this minute it's a blessing when the heavens open. The attendant runs out, quickly asks how much I want, takes the money, puts the petrol in and dashes back to his little shed. Don't think he looked at me once.

I pick up a drowned rat from the lay-by. Can't stop laughing. "On our way now Tonker mate."

"That's if I don't die of pneumonia first."

"Be shaggin' tonight." Thought that'd buck him up a bit.

"What's the score then Watt?"

"Jamaican bloke. Got a club in Moss-side, runs a string of girls. We'll be alright. He'll sort us out." I'd met him during my last spell in Shrewsbury. Him and his sidekick were in for pimping. Racking my brains for the name of his club. It'll come to me.

I'm enjoying the drive. Rides good. Like being in a little cocoon. Feels sort of safe. I glance in my mirror and yell "DOWN." Tonker dives into the footwell out of sight. A cop car follows us for about half a mile. Keep your nerve, keep your nerve. Half of me wants to roar away because of the huge adrenalin rush but the other half tells me to avoid a chase.

I keep a steady speed and my eyes firmly fixed on the road ahead. Desperate to take the next left but deciding against it, I drive past another side-road before indicating and turning off. The cop car carries on.

Tonker ain't much good at map reading. I'm trying to take the back roads and we end up miles from anywhere on a country lane. We've been travelling for ages without passing another garage. It's pouring with rain, the gauge looks grim and the car starts to splutter.

"What's that?" Tonker looks out over the bonnet and then at me.

The car rolls to a sedate stop.

"Get that pen and paper out the glovebox. We'll write a note."

Tonker stares at me. "What we gonna say, gone fuckin' fishing?"

"If it ain't been reported stolen yet and we leave a note on the windscreen 'run out of petrol', gives us more time, right?"

Tonker scribbles a few words, grabs the rucksack and we head for the hills. Nothing but trees and fields, hedges and ditches. We clamber over 'em all. Getting dark now. Still raining. We're sodden but our spirits are high as we sit under a tree and finish the sarnies.

Free. At least we're free to walk in the rain, free to eat and drink when we want, free to talk, free to laugh, and we do a bit of that under this big tree. My shoes squelch as I stand up. Ugh.

Tonker spots a light in the distance, so with collars up, and heads down against the driving storm, we set off.

The cottage is isolated and a small car is parked close to the front door. I'm hoping whoever left if there did so in the rain. More chance of it being unlocked.

We creep closer and Tonker moves towards the lit window. He darts to one side and peers cautiously through. Gives me the thumbs up.

Holding my breath I try the handle. It clicks open. Tonker leaps in and grabs the steering wheel while I get behind the car, push it onto the lane, pop the bonnet, do the business and we're away.

"We're gonna have to risk some main roads. Have a look. See where we are on the map."

Tonker opens the road atlas.

"Look there's a sign, what's it say?"

Tonker looks up as we whiz past, "Knutsford, I think."

Not long afterwards we're on a main road signposted to Manchester and Tonker has a bit of shut eye. The area is becoming more built up and we start to loose the green fields.

It's then that I see it. A giant billboard. My face is staring back at me. It must be 15ft high. I can't believe it. Armed and Dangerous the poster reads and underneath, 'The Most Wanted Men in Britain'.

Fuck me. I slow down and nudge Tonker. He starts to laugh. I start to think maybe we should have dyed our hair after all.

The Green Parrot, that's it, that's the name of the club. We turn off the main road following the sign towards Moss-side and cruise the streets.

"Stop here," says Tonker pointing to a dingy looking shop. The illuminated sign reads 'Fish and Chips'. I drop him off round the corner. Tonker walks to get some chips and ask directions while I keep the engine running, just in case.

He dashes back with a couple of newspaper parcels, which we read under the interior lights, once we've eaten the chips. Last Thursday's papers, old news.

Glancing at my watch, well, Annie's Dad's watch, it reads 8.30. If luck is on our side there won't be too many in the club. It's Monday so it might not even be open. The club isn't far and within five minutes I'm parked up on the opposite side of the road. A big green parrot flashes on and off. Not a soul in sight. We walk briskly towards the entrance.

The place is crowded and dimly lit but I can see a veritable array of girls, blondes, brunette's, redheads, all shapes and sizes, sitting or standing round the bar area talking to punters.

Loud music blares as we ask for a beer. The barman takes our money and hands us the drinks. We ain't took our eyes off the redhead sitting chatting to a bald headed bloke at the end of the bar. She's got the biggest pair I've ever seen.

Me and Tonker are mesmerized as she tilts her head back to laugh and they rise and fall almost bursting out of her flimsy top. The bald head bends down to kiss 'em and we turn away.

"Cheers" says Tonker as we chink our glasses, "made it."

There's no sign of Davey or his sidekick. They ain't here yet so we find an empty table facing the door. Everybody's too interested in their own activities to bother with us.

I glance at my wrist checking the time every ten minutes. 10.30. Perhaps they ain't comin'. Tonker digs me in the ribs as two blokes walk through the door.

Lookin' the business in snappy gear they swagger to the bar and one of the barmen dashes round to take their overcoats.

Davey gets a drink and turns to survey his world. I raise my hand. Recognition dawns, he taps his sidekick, who is busy chatting to a slim blonde girl, and smiling, they make their way over.

"Wouldn't bother you Davey, supposed to be down the Smoke by now but things went wrong."

"Yeh, man, we read about it."

"Need a place for a couple of weeks mate, just 'til things quieten down."

"I got a safe house, man, don't worry, have another drink."

Davey says to enjoy ourselves for a couple of hours. He sends his sidekick to get rid of the hot car. All I wanna do is have a bath and get out of these wet shoes. The clothes have dried on us, but the shoes…

"Pick yourself a girl, any one you want" he waves his arm around, "you must be needing a girl."

He ain't wrong there.

"And your mate," he turns to Tonker, "any one you want man."

Tonker chooses the redhead. I point towards a petite brunette 'cos she reminds me of Susie.

Davey takes us to the safe house in his swanky car, saying he'll bring the girls along later, when they've finished at the club.

It's a two up, two down mid terrace with a bathroom off the kitchen. It looks clean and tidy, although somebody's been cooking something in here that smells a bit rank.

Through the net curtains from the back bedroom window I can see a small walled yard. A gate gives access to a sort of gulley.

Where's that bath? Tonker's beat me to it and I can hear him splashing about. "Don't use all the hot water mate."

He laughs. "You might have to make do with three inches of tepid."

Slipping into a couple of dressing gowns found in the wardrobes we place our wet shoes in front of the electric fire in the parlour and head for the kitchen.

I'm bending down to grab a tin of baked beans when, CLICK. Tonker's heard it too. We slip quietly into the bathroom. Female laughter floats in the air as Davey comes through the back door with the girls in tow.

I've still got the tin of beans in my hand. Useful weapon. Davey laughs. "The girls will look after you, leave it to them."

They rustle up some food while we chat to our host. He's brought a copy of the evening paper for us to read and we don't have to look far. Front page again.

"They found that car by your sisters." Tonker points to the headlines.

"Bet it don't say anything 'bout it being a coppers car."

Tonker shakes his head.

"When?"

"Last night according to this."

Davey leaves a bottle of whisky and shoots off. The girls have gone up to 'get ready'. Tonker winks at me. "It's a hard life, but somebody's gotta do it," he takes the stairs two at a time.

"Thought you was knackered," I shout after him.

Can't venture outside and after a few days the terrace becomes a comfortable prison of its own, but with all mod cons, in more than one sense of the word.

My Susie look-alike is called Judy. She's nineteen. Turns out she had a kid last year. Her parents threw her out and the bloke didn't want to know. An Aunt took her in but money was tight. A friend of a friend introduced her to the club and at first she worked as a barmaid. Davey was short of a girl one night and offered her more than she could earn in a week pulling pints. Judy was hooked.

I feel a bit sorry for her but for now I'll take what's on offer. We can't stay here forever though and I need to start making plans to move on.

26ᵗʰ October and Davey calls in to bring us the latest papers. Still headline news.

"Listen to this" Tonker leans forward on the sofa. "According to your Mom you are liked everywhere, even the Police give you good name. You have plenty of friends and could get fed almost anywhere." He turns the page, "my Mom says I wouldn't hurt a fly and I'm easily led." We have to laugh at that one. The papers say we've been seen, here, there and everywhere but nothing about Manchester, not yet.

The manhunt is hotting up. Perhaps we *should* dye our hair. Judy and the redhead go shopping for some food and hair dye. My money ain't gonna last much longer.

Davey comes up with the idea of us working at his club for a bit, once we're disguised. We can help 'look after' the girls. Quite what he means by this I don't know. I ain't beatin' up no girl to get her to shag somebody. No way. I remember how Bishop operated.

"No man," says Davey, "when the punters won't pay, the girls need a minder close by."

Judy comes back with some shopping and the hair dye. A flame haired beauty smiles at me from the box. No, think I'll do it tomorrow. "Let's have a bacon sarnie and a cuppa girls, well done, two heaped spoons."

Davey needs the girls at the club 'til late so me and Tonker settle in front of the television on our own. Ooh good. John Wayne. That'll do me.

There's a light tap at the front door. My heart skips a beat. I shoot upstairs and peek through the net curtains. Four plain clothes cops are standing in the street. I can smell 'em a mile off. One looks up as I step back into the shadows.

Tonker is standing at the bottom of the stairs. He can tell by my face and starts racing to the back door. We're through it in a flash, jump over the wall and sprint along the gulley.

Armed police step out in front of us. We turn to run the other way but more cops are walking cautiously forwards.

They shout a warning "STOP, ARMED POLICE". Shall I jump back over the wall? No. I want to live. I stop and raise my hands. Tonker does the same.

All that planning, all that effort, six days, that's all we've had, six fuckin' days. I study the armed cops and can tell, even with their guns, they're shit scared 'cos they shuffle and fidget instead of taking a firm stance.

"THROW DOWN YOUR WEAPON," shouts the one in the middle.

I look him straight in the eye. "I ain't got a gun."

"Nor me," says Tonker.

"Turn to the wall, put your hands on your head and spread your legs."

We do as they say. Then they're all over us. After a quick body search my wrists are cuffed and I'm frog-marched to a waiting car. It isn't far to Moss-side Police Station. One interview room is much like another.

"Where's the gun?"

"I ain't got no gun."

"Don't get smart with me, you might not have a gun now but you did have one, where is it?"

There are two detectives interrogating me. Mentally I'm bracing myself for the kickin'. I need to convince them about the gun though. It'll mean extra time if I can't. I know Tonker can be trusted to keep his mouth shut.

"I ain't *never* had a gun, if I had you'd have found it wouldn't you."

They look at each other.

"Three cars have been stolen, a Wolseley from Wellington, a Rover from Walsall and a Ford from Knutsford. Know anything about them?"

I shake my head. Time to keep it shut. I'm looking round for something upon which to fix my gaze and spy a small notice on the wall.

The door opens. A uniform walks in and places a sheet of paper on the table.

"What about these?" the Detective points to the typewritten page. "You're a shop-breaker aren't you? These crimes have all been committed in this area since the 23rd."

He follows my line of sight as I scan the list. Briefly I meet his eyes, shake my head and stare at the notice.

The other Detective shifts his weight on the metal chair before standing up. This is it then. Here he comes. Don't usually do it with a witness though.

"Like a cup of tea?"

Not what I expected. "Yes, thanks."

He goes off and I glance at the remaining cop. He don't look like he's got much muscle but then again…he moves slightly…here comes the hammering.

"Cigarette?" he pulls out a packet of ten and a box of matches, placing them on the table. I take one out, light up and go to replace the packet. "You keep them," he waves his hand.

I don't need telling twice. He seems to be studying me while we're waiting for the tea. "That was some escape you pulled off there."

What's all this? No kickin' and now he's praising my escape! I ain't talking.

The tea arrives. They have one too. "We're not going to worry about the cars. We know you nicked them but there was no damage and the owners got them back in one piece."

I wasn't worried. The cars are the last of my troubles although if I got done for nicking 'em it would add extra time to my sentence. I stare at the notice. Tea was nice, sweet, how I like it, could do with another.

"You're already serving a three year sentence and this little escapade will mean extra time anyway."

As if I didn't know. If the rope hadn't broke and Dennis had managed to get over the wall I'd be tucked up in London with people I could really trust.

Was it worth it? The excitement of the planning, the buzz as preparations got under way, a focus, a goal, adrenalin rushes, almost being caught and the tremendous effort of lifting that grid, anticipation as we stood on the brink, getting one over on the screws, and for what…for a few days of freedom. Inwardly I smile… oh yes …it was worth it.

"I take my hat off to you, it was a brilliant escape," says one of the detectives. They're both smiling at me. I twist the empty cup and stare at the floral pattern. He's right. It was a fuckin' brilliant escape.

Held overnight at the Police Station, the following morning I'm with Tonker in a Black Mariah heading for Strangeways Prison in Manchester.

"Had a bit of news," he tells me.

I frown at him.

"The copper...you know."

What's he on about?

"He's off the danger list, recovering like. I asked one of them detectives to find out."

"Well at least you ain't gotta worry 'bout the rope no more."

At reception I'm given prison garb, but it has big yellow stripes down the trousers and yellow patches on the shirt.

"All the better to see you with," jokes the screw. Me and Tonker laugh at each other. It's the last laugh we'll have for a long time. I'm officially a Category A prisoner.

The Governor tells me I will appear before a Visiting Commission. They will decide upon my punishment for the escape. In the meantime I'm to be held in the Block.

Outside the cell door is a card with my information and a big A. "Leave your belt and shoes out here Groom."

It's a single cell with a red light which is on throughout the day and night. A screw comes with me everywhere I go, including the bath-house once a week and at every handover they sign a piece of paper.

No smoking, no work, no books except the Bible. I'm busy doing nothing for 23 hours a day. I pass the time shadow boxing and keeping fit. In rest periods I try to recall poems my English teacher gave me to learn all those years ago. Then I count the bricks. As a last resort I turn to the Bible.

We get two half hour exercise periods outside the cell. No talking is allowed and we walk three yards apart.

Just off the exercise yard is a recess with some toilets. I raise my hand and the screw tells me to 'fall out'. Always make use of the toilets, less to slop out.

The Visiting Commission arrives and I walk in with a screw each side of me. One is standing directly facing me and behind him sit the three people who will decide my fate. 100 days remission lost and 28 days bread and water. Sounds a long time to me.

I suppose because of medical reasons, the 28 days bread and water is spread over a period of 52 days with 3 days on and 3 days off. Although the food in here is dire, the 3 days off when I get proper meals, brought by an orderly to the cell, is something to look forward to. Especially as he often manages to leave me a roll up and split match hidden underneath my plate.

The Governor visits daily together with a Medical Officer at noon. No actual examination takes place, just a cursory "Are you alright?" to which I always respond "Yes Sir."

On bread and water days I get one jug of water in the morning and towards mid-day a lump of bread, which I'd say is about 8oz.

Tonker is in the next cell. Half the small panes in the window are broken which means sometimes it's freezing but on the other hand we can enjoy the odd chat. Mostly we talk about our hunger and the need for a fag.

On exercise, the day after my 26th birthday, I raise my hand and get permission to 'fall out'. I give Tonker a nod. He bounces in, takes a seat on the toilet next to me and pulls out a long dog end which he breaks in half. I've died and gone to heaven. We sit, puffing away.

Shadows fall and a voice growls "fuck off out."

A big, tough looking, bald headed bloke stands in front of me, legs apart, arms folded across his chest. Another powerfully built bloke with arms like treetrunks, plants himself two paces behind.

I set my face and stand up. "*You* fuck off out."

Tonker moves to stand beside me.

"Do you know who I am?" he asks swaggering and laughing, half looking over his shoulder at his mate before turning back to me, "I'm Slasher Chadwick."

Holding his eyes, I take a step towards him, "Don't care if you're Jack the fucking Ripper, *you* fuck off out." Show I ain't scared and he'll back down. Usually works, specially with bullies like him.

We glare at each other. He spits on the ground and lights a dog end before stepping outside. Baldy leans on the wall round the corner. Him and his sidekick have a smoke and fuck off.

Me and Tonker finish our fag, have a chat and re-join the orderly procession round the track.

Getting through the 52 days by sleeping as much as possible, eventually I'm taken from the Block onto a normal wing where I discover Slasher is the 'daddy' but he don't worry me.

A few days later the Governor calls me up. I'm expecting him to send me back to Shrewsbury Prison. Can't wait. At least the food is edible there.

"You are going to Durham tomorrow Groom," he tells me with some satisfaction. "They have a special punishment block and you will be there for three months."

Special punishment block! I thought my punishment was the loss of remission and bread and water. Apparently not.

Chapter 14

DON'T LET THE BASTARDS GRIND YOU DOWN

"Do you know what it is, where we're going like?" asks Tonker as we bump along in the Black Mariah.

"According to form it's where all the real hard cases go."

The screw who is sitting opposite raises his head from the newspaper and smiles. "S'right. You won't be getting through any more ventilation shafts, I can tell you that."

I pull a face and Tonker grins, "wonder if we'll be able to work and get some bacca? I'm dying for a fag."

I shrug my shoulders. "Dunno mate, bound to."

The screw crumples the paper onto his lap, reaches into his pocket and pulls out a packet of fags. Oh no, he ain't gonna light up. It's a form of torture this is.

Am I dreaming? He's offering us one. Beaming broadly I take it and he leans forward to give me a light, then to Tonker.

I draw in deeply, "thanks."

"Don't think you'll be smoking again anytime soon." The screw goes back to his newspaper.

It's not long before we're standing in Reception at Durham in the same patches prison garb. The rules are read out. There is no talking at any time either to another prisoner or to an Officer. If we do need to address an Officer we must raise our hand and he will tell us when to speak. No smoking. No library books. Oh, and bath once a week. Nothing new there then.

I am escorted to my cell. A thin mattress stands on the floor in front of a bed board, which is hinged to the wall and held in place by a catch. Bedding is neatly folded, draped over the side and a pillow perches on top. I move towards the bed catch.

"Leave it Groom" yells the screw, "your bed remains in that position until after tea. Use the chair if you want to sit and keep away from the window."

He bangs the door, turns the key and flicks the spyhole to watch me, so I sit on the chair and reach for the bible. After a few moments his footsteps echo on the landing.

The window has several broken panes, letting in the cold air, nothing different to Shrewsbury or Strangeways. What's on the other side that they don't want me to see? Cautiously, I move towards it keeping my eye on the cell door to make sure the spyhole remains closed. On tiptoe, I glance through momentarily. Just seems to overlook an exercise yard and more prison buildings.

Back to the chair and contemplation of my new surroundings. The old slop out pot is in the corner by the door, in fact, everything except the bed is similar to other prison cells. I puff out my cheeks. Only been here a few minutes and already the walls are closing in as my brain struggles with the realization that this is it for the next three months.

The screw returns and an orderly hands me three familiar canvas shapes. Mailbags.

"You do three a day Groom," says the screw ushering the orderly out.

Feeling a bit brighter I set to work. This means some pay, I hope. I'm putting the finishing touches to one when the door opens.

"Exercise" barks the screw.

He escorts me along a line of cells and through locked doors to the yard. It's the smallest exercise yard I've ever seen, walled in with a sort of steel netting over the top. I fall in behind two other cons. We walk round the track keeping a good distance apart. No-one speaks. Three screws stand watching us. No sign of Tonker.

We get two half hour exercises per day. In bad weather we walk round the landings. Like any prison it's a hard regime but made worse by not being allowed to talk to another living soul and the long lonely hours in the cell.I can buy sugar, soap, toothpaste and a few sweets with my meager earnings, but no bacca, it's not allowed.

A couple of weeks later as my feet hit the exercise track a familiar mop of curly hair dances in front of me. It's Tonker and he gives me a wink as we share a grin. Good to see a familiar face, even if we can't speak.

The other con walking is dark haired, about 6ft and thick set. I'd seen him before a couple of times and he makes a beeline for me. I shove my hands in my pockets and keep walking, eyes firmly fixed on Tonker's back.

"I'm Frank," he says falling into step alongside.

We ain't supposed to talk to a screw let alone another con. What does he think I'm gonna do, start chatting?

"They call me the Axe Man."

I've heard of him. Who hasn't? I glance at the screws. Hope they don't think I'm instigating this.

"Don't let these bastards grind you down," he waves at an officer walking towards us.

I just wanna get out of here back to a normal prison. Me? I don't need any hassle. Keeping my mouth firmly shut I carry on walking. Frank keeps pace.

The screw shouts across. "C'mon. No talking, you know the rules."

He just seems to ignore the warning and continues making small talk. Amazingly they leave him alone but I'm not taking any chances so it's eyes front and lips sealed for me.

The days are long and although sewing mailbags keeps me busy, sometimes the temptation to look out the window is too much. Must be something worth looking at 'cos after dinner most days I can hear shouting from cons and what sounds like female laughter.

Placing my chair under the window, I hop onto it for a better view. The exercise yard is full of women. Raucous banter fills the air "get your tits out love", "fancy a ride on this", "show us your arse."

It's just a laugh and the women are up for it. One gets her knickers off and waves 'em towards our windows shouting "Bet you'd like to get into these?"

Normally a pin could be heard dropping at twenty paces on this Wing but there's a right old racket going on as more voices join in the fun.

My face is pressed against the tiny panes. You never know, perhaps one will open her shirt and give us a flash.

BANG. I feel myself being pulled backwards off the chair. Two screws pin my arms and march me off. We approach a cell door and they throw me in. It's padded. I ain't no looney. What the fuck...

They're laying in to me with body punches and kicks to the legs. "You'll be up in front of the Governor tomorrow," the one screw tells me as my ribs feel the weight of his fist.

True to his word, the screw hauls me in front of the Governor who gives me three days bread and water and three days loss of remission. With the 100 days I got for the escape and now an extra three for this, time is stacking up. I'm already being punished in this Special Block. What do they want, blood?

Back in my cell I still have to do the mailbags, even though there's only bread and water for the next three days. What I wouldn't give for a chat, a smoke and a nice cuppa with two heaped spoons.

The once weekly bath and change of clothes is something to look forward to 'cos at least I feel clean for a couple of hours. No privacy. A screw stands watching and waiting as I splash about in three inches of warm water, a luxury in itself. There's only cold taps everywhere else.

Beds are changed once a week too. An orderly brings clean sheets and pillowcase. Dirty ones are left outside the cell for collection. Most sheets tend to 'walk out' on their own and stand to attention.

Some of the screws take a perverse interest in what cons get up to in their cells of an evening. Often the spyhole will flick and a voice shouts, "wanking again Groom." Sort of spoils the moment.

Frank comes over to me again during exercise. This is the third time in as many weeks. "Fuck off" is directed at the screw when he's reminded of the rules. They don't seem to bother after that.

I speak out of the corner of my mouth to him. "I'm Watt, Watt Groom."

He smiles at me.

To have a chat is like a gift from the gods. From then on, if he's in the same group, we walk alongside chewing the fat. Suppose it happens about six times in three months.

With only a week to go I'm counting the days as well as the bricks in my cell. It's after tea so my bed is down and made up. I'm lying here daydreaming, a sure mistake. Thoughts of 'the Shape' wend their way and I'm visualizing her here lying next to me, nuzzling my neck, nibbling my ear and touching….No, I roll over and stare at the ceiling. This time next week I'll probably be back at Shrewsbury. Anything's better than this.

The bed-catch takes my eye and absently I spin it round. It clicks and whirrs so I do it again. BANG. Two screws burst in and tower over me as I lay prone on the bed.

"You'll be on report tomorrow Groom," says the one.

I'm open mouthed. What the fuck have I done?

They must sense my confusion 'cos the other one adds, "for making a racket with that catch. Leave it alone."

Another three days bread and water and three days loss of remission. As I'm walked back from the Governors office to my cell the injustice of it all rises up but, deep breaths, not long to go now.

Second day into this bread and water spell, I'm sitting thinking about the other cons eating their tea. I've scoffed my 8oz of bread. Looking into my water jug there's a smidgeon left in the bottom which I'll save until bedtime.

I'm staring at the bars watching the clouds roll by when a sandwich appears. I blink. I've heard about people hallucinating. Blink again. No, it's definitely there.

Approaching the window I pull it carefully through one of the broken panes and tug on the string.

Cheese. Ain't bothered what the fuck it is. Afterwards I wish I'd taken the time to savour the taste a bit more, don't think it even touched the sides. A scribbled note attached to the string simply says 'Frank.'

He's sent me half his food. I never see him again but won't ever forget this act of compassion from a fellow con.

One week later I'm in the Black Mariah heading for Shrewsbury prison. It's a bright spring day and I ain't sorry to be leaving Durham. Me and Tonker travel together.

"He was a nutter that bloke who kept talking to you."

"You know who that was, don't you?"

Tonker shakes his head.

"The Axe Man. Big name down the Smoke."

Tonker seems impressed. "What'd you talk about then?"

"Just chit chat, family and stuff," I raise my eyebrows, "and Durham."

"Shrewsbury nick. I can't wait to have a fag and talk to people."

"Wouldn't be too confident about that," pipes up the screw.

What the fuck does he mean?

"When you two birdbrains escaped all priviledges were cut. There's been no association for months. Don't know about talking to you, they probably want to lynch you."

Me and Tonker grimace at each other.

"No doubt the Governor will ask if you want to go on protection."

No way. I ain't going on protection. Only for nonces, that. Sooner take my chances. Tonker shakes his head.

Within a couple of hours I'm standing in the Governor's office. He doesn't look happy, then again, he never does.

"I have to warn you Groom, my Officers have reported unrest among the prisoners. There may be trouble. I am offering you Rule 43 if you want it."

Rule 43 is protection and I shake my head vigorously. "No Sir, but thank you."

He nods and a screw steps forward to take me to my cell. Category A prisoners, wearing patches like me, are housed in one row of single cells. The dim red bulb glows as I walk in.

"Better watch your back Groom, the whole nick is out to get you. Governor hasn't re-instated association yet." The door bangs shut.

Being so closely guarded at all times, a one on one situation, it's more difficult for cons to get at me in any event. But, it only takes a second for someone to jump out of line in the meal queue or during slop out, slice me with a dinner tray or stab me. I've seen it happen. It's not unknown either for screws to turn a blind eye whilst prisoners beat up other cons mob handed. My weather eye is officially back in business.

A screw accompanies me everywhere and signs the sheet at each handover. I've been allocated to work in the Mailbag shop. No more bake-house, extra sugar and cups of tea.

In the Mailbag shop, 'A' list cons work separate from the rest and we are watched constantly by one screw. There are lots of nudges and serious stares as I make my way towards an empty seat. Picking up the canvas shape, before starting to sew, my eyes slowly sweep the room, holding those that dare to stare back.

Tonker takes his seat next to me. The other would be escapee, also an 'A' list prisoner, looks worried as he sits alongside. Last time I saw him he was plummeting from a broken rope towards the ground.

"I had no choice," Dennis whispers, "they kicked the fuck out of me, on my bad leg an' all."

"You didn't have to tell about the g...u...n." I don't look up from my sewing.

"They said they'd go easy on me if..."

"Don't wanna hear it, no excuses." Under my lashes I can see the screw is watching us intently.

"I was in agony Watt, you don't understand."

Tonker glances at me and rolls his eyes. "What's done is done mate."

"Suppose so." We made it out, if only I could have got to London.

I finish a bag and take it to the screw for checking. He makes a mark against my name in the ledger and nods. I move past a row of three cons to get a new canvas.

"Bastard," says the one out of the corner of his mouth.

"We're gonna get you," the next one murmurs.

"and your fuckin' mate," the other growls.

I turn my head slightly and hiss through clenched teeth, "Fuck off."

With a needle secreted in my clenched fist and covered by the canvas, on the route back to my seat I accidentally trip over something and manage to jab it into the shoulder of the one who called me a bastard. Lewis, I think his name is.

He cries out, clutches the top of his arm and goes to stand but I lean over pushing him back down. One of the screws pricks up his ears and starts to walk over. "Sorry, Lewis mate, just tripped," I say loudly. Whispering in his ear, "next time it'll be your fuckin' eye." I pat him on the head, smile and move towards my seat. The screw looses interest.

"What was all that about Watt?" asks Tonker.

"Just watch your back mate."

Tonker frowns and the curls cavort vigorously as he nods.

There's always a fair bit of shouting, banter and general clatter as meals are collected from the servery. The 'A' listers, only four of us, are kept some distance from the rest of the prisoners, but such is the ill feeling towards me and Tonker that I am on my toes, watching and waiting, every mealtime in case of some nutcase wielding a knife, fork or tray. One of the orderlies at the servery spits onto the pie just before he serves me. It turns my stomach and for a few days I can't eat anything.

One thing about time, it passes, sure as day follows night and that's what keeps me going. Only one more birthday and Christmas, then I'll be out.

It's Tonker's release day tomorrow and he tells me his address as we sit sewing. "Come and see me when you get out Watt."

"Lucky beggar, you'll have Christmas at home."

"You won't be long after me. Don't forget. Keep in touch."

He walks out of the Mailbag shop, his bright yellow patches glowing, and I follow him, only difference is, I'll be here again tomorrow.

It's early January when my feet finally walk free out of the prison gates. Another con is released at the same time and a girl comes rushing over. Nobody's waiting for me. Carol had sent a couple of letters right at the beginning of my sentence but I ain't heard nothing since. Halfway down the hill I turn and glance briefly at the walls. No, *this* time I ain't *never* comin' back.

Tonker has written inviting me to live with his family when I get out and says he's got me a job working with him on a local building site. Sounds good, a shot at going straight.

I follow the directions he'd written. It's not all that far from the prison and I ain't in no hurry. Tonker's at work but his Aunty makes me very welcome and shows me into a nice, clean bedroom. I bounce on the mattress, feels soft and comfy.

"Would you like a cup of tea, Watt isn't it?" she shouts upstairs.

Chatting to Tonker's Aunty and drinking tea, I feel normal again. She makes me a sandwich for lunch and in no time at all Tonker bounds through the door.

"Watt, good to be out eh?"

"You can say that again mate."

"Bed comfy enough?" We laugh and there's a lot of backslapping.

"My girls coming round later, bringing her sister for you," Tonker winks.

Pleasant girl, she ain't bad and seems to like me. It doesn't take long to settle into a new way of life. Tonker sorts out some old workclothes and for the next few weeks I work as a brickie's labourer which involves keeping the bricklayers supplied with bricks and cement as and when needed. Hard graft carrying the hod but at least it's honest.

The wages aren't brilliant but with my first pay packet I manage to buy some new clothes. Fashions have changed!

The four of us, that is Me, Tonker, his girl and her sister go out together at weekends to the local clubs and pubs. I pay board and Tonker's Aunty cooks a meal and generally looks after me well.

Then Don arrives. When I get home one night there's another lodger and he's gonna share my room! I don't think so. Thanking Tonker and his Aunty for everything, I make my excuses and leave.

On the train journey to Wolverhampton I resolve to keep going straight and get some paid work. Anything will do. The family is pleased to see me.

Mom gives me a lecture saying as how I should be like Roy 'cos he's got a good job now working with Dad at the brickyard. Dad doesn't say much, his usual grunt. It's Friday and Roy's off to the Toc H.

"I can drop you a few bob," he tries to persuade me.

"It's not that, I've got some money. Bit old for the Toc H Roy."

"Older people go there as well now."

"What do you mean, *older* people?"

Toc H is crowded, all ages. Some of my old mates are propping up the bar including Rob who turns to greet me. Maud catches hold of his sleeve to try and drag him back.

Ignoring her he comes walking over. "Good to see you mate."

"Long time, no see Rob, how's the old married life suiting then?"

He pulls a face then breaks into that wicked grin. "Ain't bad. We've got a little 'un you know. Maud's Mom is babysitting so we can get a night out."

A little 'un of his own. Susie. I could have had...

Steve appears and slaps me on the back. "How you doin' Watt?"

Ian joins us and waves his wife across. It's like the old days, drinking and chatting with the lads. Glad I came. Great night.

Saturday evening me and Roy hit the dance at Willenhall Baths. I'm at the bar when, "hello stranger, how's *Carol* then?"

I'd recognize that voice anywhere and swing round to see Jean. She's a stunner. Same beautiful figure. Breaking into a laugh I give her a twirl.

"You know very well I've been inside. I ain't seen Carol in nearly three years."

"Dance?" Jean was always a good dancer and I'm itching to get on the floor. They're playing a rock 'n roll. Didn't hear too many of them last night at the Toc H.

I swing her onto the floor. "You ain't lost your touch Watt," she giggles as we get into the old routine.

Catching her breath when the record finishes, I grab her waist and steer her towards the bar, "drink?"

"Oh, could do with one after that."

"Usual?"

"You remember then?"

"Course I do, Cider and a pint of Mild please mate."

I pass the drink and stand with my arm around her shoulders.

"I'm married now you know."

Doing a double take, I step back.

"When? Who to?"

"Not long after you went out with Carol really. I did it to make you jealous Watt, but you never even noticed."

It's true, I didn't know or if somebody did tell me it never registered. Too busy riding my motorbike and having a good time.

"He's working away at the minute."

I don't know what to say.

"I never wanted anybody else, only you." She's sidling up to me again.

Whoa. I take her hands from round my neck. "And you a respectable married lady."

"No harm in a dance is there?" A romantic ballad starts to play and she sways her hips against me.

We're onto the dancefloor and she's close, real close. Take a deep breath, think about something else. Can't. Won't. Feels nice. She raises her head from my shoulder and our eyes meet. Her body presses closer. I'm trying to control the urge but failing miserably. It's agonizing. I can't pull away, not at the moment. It would be too embarrassing. The record finishes.

"You'll have to stay in front of me." Grateful of the cover provided by her swirly skirt we walk slowly towards the chairs.

She's married. Can't do this. Someone else's bird an' all that. Jean disappears to the toilets and I join Roy at the bar who is chatting up a curvy blonde.

When Jean returns she makes a track towards the bar. Our eyes hold for a moment. I swivel round and start chatting to my brother. She stops dead and wanders over to her girlfriends.

What the fuck! Some drunk smashes our kid in the face. The sound of breaking glass fills the place and birds start screaming. Roy literally picks the guy up and throws him over the bar. The barman reaches for the telephone as I pull Roy back and drag him outside. The blonde piece he was talking to is the bloke's girlfriend.

Next morning I'm awake bright and early. Got some stuff to do today. First thing is take this watch back. I catch the bus into Walsall and walk past the old garages, stopping for a minute remembering the Rover.

A few steps further and Annie's front door looms large. With a little note of thanks attached I push the watch through the letterbox. A thought strikes me. I might as well visit our Pearl while I'm over this way.

It's a short bus ride to Pelsall. Within twenty minutes I'm sitting in her kitchen and she's got the old fry up going. "Cuppa Watt?"

"Do I ever say no?"

She prods me in the shoulder and laughs. Always there for me, our Pearl, visiting me in nick and writing whenever she could.

We chat about the escape and what happened in Moss-side. Pearl tells me the Police arrived just after I'd left.

"I was dyeing your prison uniforms in the boiler, stirring 'em round with a big wooden stick I was" she says "and he was standing there, the copper, standing right there." We laugh and Pearl makes another cuppa.

"C'mon then our Watt, what you gonna do now? Always a bed for you here, you know that but you need to get a proper job."

After the bacon, egg and beans we move into the living room. My old guitar is propped against the side of the fireplace. Tom is an avid Country Music fan with a huge record collection. When he's at home the radiogram is always playing. Music lifts the spirits so I pick it up and strum a few tunes.

"Can I leave it here a while longer?"

"Course you can."

Might take Pearl up on her offer in the future. I like it at Pelsall. Tom and Pearl seem to have a nice life, he's got a good job, they're happy.

Back at Bilston next evening Mom's brother, Joe, calls in to see us. He works at the potted meat place, the Butchers Hide Skin and Wool

Company on the Moseley Road. I've walked past the place many a time. Bit of a foul smell.

"Need another bone-dryer," he tells me, "just come along tomorrow morning if you're interested."

I've no idea what a bone dryer does but I'll give it a go. Joe introduces me to the foreman and he gives me the job to start right away. It don't pay a lot but as my dear old Mom would say, "the devil makes work for light hands."

We put offal into a machine which renders it down to make dripping. Bones are put into a drying machine and then they are taken to be ground up. Me and Joe sing as we work *"dem bones, dem bones, dem dry bones."*

I stick it for a week. The foul smell seeping through the walls to the outside world is nothing compared to the stench inside. All the dogs in the neighbourhood follow me home, sniffing at my trouser legs. I have to fight 'em off while the school-kids laugh at me. No, it's not the job for me.

On Saturday I head to the Table Mountain. Ain't been in since I came out. A young woman is serving behind the counter.

"Where's Doris?"

"Oh, she's retired. What can I get you?"

"Bacon sarnie, well done, cuppa with two heaped spoons."

Glad to see the Juke Box is still in the corner. Some of the old record titles stare back at me. Pressing a selection I sit in the window seat and look round at the old red leatherette chairs, bit ripped and shoddy now, lots of memories in this place.

I'm hoping some of my old mates will appear, but they don't. Most are married with wives and families to go home to. There's a new, young crowd but they know who I am alright. I see the nudges, the way they look at me and can hear them talking about my escape. Not in a bad way, it's like I'm some sort of hero.

Tuesday sees me at the Labour Exchange. The friendly lady smiles at me as she flicks through the big boxful of jobcards. It seems like forever until she plucks one out. "This one might suit."

The job is at the Criterion Stamping Works on Willenhall Road. Walking distance. Good rates of pay. In jig time I'm standing in front of a bald headed bloke who looks exasperated, doesn't ask me any questions and says he needs somebody, and fast. "Start tomorrow, be here at seven."

The work is heavy, I'm hot and sweaty and the VERY LOUD stamping noise hurts my ears. The foreman says I'm taking too many breaks for drinks. I have a bit of a 'personality clash' with him in any event. He knows my past and makes it plain he doesn't like me. To be truthful I hate this job anyway. Friday, I collect my money and cards.

I've been out of prison for a couple of months now. Still no proper job, although I've tried. Perhaps I'll have better luck at Pelsall. Packing my gear, I catch the bus and head to Pearl's.

Whistling, I walk towards the pre-fab with its whiter than white nets and pretty windowboxes. In the fading afternoon sunshine Pearl greets me on the step and gives me a big, welcoming hug. She sits me down with a cuppa and I strum a few tunes before nipping to the local for a pint.

Propping up the bar my eyes scan the drab, smoke filled room. Men of all ages sit chatting, playing darts or dominoes and swigging their beers. They'll go home half cut, kick the dog, shag the missus, work for a pittance in dead end jobs and be back in here again next weekend.

Turning to the busty blonde barmaid for another pint, I watch as the glass is re-filled. I'm twenty eight years old, no job, no home of my own and hardly any cash in my pocket. There's a better life waiting for me, I can feel it in my bones and it won't be like the lives of these losers sitting in here either.

Chapter 15

CATCH ME IF YOU CAN

Shirt off, showing my tanned, toned, body to all the passing girls, I'm working on a building site with Tom.

His brother, Morris, nickname Moggy, is the site foreman and he's given me a chance. We're installing massive sewerage pipes and I'm helping with the concrete bases.

Moggy drops us off home in the van at just turned four o'clock. Lovely cooking smells waft in the air as we hit the garden path. Wonder what's for dinner tonight. Me and Tom smile at each other and rub our hands. Quick wash and eat, I'm starving.

Pearl and her friend look up from the table as I walk in with my shirt slung over my shoulder.

'Watt, this is Penny,' our Pearls got a glint in her eye.

"Hello," I nod in her general direction but am more interested in the tantalizing aroma emanating from the oven.

"She ain't got a boyfriend Watt." If nothing else, Pearl is direct. "Why don't you take her for a drink tonight then?"

Not really my type but nice enough. Early twenties I'd say, brownish hair.

Pearl seems intent on my going out with her friend, and so, to shut her up as much as anything, we arrange to meet at the Red Cow later.

"C'om Pearl, get the grub up," Tom comes into the kitchen as Penny disappears out the door, "then we can go for a pint."

Me and Tom are just getting our ale in when she appears at my side. "Drink?"

"White wine please."

"Leave you to it then Watt," Tom grins and goes to join Moggie and some mates.

We chat about Pelsall, the weather, my job and a bloke she really likes! It doesn't take me long to get the picture. He hasn't a clue Penny fancies him and she's too shy to make the first move.

Pleasant to have a bit of female company, no pressure, I don't really fancy her and she fancies this other bloke. I tell her she should speak to him and share her feelings. They've known each other, from a distance, for a while. "What's the worst that can happen?" I shrug my shoulders.

"Will you be in here Friday?" she asks, "I can tell you how I've got on."

I walk her home, only a few streets away and say goodnight at the gate. Pearl wants to know 'all' when I return. Don't think she believes me when I say "nothing to tell."

Friday night comes and, as usual, me and Tom head for the pub. There's a very pretty young girl standing at the outdoor and she steps back for us to walk through. Lovely eyes. I smile at her and she blushes.

"Hello" says Tom, "Is Hugh in yet?"

The girl points through the hatch, "he's in the bar, Tom."

Penny's sitting with a couple of friends and motions me over to their table. I get my pint in and join them. "Any luck?"

Penny knows what I mean and leans across, "I haven't quite got the courage yet, but I will."

I leave the women to their chit chat and wander back to join the men. "This is Hugh," Tom introduces me, "lives in Heath End. That was his sister in the outdoor."

Yes, I remember.

Think I'll take a visit home, catch up with the lads, see who's about, so come Saturday morning I'm off to Bilston. Two buses later I'm sitting in the Table Mountain.

Haven't seen Russ since before I went to Rochester and that's a good many years. I'd climbed a couple of drainpipes for him and his mate back then. We catch up on the news of what Bishop, Taylor, Mad Jack and the rest are up to these days and, of course, he wants to talk about the escape.

"Gordon gave me the low down when he got out," Russ looks at his watch, "should be here any minute, it's a wonder he didn't escape with you."

"His sentence was almost finished. Last time I saw him…"

"Hello Gord, me old mate," Russ stands up and shouts for another cuppa as Gordon walks through the door. Smiles and handshakes all round.

"How you doin' then Watt?"

"I'm good, living with Pearl, working on the building."

Gordon screws up his face. "Going straight. You! That's a laugh."

Russ looks at Gordon, their eyes speak and Gordon nods. Russ lowers his voice, "we got a job on if you want in."

That's all it takes. The old adrenalin rush at the mere thought of it. Nearest you come to one of them on the building is when the hammer hits your hand by mistake. Turmoil. My teacup suddenly becomes fascinating. Wrestling with the part of me that wants in, I shake my head.

Staring out of the window as they make their final arrangements, I think back on the times I've sat in this very place doing the same thing.

Russ finishes his tea. "Gotta go, see you around Watt, good to see you out mate," he taps me on the shoulder and gives me the thumbs up.

Gordon pushes back his chair, "catch up some other time, stuff to do, you understand."

I smile and nod as he makes for the door.

Mom's pleased to see me when I nip home before catching the bus back to Pelsall. In the Red Cow Hugh pulls me to one side, "my sister fancies you, wants a date."

I frown at him remembering the young girl I'd seen in the outdoor. "How old is she?"

"Sweet sixteen," he laughs, "you look after her mind."

"I'll take her to the pictures on Friday night. Tell her to pick which film she'd like to see."

He nods and we carry on chatting with the rest of the blokes, mainly about football, work and women.

Lying in bed that night, with my hands clasped behind my head, staring at the ceiling, its not football, work or women on my mind. It's Gordon and Russ. Wonder how the job went.

Friday comes and I'm standing on the steps of one of the Cinema's in Walsall. There's a good John Wayne on at the Savoy but the film

Mandy wants to see is a romantic saga. Still, I buy some popcorn and tickets for the back row and we're soon settled.

I look at her young, fresh face, as the lights go down and she turns to me, smiling. Happy. Yes, she's happy. Was I *ever* that happy?

It's a slow moving film with no real action. As the lights dim for the second half my arms slides round the back of her seat. A while later, my hand finds its way onto her shoulder and sometime after that I pull her closer.

Mandy is good company and chats away in the café opposite before we catch the last bus to Pelsall. She's enjoyed the film; her eyes are sparkling as she recounts various bits I'd not even noticed. I leave her at the front gate and wave to Hugh as he lets her in.

Saturday, so I'll just pop to Bilston and see Mom. That's what I tell Pearl. Actually, I can't wait to get to the Table Mountain. Gordon's sitting chatting to a bird but he fucks her off as soon as I walk in. He ain't looking too happy.

"Idiot, he is, that Russ," Gordon's in a mood so I just let him ramble on waiting for my bacon sarnie. It seems they never did the job last week because Russ got nabbed in a stolen car. "He runs a light, in a stolen car, he runs a light. Can you believe it Watt?"

I shake my head. Golden rule number 5, or is it 6, drive real careful in a stolen car. Gordon is sick to the stomach, I can tell.

"Look," he takes a bite of his sausage and egg sandwich, "it's a warehouse … safe as houses… me and you."

I raise my hand and look away.

He looks disappointed.

"No, I don't mean that." I've got my eye on the bacon sarnie heading my way!!

"Always was a pig, me," Gordon grins, wiping some egg off his chin, "you're in then?"

Laughing, I nod. The buzz is back, ain't felt this good in ages. I'll just do this one to help Gordon out.

We go off together and he tells me more about the job. Arranging to meet at nine o'clock, I nip to the shops to buy me a small torch, a roll of black tape, a pair of gloves, some meat and a bar of chocolate. Heading towards Mom's I'm planning to borrow a dark coat off Roy, my mind racing, feeling so *alive*.

"What you doin?" asks Barry, my young brother, as I sit at the table doctoring the torch.

"Here, you can help. Cut a couple of strips off that tape."

Barry hands me the strips and I place them over the front of the torch leaving a small open circle in the middle. Just need enough light to see what I want, not a bloody beacon.

"Can I have that chocolate?"

"No you can't." Delving into my pocket I pull out a few bits of change, "here, go and get your own."

Me and Gordon meet in town on one of the back streets where partygoers leave their cars before hitting the nightclubs. We've barely lit our fags when a couple of likely lads pull up in a nice black saloon. They disappear laughing and joking in the direction of town. It will be hours before this one is even missed.

Within moments we're into the car and gone. The warehouse is five miles away. An imposing red brick building faces the main road. I drive past and turn into a side street.

Gordon points in the direction of a small gate set into the wall. According to his source there's a guard dog, but no need to panic 'cos it's on a chain.

Out of the car, over the road and we're standing by the gate. Gordon produces a small jemmy and with very little noise opens it. We step into a large yard and close the gate behind us. So far, so good.

An outside light glows dimly across the cobbles. Gordon moves along the wall, jemmy in hand, and I follow. No sign of any dog yet.

My eyes are glued to a large wooden door. We've only taken a few steps and suddenly there's light, much more light as it opens. Shrinking into the shadows of the wall, I flatten myself against it, holding my breath, and watching.

The nightwatchman appears with something in his hand and he's whistling. A chain rattles. I see the glow of its eyes as a Doberman looms from the darkness.

For a split second the eyes turn towards us. I go cold. Another whistle and the eyes turn towards the bowl of food which is placed on the ground. The door closes and I breathe out slowly.

"C'mon," whispers Gordon, "got about fifteen."

The Doberman is nose down in the bowl as we reach the door and raises his head for a second as I push the handle. Watchman didn't even bother to lock up. We're in.

Gordon smiles at me, his information is spot on. Less than ten minutes later, having darted twice past an open door from where the sounds of TV, laughter and munching of sandwiches can be heard, we emerge into the yard.

A week's takings are safely stashed in a large rucksack which hangs heavily on my back. We stand under the dim light. I can see the empty bowl. A chain rattles and we are confronted by the dog. He looks from me to Gordon and back again, takes one step forward and nuzzles my pocket. He's after the meat!

I throw it to him, wrapping an' all, and leg it towards the gate. Gordon follows. Unfortunately it's a small piece of meat and a very large dog. He wolfs it down in one go.

The chain rattles like fuck as he barks and gives chase. I turn to throw the chocolate and see him take a flying leap at Gordon's arse. The chain reaches full stretch and the dog's neck twists as he's jerked back.

Gordon clutches his backside, "I've been bit. I've been bit."

Abandoning the car about a mile from Gordon's house, we leg it over gardens and through alleyways until we hit the rear fence. Through his back door, laughing, we fall onto the sofa.

I tip up the rucksack and cash, lots of lovely cash spreads across the floor. Gordon's missus tends to his bite wound before making us a cuppa and the old fry up. I never eat before a job. Sharpens the senses. Like to make up for it afterwards though!

We count the money and split it equal. I kip on the sofa while Gordon goes to bed. Not much sleeping going on upstairs. I think at one point the ceiling's coming down.

I'm back to Pearls on Sunday in time for a nice roast dinner and slip her a few quid extra board money.

"Mandy came round yesterday, wants to know if you'd like to go for a walk this afternoon, if it's nice. Pick her up at three" Pearl's giving me the order. She wants to see me settled with a girl.

Although I planned to have a bit of shut eye this afternoon, meeting Mandy has its attractions, so at three o'clock my knuckles are rapping on her front door.

We walk across Pelsall Common chatting and watching the kids play. Her hand slips into mine and we stop under one of the big trees near the Church. She leans back and gazes at me with those lovely green eyes. My arms encircle her body as I kiss her gently at first and then with more passion. She responds momentarily and then pulls away, "someone might see."

"Nice walk?" asks Pearl.

"Mmmm, got the kettle on?"

I light a fag and sit with Tom in the living room listening to his records. "Have a go at this one Watt," he says, playing one of his new 45's. I pick up the guitar and between us we learn the song.

"There's music on at the Oak tonight, you coming?" Tom goes off to get ready.

Tom's got a good Country voice and likes to sing with all the local artists. Think I might give it a go myself, so at eight o'clock I'm in the Oak.

Penny's sitting with a bloke in the corner. On her way to the toilets she tells me that he'd fancied her all along. I'm pleased.

After the mid time break the guitarist gets singers up. I lean on the bar watching and listening. Towards the end of the night Tom performs 'From a Jack to a King' and brings the house down. He whispers in the guy's ear and next thing I know my name is being called.

'Singing the Blues' is one of my favourites. Everybody knows it and sings along. The crowd wants more. This feels good, I like it.

Tom shouts up, 'Take These Chains'. My song finishes to rousing applause and I grin like the proverbial Cheshire cat all the way back, through a sea of clapping hands, to the bar. I'll bring Mandy here next week to show her my other talent.

"Why can't we go out Friday night?" Mandy drops her bottom lip.

"Now don't start, I've got a bit of business to sort. I might be home but then again, might not."

"Aren't you at work on Friday then?"

Ignoring her question, "We'll go to the Oak on Sunday."

Gordon has been in touch. He'd got Pearls address from Roy and came over last night. We'd spent some time admiring his new car, a nice two tone Vauxhall Cresta, and then gone for a drink. He's got something lined up. Friday morning at eleven fifteen, a wages heist. Neither of us have done anything like this before. I'm a bit wary.

The plan is for us to lie low at Gordon's until Sunday, less chance of being picked up with the dosh.

Friday dawns. At seven Tom gives me a knock.

"Don't feel too good, been up half the night," my voice sounds croaky.

Tom goes to work on his own. I turn over, smile to myself and snuggle down for a bit more kip. At eleven I'm waiting for Gordon outside the Alhambra in Bilston. He pulls up in a black car and it's hi ho, here we go.

One old dear in the wages office at eleven fifteen, that's what he'd said. It's agreed if she does anything other than move away from the money when told, then we leg it. No violence on my record and that's the way it's gonna stay.

From our vantage point in the car Gordon points to a small door at the side of the factory. "Through that door, it's the first office on the left. Window looks onto the street. We can walk past first."

The lady sits there behind her desk, counting out money, and placing it into wage packets. The side entrance is not locked; we walk briskly towards the office door. I'm just about to pull the stocking mask from my pocket. Voices drift along the corridor before we see 'em; two blokes carrying mugs of steaming tea. They turn the corner and almost knock us flying.

"Oops, sorry" says the one who spills half his tea down my jacket.

"Can I help?" asks the other politely, passing his mug to his workmate who proceeds to kick open the wages office door.

Quick, think of something. We ain't prepared for this. Gordon's busy looking at the money which is neatly stacked on the desk.

"We've come for a job," I nudge Gordon who drags his eyes from the dosh towards the bloke.

"Have you got an interview? Didn't think we had any vacancies. I can check for you."

"No, we just came on the off chance." I raise my hand to my hair knowing he'll see the tattoo's. It will stop him going to check. Don't want to hang around here now. Too many people have seen us.

He takes one look and shakes his head, "No, no, I'm sure we don't need anyone at the moment," and shows us the door.

Abandoning the car on the outskirts of Wolverhampton, we bus it back to Bilston and our laughter fills the Table Mountain as we re-live the moment.

"What about that fancy fur shop up town?" I prefer shops. No dogs to contend with for one thing!

"Mmm, suppose. Know a fence where we could offload 'em then?" asks Gordon, interested now.

"Leave it to me. I know somebody who'll take the lot. Let's do it tomorrow."

I've had my eye on the fur shop for a while. Easy access round the back too. Gordon agrees to nick a biggish estate type car and pick me up tomorrow night on the Bilston Road by the Fish 'n Chip shop at eleven o'clock.

Gordon goes home to his wife and I think perhaps I'll nip round and see Mom before heading back to Pearls. She's just put the kettle on when there's a screech of brakes outside. Next thing, BANG, "POLICE OPEN UP." Not waiting for anyone to actually answer the door, four Officers barge their way through. "What the fuck......" I'm handcuffed and led to the waiting car.

It's the usual good cop, bad cop routine. Good cop brings tea 'n sympathy while trying to get me to confess. Bad cop brings his fist while trying to get to me to confess. A ruddy great long list is waved in front of my nose. Seems there's been a spate of warehouse jobs and they wanna pin 'em on me.

After a couple of hours the good cop tries a different tack. If I haven't done these jobs then I must know who has. Even if I did know, which I don't, ain't no way I'm telling *them* anyway. Surely they must know me well enough by now, or is it they just enjoy the bully boy tactics?

Bad cop returns and walks behind my chair. "Stand up," he growls.

Slowly I place my hands on the table, push back the chair, stand, turn and stare directly into his eyes. He draws back his fist and I brace myself.

A knock at the door. Hesitation. He drops his arm and disappears. Murmuring outside but I can't make out what's being said. Perhaps it's on record about the time they beat me up and left me pissing blood!

Ten minutes later I'm released without charge. Ten minutes after that I'm on the bus to Pelsall. Can't wait for a nice hot bath and my warm comfy bed.

Mandy pops round on Saturday afternoon and I strum a few tunes on the guitar. She loves music and is enthusiastic about my singing. We pick out my best songs ready for Sunday night. At eight o'clock I make my excuses, leave Mandy at Pearls and make my way over to Bilston.

The smell of chips is driving me mad. I'll have to nip in and buy some if Gordon don't hurry up. Every car that passes I think it's him. Always fuckin' late is Gordon.

Eventually he pulls up in a spluttering Morris Traveller. There's a parade of shops and the one full of pricey furs and sheepskin coats is third from the end. As we enter the rear car park Gordon kills the lights and then the engine. The Morris glides silently to a halt.

I peer through the small barred rear window into what appears to be a stockroom. My grin spreads from ear to ear as the hanging rails of goodies, shrouded in white covers glow in the darkness. I elbow Gordon. He looks through and gives me the thumbs up.

"Need a jack," I whisper and motion Gordon towards the car. Within moments he's back with a scissor jack.

Getting down to business, the jack is placed between two bars and turned. With some groaning they expand enough for me to cut a small hole in the glass of the window next to the door. I reach through to pull the latch, yes got it, no bolts, we're in.

Armfuls of white shrouded gear on hangers are piled into the boot and onto the back seat. Few quid's worth here. The old car splutters into life and we make for Gordon's house to drop it off, before dumping the Morris Traveller on some waste-ground by the fiery holes and legging it to safety.

Gordon's missus is in hysterics when we get back. "What d'you call this then?" She can hardly stand for laughing.

We stare in total disbelief at the pile of stuff in the middle of the living room floor. She has removed the white covers to reveal old coats, trousers, shirts, blankets, sheets, curtains, you name it, anything but sheepskins and certainly no furs. We've only gone and done the dry cleaners cum laundry next door!!

Horror. Shock. Laughter. Well you have to see the funny side. "Get the kettle on luv." We sit up all night planning our next escapade.

Before going to bed Gordon's missus takes first pick and he drops the rest at Mom's. She has what she wants, then sends Barry round to fetch the neighbours.

"Like a jumble sale without having to pay," says a delighted Mrs. Clegg. "Feels like Christmas come early," Mrs.Jones remarks holding up a woollen coat, "might keep a bit warmer this winter. Look at this our Phyllis."

Pretty soon the stuff has gone and a germ of an idea implants itself in my brain.

Good crowd in the Oak Sunday night. Even more singers in so

there's only chance to sing one. It goes down well. The applause feels good. "Getting better Watt," comments Tom. Praise indeed.

Ten o'clock the following Friday night, although it's summer and quite pleasant, I've been stood here for fifteen minutes. Another dog-end joins the group lying at my feet. Where's Gordon? I see headlights coming towards me. Thank fuck for that. "Sorry mate, had to wait for the car. Took the geezer longer to lock it up than it took me to get into it," he glances across at me. "Got everything?"

Check my pockets. Torch, yes. Wire, yes. Glass cutter, yes. My gloves are already on. None of my prints will be on this car. I nod.

These warm nights are good for burglary. People leave their windows open. Less noise in gaining entry. My information tells me they don't keep a dog so we should be easy on.

The house sits in its own grounds fifteen miles away. Parking up in a lane almost opposite we sit chatting and smoking 'til the early hours watching the lights go out. After almost an hour we walk towards the driveway, creep along in the shadow of a tall hedge, across the front and round the side of the house.

Once in the back garden I motion Gordon to keep watch. He stands at the corner while I move along checking the ground floor windows. All are secure but I spot one open about ten foot up the wall at the side. Must be on a half landing.

It's close to the drainpipe so I shimmy up, reach through, lift the catch and climb in. A small ornament drops to the floor with a clatter but my quick reflexes allow me to catch the other one before it falls. Perched on this tiny window ledge I'm holding my breath. The snoring stops momentarily, becomes a grunt and starts up again. The sound is coming from a room at the front of the house and the door is ajar.

Gently I ease myself onto the stairs and creep down slowly into the kitchen. Gordon's ugly mug is pressed hard against the window pane. No key in the lock. I pull the top and bottom bolts and look round. Don't have to search far. It's hanging at the side of the door.

Gordon does the downstairs while I reccie upstairs. Heading towards the snoring sound, inch by inch I make my way to the wardrobe where the thin beam of my torch picks out a briefcase and handbag set at the side.

Silently I lift the handles and take them onto the landing. Back into the bedroom I make for the dressing table. A large jewellery box sits in the middle and it soon joins the other loot on the landing.

A brief look see in the other bedrooms tells me they are unoccupied and there's nothing else around. A break in the snoring sends my spine rigid. I freeze and hold my breath. The bed creaks. Someone is getting up.

I dart into a spare room as the pad of feet comes within inches of me. Surely to god they must see the stuff at the top of the stairs. I'm trying to listen but my pounding heart drowns out every other noise. Deep breaths.

The toilet flushes. Feet walk past, creak, they're back in bed. A few minutes later the snoring resumes. Looking to the ceiling, I thank sweet Jesus and move swiftly onto the landing.

Carrying the stuff downstairs I can see Gordon grinning. Must have found something good. I follow him into the large lounge and my torch follows his pointing arm. "Look at these" he whispers. There's an array of small silver boxes on the sideboard.

Cash from the handbag and a couple of hundred pounds from the briefcase is stuffed into my pockets. A couple of diamond necklaces and bracelets shine up from the jewellery box. Nice. We fill our rucksacks with the silverware and let ourselves out of the back door.

At Gordon's we divide the cash. Within a couple of days the little silver boxes and diamonds have fetched a princely sum. My fence tells me diamonds and silver are much sought after. If there's any more…

Yes, with a bit more dosh I can buy a motor bike. That's all I want. Me and Mandy, wind in our hair, zooming down Hermitage Hill. Picnic by the river. She'd like that. I'd like that.

My brain is working overtime. There used to be a jeweller lived on the main road in Bilston. His house is probably rammed with the stuff. We can reach it on foot, through the gulleys and over the back gardens.

Friday night and we're sitting at the bottom of the garden, hidden behind a clump of bushes, waiting for all the lights to go out. An hour or so later I give the 'wagons ho' signal to Gordon.

Inching our way through the shrubbery we get to the house. We're in luck. A window in the back kitchen appears to be open, only slightly, but if it's on the latch I can get in. Sure enough, insert the magic wire, pull and hey presto, the large window swings open.

Noiselessly I climb in and clamber over the sink. Gordon's bigger built than me, put a bit of weight on lately, so he comes through the back door, which is bolted but still has the key in the lock.

Hearing a pitter patter of feet I turn to see a big brown dog run towards us. Gordon freezes. Reaching into my pocket I pull out the meat and chocolate. A low throaty growl turns into munch, munch as the food occupies him for a while.

Through the open door is the hallway where some coats are hanging with a couple of bags underneath. I signal to Gordon and we creep towards them. Pitter patter, pitter patter, the wretched dog runs in front of me, bares his teeth and starts to growl again. He barks once but I'm back to the kitchen. Here it is. A glow of light from the fridge flickers round the room. Pulling out the family's Sunday joint I throw it at him. He's onto it, holding the meat with his paws. Got a big bone in the middle.

We stand like statues, hardly daring to breath. Has the barking woken anyone? Seems to be all quiet. I move slowly towards the bags.

I've just reached them and Gordon is standing at the entrance to the kitchen keeping an eye on the dog, when light floods the hallway. I turn and look into the barrel of a shotgun.

"You just stay where you are sonny boy. I'll shoot if I have to." He looks a bit useful for a jeweller!

A big ugly bruiser is stood standing at the top of the stairs pointing a gun at me. He don't look worried at all. He might just shoot. Shall I make a run for it? How are his reactions? Would he have time to pull the trigger? Will I take the risk? Is it worth it? He starts to walk down the stairs.

Don't think he's noticed Gordon. Out of the corner of my eye I see his shadowy figure receding. All hell breaks loose when he trips over the dog.

I make a bolt for the back door, the dog starts barking, the coat-stand has been blasted and I can hear the gun being re-loaded. He ain't fuckin' kiddin', he's gonna shoot us.

I ain't never seen Gordon run so fast. Come to that I ain't never run so fast myself. We sprint in a zig zag across the lawn and take a flying leap over the conifers as the 'jeweller' fires again. Gordon cries out but carries on running. Not looking back, we leg it over as many gardens as we can, along the gulleys and away to Gordon's house.

"I'm shot, I'm shot."

"Calm down mate, lets have a look."

Gordons drops his trousers to reveal a wound in the back of his leg, caused by what looks like sharp pieces of flying shrubbery!

He gets his missus out of bed to remove the splinters and make us a fry up.

Hungry work using all this adrenalin. We laugh, chat, smoke and drink tea 'til first light.

Turns out the jeweller had sold the house to a scrap metal dealer a few months ago. It pays to do your research. Don't go in blind. I remember Gallagher, down the Block at Rochester, telling me that. We were lucky. Could have ended up six foot under!

I'm still working on the building with Tom but the contract's coming to an end this week. Moggy promises me another job on the new site. He'll let me know when.

Mandy and me are going steady. Still ain't had much more than a kiss and a cuddle but we get on together, have a laugh. She's Tom's mate's sister so I need to tread a bit careful. Promising to see her on Sunday night, I set off on Saturday to meet Gordon.

"One bacon and one sausage sarnie over here when you're ready luv," Gordon's already sitting at the window seat in the Table Mountain with a cup in front of him, "and one tea, two heaped spoons."

"Was pulled yesterday."

"Got nothing on you had they?"

Gordon laughs. "No, course not, but you know the game, bit sore today," he rubs his ribcage.

"Bastards. You still on…?"

"Yes mate, what you got?"

"Got two possibles lined up Gord mate. No fuckin' four legged friends or maniacs with shotguns to worry about either."

Heads together, I'm giving him the info when a familiar laugh makes me sit back. Elaine. Turning, I notice the shapely legs before looking up. She's with a bloke and introduces him as her husband. I'd seen him around, local chap, been inside, got a bit of form. Turns out they've got a kid.

"Settled down then Elaine?"

She smiles and whispers in my ear when he goes off to fetch their drinks, "I could still turn the odd trick for you handsome."

"I'm courting, going steady."

"Don't see you much over this way, where you living then Watt?"

"With our Pearl, at Pelsall."

Elaine looks blank, "never heard of it, you ever heard of Pelsall?" she asks her husband as he returns with tea and toast.

During the ensuing conversation, which is a bit inconvenient 'cos me and Gordon need to talk about stuff, I find out 'the Shape' has moved away, living somewhere in Sheffield or Leeds. Elaine can't quite remember. Rosie married a bloke from the Bank, has two kids and is well set up living the on other side of Wolverhampton. Susie? No, Elaine doesn't know what's happened to her.

They move off after a while. Me and Gordon get back to business. We'll do the one job tonight and the other early next week.

The first **is** a jeweller, but a shop, not a house. I've done the research and we're all set. Gordon's gonna get the car and we're to meet outside the Alhambra at the usual time.

Always park up when it's busy. A tip from Mad Jack. Always use alleys and gulleyways where possible and keep off the roads. I can hear his voice in my head as I'm waiting for Gordon.

I'd spent the best part of this last week casing the joint. Glancing up at the roof, clearly visible from the opposite side of the road, I'd spotted the skylight. Several days I'd walked past. Never closed. That's the in. My fence is ready and waiting.

A few minutes each time, browsing in the window, but really looking through into the shop gave me the information I needed. The safe was clearly visible when the door to the back room was opened. Bernie Watkins had taught me all about safes, how to break 'em, what to look out for. I can do it.

Here comes Gordon. Adrenalin starts to rush as soon as I slip on my gloves and get into the car. We park up and walk along the alley towards the barred rear door. Gordon positions himself twenty yards away, lights a fag and leans against the wall. Taking a deep breath, scanning for cars and people, I start to shin up the drainpipe. Am I putting on weight? Seems harder than before.

I'm just about to clamber onto the roof when voices drift up from below. A bloke murmuring something and a girl laughing as they stroll arm in arm, totally oblivious to me perched above them. They stop at the bottom of the drainpipe for a kiss. If they were to look up now, I've got one foot on the gutter bracket and one knee onto the roof. Can't afford to move in case of making a noise, a tile might slip or anything. Wish they'd hurry up. Eventually they move off.

The rooflight beckons and in no time I'm through and standing on a dark landing. Torch in hand, I make my way down two flights of stairs and head for the back door. There are enough bolts on it to stock a hardware shop. Keys on a rack nearby with neatly written labels underneath come in very handy! Once Gordon is in I draw one bolt back across the top. This is our getaway route.

Turning towards where I believe the safe to be, our first hurdle is a locked door. None of the keys from the rack fit so Gordon produces his jemmy and we're in. A beautiful large wooden cabinet lines the one wall with dozens of neatly labelled drawers. We grin at each other when the torch beam shines on 'Gold watch M.', 'Gold watch L', diamond this, diamond that, silver this, silver that. I leave Gordon filling the rucksacks but interrupt him seconds later for the jemmy treatment to another locked door.

The big fuck off safe sits there with an air of defiance about it. Trying to remember everything Bernie had taught me, I kneel down and reach carefully into the alcove feeling all the way round for wires or any sign of connection to a telephone line. None. Good.

The combination dial is set in the middle and underneath a steel flap reveals the keyhole. Keys for this type of safe usually come in two parts. They will probably be locked away separately, perhaps in that room with the cabinets.

Gordon is busy checking out the merchandise when I re-enter. "Look at this little lot," he points to the array of silverware, watches and rings he's taken from their boxes, "we're in the money here alright."

"Seen anything resembling a key?"

He shakes his head and carries on filling the second rucksack. There's a desk in the corner with locked drawers. "Pass me the jemmy mate."

In the centre middle drawer lays the long steel shank. Now all I need is the end piece to screw onto it. Making my way to the line of cabinets I shine a light on each label one by one. I notice an unmarked drawer in the bottom left hand corner. The steel teeth reflect in the beam of my torch. Oh yes.

I screw the two parts together and slide the key into the hole. It turns, a click, and the first part is complete. I sit back on my haunches and study the numbered dial. Now for the tricky bit. Bernie, who knew an employee at a local safe manufacturer's, had taught me the easy way in, only works if the owner's are a bit lazy though, so here's hoping...

Twenty seconds later I've pulled the giant handle and sit staring at a nice pile of cash, an even bigger pile of documents and a dozen or so boxed items.

Slipping the rucksack off my shoulder, I pull a smaller one from inside and stuff that with dosh. The larger one is filled with boxes. Ain't gonna bother opening 'em 'til we're back at Gordon's.

As we sit at his table eating bacon, egg and beans Gordon's missus lays out the stuff on their new hearthrug. The cash is piled up in front of us on the table. A good wedge, without what we'll get for the merchandise. My fence will be well pleased.

Sunday morning I ring him and arrange to meet on Monday by the fishing pool at a local park. Gordon will pick me up from Pearls at lunchtime; we'll collect the goods from his house and take it from there.

Sunday night I'm on top form and Mandy say's it's the best I've ever sung. "Next Sunday we'll go for a picnic on my motorbike," I tell her as we kiss at the gate.

"You buying a motorbike then?"

I nod and she giggles.

"Really?"

"It'll be great."

I watch as she walks to the door, turning to blow me a kiss. This time next week, riverside, picnic rug, romance, she'll melt.

On Monday, after close inspection of the gear in Gordon's car boot, the fence gives us a good price.

On the way back to his I divide the cash. "We still on for tomorrow night then?"

Gordon looks across. "Last one for a bit eh, taking the missus away next week to a caravan in Wales." He thinks for a minute. "Why don't you and your girl come with us?"

I shake my head. "Mandy wouldn't be able to go mate."

"Well you come then, we'll have a right laugh. Might even be some rich pickings round there, never thought of that. Missus won't mind, long as you have a separate caravan."

Never been on a proper holiday apart from my trip to Devon, which given that I had to walk all the way back, is not remembered with any particular pleasure.

"You better ask your missus first, but if she don't mind, then I'm up for it."

Tuesday night finds me waiting outside the Alhambra at ten o'clock. Gordon pulls up in his own car. Opening the door I slip inside and raise my eyebrows.

"Loosing my touch Watt, tried two but was disturbed, thought fuck it.

Where we off then mate?"

"Take the main road into High Town and park up."

An antique shop I'd noticed on one of my trips with Carol. Lots of them small silver boxes the fence liked so much.

"You coming with us to Wales then, we're off on Saturday morning, eight o'clock sharp. Missus says you're welcome, plenty of room in the car."

Gordon senses my hesitation. "Go on, if you come then we can work a couple of nights and it'll pay for the holiday," he smiles and winks.

"Great. Take a left here." We pull onto a small car park at the back of the antique shop. Not a soul in sight. All very quiet.

Sitting in the car it's plain to see the windows are barred. Bit exposed to start using a jack. There are no rooflights. Gordon glances over at me. "You ain't cased this have you?"

I shake my head. "Stay in the car mate, got an idea."

Shinning up the drainpipe I'm soon creeping over the roof. Crouching down I carefully start to remove some roof tiles. One slips gracefully out of my hand, slides down, tips into the guttering, flips over and crashes to the ground. I hold my breath and become motionless for a few minutes.

Apart from the hammering of my heart there's a deafening silence. Continuing with my mission, the tiles form little stacks around me. In no time at all I'm lowering myself between the joists into the roof-space.

A big grin spreads over Gordon's face as I open the back door and he comes galloping from the car, holdalls in hand. "Watt, you're a fuckin' genius."

"Not just a pretty face, me."

Small silver items adorn every surface. There are some nice looking candlesticks, teapots, condiments, cigarette cases...the goodies are quickly deposited in our bags.

Into the boot they go. Gordon forgets himself for a moment when he slams it shut. I wince. We head out of the car park and away.

"Risky this, using your own car Gord, mate."

We've got a boot jam packed with stolen gear and it's roughly twenty miles back to his house. I glance at my watch. Eleven thirty. One good thing, it's not too late.

I'm tense as we drive through Wolverhampton. Well, I've been tense all the way. "Now take it easy, no racing about." I warn Gordon.

His missus makes us a strong cuppa with a tot of whisky as we unpack the loot. She wants to keep the candlesticks. Much as I like her it's fatal. Another golden rule. However tempting, never keep any stolen gear for yourself.

Next day I phone my fence and within an hour we're at the fishing pool disposing of the silver and dividing up the cash.

"See you Saturday morning then," Gordon drops me off at Pearl's.

"Police have been round asking after you, our Watt."

I'm frowning 'cos I know they ain't interested in my health. "What did they say?"

"Nothing much, wanted to know where you was, they didn't search your room or anything. Have you been up to no good again?"

Pearl isn't happy about me going away with Gordon but after a bit of badgering agrees to lend me her small suitcase. Mandy starts to sulk 'cos I'm not buying the motorbike.

"When I come back, promise." Perhaps if I'm away for a week she'll be well pleased to see me home. Might get a bit more than a kiss and a cuddle. Wonder what the girls are like in Wales?

Thursday see's me in Walsall buying some holiday gear. Now, where's that good men's outfitters shop? The assistant gives me a suspicious look until I flash the cash, then he can't help me enough. Two lightweight suits, new shoes, some casual trousers, will this lot fit into Pearls case? No, better get myself a nice new one. I can afford it.

Friday afternoon I make my way over to Mom's. I can stay here tonight and walk to Gordon's tomorrow morning bright and early. My brown leather case is packed and I'm raring to go.

Got to be at Gordon's for eight o'clock sharp so I'll leave here at half past seven. Tossing and turning, I drift in and out of sleep. This sofa's got springs in some very uncomfortable places. I'm on my third cuppa and I've watched the clock on the mantelshelf round from one to five o'clock. Might as well get washed and dressed. Think I'll have a piece of toast.

My ears prick up as I hear a car turn in at the top of the Crescent. Half past five. Bit early. Nobody in our street, apart from Jake, has a vehicle and his taxi has a roar of its own.

Putting down my cup I creep to the front nets and peek through the chink. Unmistakable. Cops. Now, they could be headed anywhere but they've only got eyes for No.12.

Like a flash I sweep up my jacket, grab the case and I'm through the back door before they reach the front one. Over the garden fences and away. A commotion breaks out behind me, dawn comes up on the horizon and I start to chuckle. Catch me if you can.

Chapter 16

STOP THE WORLD, I WANNA GET OFF

Aberystwyth is further than I thought. Take us hours to get there but just after lunchtime we're sitting in deck chairs outside our caravans, which are next to each other, admiring the view. Right on the front line, sea lapping gently on the rocks, sun is shining, money in my pocket, feeling good.

Gordon and his missus go off to the little shop for provisions. She makes us a doorstep cheese 'n pickle sarnie and we decide to climb the big hill that towers above the caravan site. Afterwards, suitably knackered but refreshed by the sea air we drive into town, hit a few pubs and then hit our beds.

Next afternoon, with some misgivings me and Gordon decide to have a swim. Neither of us have any trunks so we decide to go in our trousers, rolled up to the knees. Big mistake.

The stones dig into my feet as I make my way to the sea, which is freezing. Only one way to do it, just launch myself into the water. I remember how I'd learned to swim.

Well, actually it was by default because I was on one of Tooley's coal barges. I'd seen the other lads jump up, catch the bridge overhang and hold on while the barge continued, then they dropped down onto the back. Inevitably, when I tried to do the same, I'd missed the barge and fallen into the murky water.

Terrified. No other word for it. Thrashing about, shouting for help every time I surfaced. No-body rescued me. They just yelled instructions and somehow my doggie paddle got me to the bank.

Gordon inches his way into the water behind me. We spot a ship out to sea. "Let's swim for it," he suggests.

Been swimming for ages, the ship is still a long way off. Treading water I turn and look to the shoreline. Gordon's missus and the caravan site seem to be very small. The water is getting colder.

"C'mon mate, lets get back, fuck the ship, it's too far out."

We're struggling against the tide. No headway. Little bit of panic creeps in. My legs are getting stiff and the trousers are dragging me down. Setting my face hard, head down, I swim as if my life depended on it. Well it does!

As I haul myself out of the water darkness is beginning to descend. Gordon's missus is beside herself, crying, in a right old state. He flops onto the shingle beside me and she rushes off to put some soup on the stove.

I'm totally exhausted. Gordon looks up from his rocky pillow. Clasping hands we start to laugh. I roll onto my back. Need a few minutes to get my breath back. Mustering reserve energy from somewhere we manage to stumble our way to Gordon's caravan, where his missus wraps us in blankets and we devour a bowl of tomato soup. Within minutes we're asleep where we sit.

The two of them go off to Newquay for a day by themselves and I meander round the site before lounging in a deckchair to watch the world go by. Lots of children are playing on the rocks. Dad's doting on their daughters and being proud of their sons. My mind turns to Susie and what might have been.

Few tasty birds around. From my vantage point I spy a dark haired girl, clad only in a swimsuit, with a young lad, probably her brother, catching crabs. She squeals every time he gets one and puts it into his bucket. Perfect.

"Need a hand?" easing myself out of the deck chair.

She looks across and smiles. Good start. Down here on holiday with her family, she's twenty, comes from a place called Ludlow, works in a teashop, lovely blue eyes and nice legs. Very chatty.

I've seen some signs advertising a duo at a pub down the lane tomorrow night and ask if she fancies it. Big smile as she agrees.

"I'm in caravan number 46," she says pointing vaguely towards the back of the site.

Tonight me and Gordon have got a bit of business. After tea we spend a pleasant couple of hours chatting, laughing and drinking as they recount their adventures in Newquay.

We head out at midnight. Gordon has cased something on his daytrip. It's a big house that lies well back from the road. His car glides to a silent stop as he turns off the engine.

We've agreed to take just cash. Nothing else. Slip on our gloves, a silent nod at each other and we step from the car. No lights showing anywhere. All tucked up in bed, asleep, I hope.

By darting between the trees and shrubs we keep hidden from the house and follow the sweeping driveway to the side. I can see a vent on the latch upstairs front but don't fancy it. There's a small window open, side, ground floor, don't fancy that either. Looks like a pantry to me. Might not be able to squeeze through. Round the back I carry out a swift scan and hone in on a large picture window, must be the lounge. There it is. My invitation. An open toplight.

Leaving Gordon in the bushes I creep towards my target. Bit of a moon tonight. Feel exposed. Don't ask me why but I'm sort of bent over and looking from side to side as I cross the large paved patio. A muffled laugh comes from the bush behind me.

My skill with a piece of wire is brought into play, difficult this one, takes an absolute age but eventually the latch is lifted and I'm in. No barking, no patter of feet. Good.

Gordon stands at the rear door which leads into a room full of long boots, the lovely smell of leather greets my nostrils as I make my way through. No bolts. No key in the lock. Now I'm seeking a hook or keyrack.

Motioning him to stand still I creep out of the bootroom and into the kitchen. The narrow beam of my torch searches the room. Nothing.

Moving back to the rear door and shrugging my shoulders at Gordon, I mouth to him 'can't find the key.'

His hand is on the doorknob, he turns it and walks in. How we stifle our laughter I'll never know. Deep breaths. Can't look at each other.

Gordon moves towards the lounge and I make my way into the hall. Opening the understairs cupboard a jacket falls off the hook on the back of the door. My search reveals a wallet full of cash in the inside pocket which I quickly transfer. A leather bag, same as the sort my Solicitor always carries, is partially concealed in the corner. Not a briefcase exactly, similar, but a lot, lot bigger. It's locked. Making my way to the kitchen I find a hefty pair of scissors and return to cut the leather flap.

Mainly documents, but a canvas bag tied up with string at the bottom produces a small bundle of notes. Crouching down I relieve the bag of its contents. Turning round before standing up I come face to face with a pair of eyes and a huge hairy face.

Fuck me. My foot slips out from beneath me as the dog lurches forward; his wet tongue licks my face from chin to forehead. Ugh.

It follows me into the lounge where Gordon is still opening drawers. There must be three huge dressers in here. I motion to him and point at my furry friend who stands panting beside me.

Slowly we make our way through the bootroom. Doggie wants to come walkies too and doesn't like it much when I shut the door on him. It's a big mistake 'cos he jumps up, whining and scratching, then proceeds to make one hell of a racket. We're out of here.

Lights go on as we leap into the car and away. Hopefully the owners won't notice anything amiss right away and will just think the dog has seen a fox or something. I never make a mess, always replace drawers, shut doors and generally leave everywhere as it was found, minus the cash of course.

We don't meet any other traffic on the way back to the caravan site and coast our way down the incline, cutting the engine and lights at the top.

"Split in the morning," says Gordon, winking at me. "I'm in for a good night."

Noiselessly I click the car door shut and wave as he enters his caravan.

Kettle on first, then count the money. Ha Ha. Looks like enough here to keep us going for a bit. Don't know what Gordon managed to get 'til tomorrow. I fall asleep fully clothed on the seating area, my hand clutching the dosh.

A rap on the door startles me. Some of the notes have scattered onto the floor at my feet and I quickly scoop them up before peering through a chink in the curtain. Only Gordon. "Why didn't you shout something?"

"Missus has got some bacon on, coming over?"

Smoothing my hair in the mirror and collecting the dosh, my nose leads me to the caravan next door where scrumbly bacon and eggs await.

"Four hundred and twenty pounds altogether then, Watt. Two hundred and ten each, not bad for a night's work eh?"

"Can we go into Aberystwyth today then, I saw a lovely dress in that shop by the castle?"

While Gordon and his missus go into Aberystwyth I keep an eye out for my date. She might be crabbing with her brother again today. No such luck so I get my head down in the afternoon sun and wake when Gordon gives me a tap on the shoulder.

"Thought you had a date, cutting it a bit fine."

Grabbing my soap and towel I dash to the shower block and twenty minutes later I'm ready and searching for No.46. That much I have remembered. For the life of me I can't remember her name though.

I rap the door and stand waiting with my hands behind my back as a very pleasant, cheery faced lady, presumably her mother, opens it. "Sandra," she shouts. That's it, Sandra.

I can't take my eyes off her shapely legs as she gingerly negotiates the rickety steps in her high heels. Reaching out to offer my hand I'm immediately conscious of her mother staring at the tattoos.

The pub is about half a mile walk and we chat on the way. Apparently her folks own their own caravan. Her mother and brother are here for the whole summer. Sandra comes down most weekends and when she has time off work.

The duo is quite good. A man and woman, both singers and he strums the guitar. Wish I'd thought to bring my guitar now. Could have played a few tunes for Sandra. I'm sure she'd be impressed.

It's dark on the walk back and several couples, arm in arm, spread out along the lane. She leans into my chest and slides her hand around me so as to steady herself on the uneven surface. The warmth of her body against mine and the gorgeous perfume wafting into my nostrils make me quicken my pace.

"Fancy a cuppa in my van?" I'm trying to sound casual but inside I'm feeling rampant.

"Better not," she blushes under the light that shines at the entrance to the site.

We veer off left towards No.46. Stopping just short there's a big leafy tree with branches almost touching the ground and I guide her into its shelter. She giggles as I place my fingers over her lips.

A gentle kiss leads to several, each one more intense. My hand wanders underneath her blouse to unhook the bra.

Crunching footsteps in the gravel grow louder. Sandra tenses and pulls back against the tree trunk.

I groan inwardly and loosen my hold.

"We better go, it's getting late." She fastens her bra, straightens her top and smoothes her hair before we part the branches and step into the real world.

At the door of No.46 she pecks me on the check and runs her fingers through my hair. "See you tomorrow if you're on the beach."

Gordon and his missus take a ride to a place called Ynyslas which they say has beautiful sand dunes. Sandra is far more attractive to me than sand so declining their invitation I decide to stay put. No cooked breakfast this morning 'cos there's no bacon left. I wave them off and make my way to the shop.

Half an hour later I'm cooking a fry up. It's a bright sunny morning and all the windows are open. Sandra walks past the front end of the van and waves. She looks stunning in a blue bikini. I motion her in and she comes round.

"Oh, that smells lovely, we've only had cereal."

"Want some then, can put another couple of rashers in if you like?"

She nods and sits in the window seat staring out to sea. Over breakfast I tell her about my swim to the ship, which is still there and looks even further away.

We stroll along the shoreline, paddle among the rocks, jump the waves and head back for a cuppa.

Moving along the window seat I draw the front curtains and pull her to me. She kisses me with passion, my mouth, my neck, my cheeks, mouth again.

I grab her shoulders and raise my hand, "Don't move, hold that thought."

I'm racing to lock the door and pull all the curtains shut. She laughs. Now we're in our own little cocoon.

"Have you got any…" her voice trails off.

"You mean these," reaching for a pack of three I'd cadged off Gordon, just in case.

Hate the wretched things, but she seems insistent so here we go. The thought of Elaine, who had this knack of putting them on, first with her fingers and then rolling 'em down with her mouth, makes things more urgent. No other girl I ever met could do that.

Me and Sandra spend a wonderful afternoon. Mandy doesn't know what she's missing. An ashtray full of dog-ends later Sandra wants us to walk up the hill. Feeling a bit knackered and needing some shut eye I make my excuses.

Gordon had said he wants us to work tonight so as to leave the rest of the week free. His aim is to go home with money in his pocket, having paid for the holiday and treated his missus to whatever she wants.

I'll get Mandy a present tomorrow. Pop into Aberystwyth. If I take her something really nice, perhaps, who knows...

We head off the site at about ten o'clock and arrive in the middle of nowhere about half an hour later. No moon tonight.

"Follow me," says Gordon climbing over a stone wall.

I stand with my arms outstretched either side. "What are we doin'?"

"Need to get at the back 'cos the place is right on the road."

"Can't see any lights, how far is it?"

"Not far, stop grumbling, I drove all the way round this afternoon. I'm sure this field will lead us there."

I hop over the wall and follow Gordon. We've been walking briskly for a few minutes. I stop to light a fag and look up. One minute he's there, the next he's disappeared. My feet are rooted to the spot. "Gordon mate, where are you?"

A strangled cry emanates from about five yards in front of me. Can't help but laugh. Creeping slowly forward in the short grass I reach the edge of some sort of circular pit. Gordon's face peers up at me. He seems a long way down.

"Are you hurt?"

"Don't think so mate, can you get me out?"

I lie belly down on the grass and stretch out my hand. Gordon tries for several minutes to scramble up the side. Our fingertips touch once but that's as close as we get. No good, he can't get out.

"Have you got anything in the car?"

"Don't know mate, have a look," he tries to throw the keys up to me. At the third attempt they make it to the top and I walk *very* gingerly back across the field. If I end up down one of these holes, neither of us is going anywhere.

In the boot he has a turning handle for the jack. Grabbing it I return, shouting Gordon to make some noise so I can locate the hole.

"Try and dig some footholds with this."

Ten minutes later, with a lot of scrambling, clutching, heaving and pulling, we're both lying on the damp grass. Gordon, although caked in mud, is intent on continuing so off we go.

I feel myself slipping and desperately try to retrieve my balance and foothold on the side of a shaft. This time it's Gordon who is laughing and throwing down the handle and me who's digging footholds to get out.

"Let's stick together Gord mate so we can catch each other."

The field is riddled with shafts. It's pitch black and progress is slow. Despite my best efforts to save him Gordon plummets down another shaft, this one much deeper than the other two. He ain't laughing and neither am I.

An hour later we're both sitting on the grass. Gordon's nursing his ankle. The lights of the isolated house can be seen, turning out one by one as the occupants retire to bed. We are three quarters of the way across this field. No way am I going back. Could end up dead.

Helping Gordon to his feet and with his arm round my shoulder, we make our way past the back of the house to the road. No streetlights out here. I stumble and Gordon hobbles however many miles it is to the car.

Neither of us have the stomach for anything tonight. Laughable at first, 'now you see him, now you don't', it had quickly turned into a nightmare scenario.

"You'll have to drive, my ankle is killing me."

Nice little runner, this Cresta. Might be better to get myself a car rather than a motorbike. Roomy back seat an' all.

Covered in mud we make a sorry sight and I can hear Gordon's missus laughing well into the early hours. The shower block is obviously locked so I have to make do with a strip wash. My clothes are absolutely ruined and end up in the bin. Definite shopping trip tomorrow.

Gordon's ankle is bandaged up this morning and I watch him limp across. I've just put the kettle on and he stays for a cuppa. "You planning on going anywhere today then?"

"No mate, staying in the deckchairs. Missus has gone for a couple of newspapers."

"Any chance I could borrow the car, do some sightseeing? Thought I might take Sandra."

Gordon agrees and within the hour me and Sandra are browsing the shops, the castle, the sea wall. At teatime we return happy, laughing and fully loaded. It feels like a real holiday. She goes off to show her Mom the new frock, a gorgeous, if a bit expensive, blue number to match her eyes, lacy white gloves and slingback shoes. I get showered and into my new suit ready for our date tonight.

The rest of the week is spent with Sandra and we make up a foursome with Gordon and his missus visiting local pubs each evening. Daytime finds us sun worshipping in the deckchairs, apart from late afternoons when we make our excuses and disappear into the caravan.

Saturday comes all too soon. Sandra gives me her address and asks me to keep in touch. Good while it lasted but I'm going home to my Mandy with a couple of nice presents, some perfume and a new top.

I take over driving because Gordon's ankle is giving him some pain. We relive our adventures on the way back and my stomach aches 'cos we laugh that much about the open door, the sloppy great dog and dropping down them shafts.

Mandy throws her arms round my neck and gives me a big kiss. She's been waiting at Pearls for me since dinnertime. Good news. Loves the presents. She ushers me to the kitchen table, wants to know all about Aberystwyth.

Not much to tell really 'cos I have to leave out all the best bits.

Pearl's had a telephone installed while I've been away. Now who do I know with a phone in the house? Great news from Tom. Moggie has managed to get me some work on the new site to start in two weeks time. I think Pearl has been badgering him.

Mandy's gone home to get ready for our date and I'm contemplating how I can get her into bed when, ring,ring, ring,ring. Pearl comes running through to my room. She's flustered and upset.

"It's our Barry. The Murphy's have beat him up, mob handed. He's in a bad way."

I'm off the bed and grabbing my coat. Bastards. The Murphy family live back of the Cock Pub, there's five brothers, if they've all had a go at him…

Racing to the door I shout over my shoulder, "tell Mandy."

Need to get to Bilston, and quick. An elderly couple live next door to Pearl. I'd done a bit of work on their garden to help out and dropped 'em a few quid when I'd been flush. They've got an old Morris

Minor, very battered but it goes. Saying my brother's been rushed into hospital and I need to get there fast, they offer to lend it me straight away. Well, a little white lie never hurt anybody.

A Groom pow-wow at Mom's. Mike, Malcolm and Roy are already here.

They've waited for me. I'm the eldest. Barry is lying on the sofa, black eyes, cuts and bruises everywhere. He's pretty battered but doesn't want to go to hospital.

Don't know what it's about, don't wanna know. No excuse for five onto one. Hyped up the four of us pile into the Morris Minor and go looking for the Murphy's.

Driving like a maniac, I screech to a halt outside their house. Leaving the car doors wide open, me and Roy race to the front while Mike and Malcolm charge round the back.

We burst through the front door shouting for the Murphy bastards to come out. Old man Murphy is sat by the fire. Big fella, he grabs the poker and leaps to his feet.

Mike and Malcolm run up the stairs, their heavy boots thudding against the wood. I can hear 'em clumping across the bedroom floors as they check each room.

Old man Murphy is standing in front of the fireplace, poker in hand. He places an arm across his wife and pushes her behind him as she comes scurrying from the kitchen.

"Your fuckin' sons, they beat up my brother mob handed, five onto one, the bastards" Roy squares up to the old man. Can tell our kid is angry by the way he bites the collar of his jacket and roars. A habit of his. Nobody messes with Roy when he's in this mood.

I raise my hand. "Got no quarrel with you or your missus. Where are they?"

"Out of my house, get out," screams Mrs.Murphy.

Mike pokes his head through the door. "They ain't here Watt."

"Check the garden shed."

The Murphy boys are nowhere to be seen. Part of a big gypsy family they've probably got wind and gone to get reinforcements. Sure as eggs is eggs they must know what's coming.

Next stop, the Cock pub. We storm in but nobody's seen 'em. Knowing they won't go far I decide to drive round town for a bit. They ride about in a sort of truck, three in the front and two on the back, so not hard to spot. No way are we leaving this unsettled. If we have to search all night we'll get 'em.

I'm at the fork in the road by the shoe factory in Priestfields when their truck comes cruising into sight. "Hold tight," my foot thrusts to the floor and the old car lurches forward.

We're on opposite sides of the road. Got two choices here. Can either sweep round the back and give chase or head 'em off. Split second instinct takes over and I'm steering across in front of the truck.

It all happens in the blink of an eye. The Murphy's aren't expecting this.

Just before the Morris Minor hits their front wing I glance up to see the eldest brother, Jimmy, laughing. Seconds later his face contorts as he tries to swerve and avoid me.

Metal meets metal in a clanging, screeching, scraping, melee. We're out of the car before it's brought to a shuddering stop. Mike and Malcolm take on the two in the back while me and Roy drag the eldest three from the cab.

Me and my brothers are all good fighters, but so are the Murphy's. No need for words. They know what it's about.

Jimmy tries to put the nut in straight away but I sidestep and whack him on the head while kicking out at his brother Joe. I catch him in the groin and he goes down.

Jimmy lunges at me with a good body punch. It hurts, but the one I give him back hurts more. He winces. I follow it up with a smash to his face and another good body shot. As Joe tries to get up I crack him on the back of the neck and he goes down again.

My jaw feels the weight of Jimmy's right hook. I turn, flick my head and nut him. He reels backwards. Hearing a scuffle and whirling round just in time to block a punch from Joe, I pummel him in the ribs and whack his head as he keels over sideways.

Quick glance over my shoulder tells me Mike and Malcolm are holding their own. There's lots of grunting, roaring and shouting of obscenities in the middle of the road. Won't be long before the cops come.

"Need to finish 'em," I shout above the calamity.

Grabbing Jimmy's head between both hands and forcing it downwards, I bring my knee up and he jerks backwards clutching his face.

Kicking Joe in the back as he gets to his knees, I turn to see Roy's opponent is out cold. Jumping into the Morris Minor, which is still running, I extricate it from the truck.

The two younger Murphy brothers sit against the rear wheel of the truck, dazed and bloody. "C'mon, cops," I yell. Blue flashing lights are converging.

We're into the car and away home round the back streets. Murphy's won't grass, that's one sure thing. Families like ours don't involve the cops.

The four of us get cleaned up, we ain't come out of it unscathed, all got cuts, bruises or black eyes. Barry bucks up no end as we tell him, over a fag and a cuppa, how we got 'em and more to the point, how we left 'em.

Curious now, I ask Barry why? Turns out he'd fancied the same girl as one of the Murphy lads and was chatting her up. Instead of them two sorting it out, young Murphy had gone to fetch his brothers!

The Morris Minor is in a terrible state. Half the nearside front wing is missing, the chrome bumper is battered with one side resting on the road, the radiator is dented, water has leaked and clouds of steam spiral into the air. Wasn't worth much when I borrowed it, but now…don't know what they're gonna say.

Me and my brothers study the wreck and after a long period of silence, burst out laughing. Need to get it shifted. "There's a scrap yard open tomorrow morning, down by old man Coles place," suggests Roy.

"It don't belong to me, can't do that."

Nothing else for it but to drive back to Pelsall tomorrow morning. Only thing I can do is offer to buy them another. Was gonna buy a car or motorbike myself, got the money put by. Tying up the bumper I head off.

Surprisingly, the elderly couple aren't too upset, especially when I give them two hundred pounds to buy another car. The old chap is overcome and gives me a hug!

I'd spent a fortune on the holiday in Wales, the caravan, couple of new suits, presents for Sandra and Mandy, drinks every night, chipped in with the petrol money. Ain't got much dosh left.

Mandy drops her bottom lip. She has a habit of doing that when my plans to buy a motorbike are put on hold. I'm walking her home from the Swan on the Wolverhampton Road. Our route takes us across both commons. Lots of tree's and I whirl her round under the branches of one and pull her close.

"You said you'd get a motorbike, we'd ride down that big hill and sit by the river in Bridgnorth, you promised."

I let go and start walking again. She falls into step alongside, stumbling a bit as her heels dig into the soft grass of the common. "Look, I'm thinking of getting a car instead. Just take bit longer to put the dosh together that's all. Had to buy other stuff, ain't started the new job yet, you'll have to wait."

We walk in silence and I peck her on the cheek before she waltzes off. Not looking back or blowing me a kiss she slams the door shut.

Seeing all those happy families on holiday in Wales has come to haunt me. Really what I want is to start this new job, keep my nose clean and settle down, maybe start a family of my own.

There's entertainment at the Queen's this Friday. The guy sings mostly Roy Orbison numbers. Looks a bit like him too what with the sunglasses an' all. Promises to be a great night. I ain't seen Mandy since she went off in a huff and as my knuckles rap on her front door I'm wondering what reception I'll get. Her beaming smile tells its own story as she flings her arms round my neck. Women! I'll never understand 'em.

Gordon rings me on Sunday afternoon. Pearl's listening at the door, I can hear her breathing. She answered the phone so knows who it is on the other end of the line. Gordon soon realizes I'm talking in some sort of code.

He's got something lined up for Tuesday night. Yes, his ankle is completely healed. Yes, his missus is fine. I ask him how his dog is. He ain't got one but knows what I mean. "No dogs," he tells me.

When I wonder how his mother in law is, he knows I mean nightwatchman 'cos she's dead.

"None of them either, look it's a piece of cake Watt, a rich bastard, dodgy dealings, lots of cash, what's up with you?"

Just don't fancy it. Can't say why. A feeling, deep down. Something.

My thoughts turn to Mandy, the soft contours of her body pressed close to mine. She wants me to buy a motorbike but she'd probably like a nice flash car just as well. Romantic picnic in that secluded spot by the river in Bridgnorth. Can picture it now.

I'll do this last job, enough to get some wheels and carry me over 'til the building site contract starts.

"See you then Gordon." He knows it means I'm in.

"Ten o'clock, usual place," he hangs up.

Tuesday night finds me waiting outside the Alhambra. Gordon pulls up in a long estate car. What the....

I slip on my gloves and get in. "Why'd you get a fuckin' great thing like this?"

He thinks for a minute. "I liked the colour."

Any other time I'd laugh. "Prat!"

He looks over at me. "Well it runs good don't it, roomy, comfy an..." he turns to see the traffic lights change to red but in the blink of an eye he's gone across.

Less than twenty seconds later I see the reflection of blue flashes behind us. My stomach turns over. I'm already pumped up. Soon as I got in the car, adrenalin had started to flow. Don't panic.

"Just keep calm, won't be reported stolen yet. Bluff your way..." I never get to finish the sentence 'cos I'm clinging on for grim death as he slams his foot to the floor. Although Gordon knows these streets like the back of his hand we ain't got a chance in hell. I know it, he knows it and the cops know it. Gotta try though. Three blue flashing lights behind us now.

"Take a left," I yell at him. My mind is racing. If we can ditch the car and leg it along the canal we may be able to slip away over the back gardens.

A motor bike appears from nowhere in front of us, Gordon swerves to avoid it and we career out of control towards a wall. Slamming the anchors on we twist and judder to a halt facing the line of flashing lights.

A swarm of cops surround the car and drag us out. Cuffs on and within five minutes I'm standing inside Bilston nick.

The Custody Sergeant, name of Flanagan, knows me of old. I empty my pockets. He places the contents into a bag and seals it. "Sign here Watt," he smiles, "I'll bring you a cuppa through."

If there's such a thing as a nice cop, it's him. I remember once he'd leaned over and told me "if it wasn't for the likes of you, young man, the likes of me would be out of a job" and winked. He doesn't bang the door as hard as some of the others either.

Seeing as how he was driving, Gordon does his best. Tells the cops he nicked the car, was just giving me a lift and I didn't know it was stolen. They don't buy his story saying I was 'going equipped' for theft because of the gloves, torch, small jemmy, glass cutter and stuff found in my pockets.

No bail. Held in custody. Found guilty. I suppose because of my record, the escape, who knows what, suddenly I'm the ringleader.

The Judge's voice rings in my ears as I'm led from the dock. Gordon gets eighteen months and I get three years, three fuckin' years!

Stop the world, I wanna get off.

Chapter 17

SHANGHAI'D

The familiar red glow meets me and Officer Pugh shakes his head as he closes the cell door. Back in Shrewsbury Prison and back in patches. Because of my previous escape I'm considered high risk and therefore Category 'A'.

The key turns and I throw down my bedroll before moving to the window. Five broken panes in this one. Going to be real cold come winter.

Gordon had travelled with me in the Black Mariah but he's an ordinary con, not being watched one to one and he ain't got this red light over his head day and night. No good trying to break it. That's one thing they replace immediately, not like the window panes!

Sitting on the chair, my eyes wander round the familiar surroundings, finally landing on a dog-eared bible lying on the table next to where my elbow is resting.

If I keep my nose clean I'll do two years out of the three year sentence. In here it's not what you do, it's not being found out that counts. Officer Pugh has told me I'm allocated to work in the Mailbag Shop.

My mind is already racing ahead. Maybe I can make things more interesting, do a bit of baroning. Depends if there's anyone I know and more importantly, can trust.

Six of us in patches make our way to the recess, slop out pot in hand. The bloke in front catches my eye, being so much taller than everybody else, standing about 6'3" he has light brown hair and thin features.

Teatime. I'm starving. The unmistakable frame of Crusher stands at the servery. Perfect. Might be able to do a bit of business after all. Wonder if he's in the Mailbag Shop. Will have to wait 'til tomorrow. Crusher turns and we acknowledge each other. He must have been out and come back in again, just like me, just like a lot of cons.

This morning, I take my seat in the Mailbag shop next to mister tall with the long features. "I'm Bobby," he introduces himself.

"Watt, Watt Groom."

"Oh, so you're the one who escaped."

"That's me," I smile and carry on sewing. Obviously it's still being talked about, my notoriety precedes me.

"What you in for?"

"Nickin' a car and going equipped, got a three stretch, You?"

"Robbery."

Glancing across at the ordinary cons my eyes light upon Crusher. I give him a serious slow nod and he makes his way to the toilets. A couple of minutes later we're both standing at the urinals.

"How you doing then Watt?"

"So, so, me old mate. How long you been back in then?"

"Two months, another ten left to do."

I lower my voice, "fancy a bit of baroning?"

"You know me, smoke like an old trooper. Fancy it, yes, but I'd never be able to save enough burn."

"I get the bacca, you baron it and we split the profits."

"Sounds good to me mate. When can we start?"

"Pay day."

Crusher leaves first and I wait a couple of moments before returning to my seat. The screw is watching me intently.

"He looks a bit useful," remarks Bobby, nodding towards Crusher.

"Yes, he was in with me before, comes from Wales but runs with some pretty heavy people down London, if you get my drift."

Bobby smiles knowingly as we sit sewing our Mailbags. I chat to him about Mandy and my plans for the future. Can tell from the accent he's from London. Pleasant chap, quietly spoken, doesn't come across as the type to do a robbery. Still, I remember Fuzz. He looked like an armed robber but was in for embezzlement. Appearances can be deceptive.

Something strikes me as I'm walking round during exercise. The short, stout bloke in his forties talking to one of the screws is doing just twelve months for sticking a knife in somebody. It hardly seems fair that I get three years for a bit of pinching. Turning to Bobby, "I remember an old chap at Court with me a couple of years ago. Had a long record. Got ten years preventive detention for taking a bottle of milk off a doorstep."

"Ten years?" His voice sound incredulous, "for a bottle of milk?"

"Yeh, living rough, probably starving. Jailer in the Court cells said he'd have to serve eight years and four months. Can you believe it?"

"Oh, I believe it alright Watt."

"There's something wrong with the system. Don't seem right does it, that you get a longer sentence for thieving than if you stab somebody or beat 'em up."

Bobby shakes his head.

"How long you doin' then Bobby?"

"Thirty."

"Thirty months? It'll pass in no time, a breeze."

"No, not months, thirty years, *three live sentences.*"

"What did you rob, the fuckin' crown jewels?"

"A train…and before you ask, I didn't do it."

With that we are ushered from the exercise yard and back to work.

The screw raises his eyebrows as I take my fourth finished mailbag for checking at the end of the day. Need to clock up as many as humanly possible. More bags, more pay, more bacca.

Working with a vengeance this first week, come pay day, I'm laughing.

Keeping a quarter ounce for myself, the rest goes to Crusher, which I manage to slip him during slop out next morning. Just a question of picking my time. Some screws carry out their duties to the letter but others rarely follow us into the recess, it stinks!

Middle of the week and a few cons get visits. They file out of the Mailbag Shop grinning from ear to ear. I recognize one of 'em but can't quite put a name to the face. Light haired chap with a round face. Table Mountain springs to mind.

An hour or so later they file back in. Not taking much notice I'm beavering away when Bobby nudges me. Some serious dark looks are being thrown in our general direction.

Several cons start jeering "we'll get you, you bastard," as they gather behind mister light hair with the round face who shouts and points at me, "You, you've been shagging my missus."

Blue uniforms converge as he lurches towards me with his fist clenched. Might be carrying a weapon. I stand up, sidestep the thrust and crack him one on the jaw. He goes down as two screws pin my arms and cart me off.

Now I'm in front of the Governor who gives me seven days loss of remission, seven days bread and water and worst of all, seven days loss of earnings. I've sewn my fingers to the fuckin' bone. All that hard work for nothing.

What the fuck was it all about anyway? Shagged his missus? I ain't shagged nobody's missus. Well, if I have it's been in my dreams.

Thoughts turn to Mandy while I'm down the punishment block. I wrote to her over a week ago, sent a VO and asked for a photograph to pin up in my cell. Told her how much I love her in a poem. I'm hoping it'll do the trick and that she'll wait for me.

It's cold tonight, even with the blanket pulled tight around me like a cocoon. With so many panes missing the wind is howling a gale in here. My warm breath makes a white mist in the air.

I drift off to dream of Mandy, shepherds pie, steamed puddings with lashings of custard, bacon sarnies and a cuppa with two heaped spoons. Waking to the reality of dry bread and a jug of water is sickening.

The Governor visits daily to ask if I have any complaints. Feel like saying 'yes mate, plenty' but always respond "no Sir." Wonder if anyone has ever complained and if they did what happened?

The seven days seem like an eternity but I'm soon bouncing back. A letter comes for me in a fancy blue envelope, slit at the top of course where the screws have opened it to read the contents first. Must be from Mandy. I pull out the pages and fan them open. Four. That's good. Read the end first.

Turning the last page over it's signed, 'Love you forever, Mandy'. Now I can settle down to read it through, once, twice, again, and again. She says she'll wait, loved my poem, can't visit yet because of her new job, hasn't got a photo to send but will get one done for me. 'I miss you' she writes. Now all we have to do is get through the next two years. It's a big ask.

Back in the Mailbag Shop I take my usual seat next to Bobby and work like stink to make up for the seven days loss of earnings. Mister light hair with the round face is still giving me the dead eye. I stare back and the screws watch us both.

253

Crusher makes his way to the toilets and a few minutes later we're at the urinal. "Name's Gary," he says, eyes firmly fixed on the ceramic, "comes from your neck of the woods. Ever heard of a lady called Elaine?"

Elaine, a lady, that's a laugh. Now I remember him. Gary is the bloke she married.

"I've shagged her, well so did half of Wolverhampton, but it was a long time ago, before she took up with him."

"Word is that his wife told him on the visit you'd slept with her recently."

What is Elaine playing at?

Shaking my head "no mate, I've got a girl, Mandy, we're going steady. Don't know what the stupid cow's game is."

Crusher nods. "Just watch yourself. He's out to get you."

Bobby leans back as I take my seat. "What's the score then?"

"Names Gary. I knew his missus years ago but he thinks I've shagged her recent, while he's been in here, and before you ask, no I didn't."

Bobby laughs, not looking up from his needlework.

For the next few weeks I keep my head down, notch up as many mailbags as possible and keep slipping Crusher the bacca to baron. Needing to speak with him about how our empire is doing I give him the eye halfway through the morning. Unfortunately he didn't notice or was daydreaming. Anyhow, here I am at the urinal expecting Crusher when Gary walks in with a mate at his shoulder.

My eyes focus on the gleam of jutting metal but manage to sidestep as he lunges forward. A firm grip and twist of his arm releases the blade which falls to the floor with a chink. Foot on the blade, I grab his head and slam it against the urinal.

A sharp pain in my back brings me upright as Gary's mate lands a punch from behind. I jerk my elbow sharply into his ribs. He winces as I turn to smash him but Crusher walks in, grabs his arm and sends him packing with little more than a menacing look

Footsteps. I shove the blade into my boot and head for a cubicle while Crusher and Gary stand alongside each other at the urinal. The screw takes a look round… all quiet… receding footsteps.

I leave first. Gary finally emerges looking very sorry for himself. His hair is soaking wet as if he's had his head stuck down a toilet. Crusher follows, grins and gives me the thumbs up.

Bobby seems amused at the goings on. We chat about it during exercise. Still haven't spoken to Crusher about the bacca. Best left until tomorrow.

Turns out the baroning is going great guns. Three carriers on the go for our ever increasing stash means we can relax and start smoking the profits.

"See Crusher, my old mate, a little hardship at the beginning pays off, we're laughing now."

Crusher keeps an ounce on him at all times in case I should want any, which I often do. I've got more earnings to spend on other stuff and decide to treat myself to some liquorice.

I reach into my pocket and chuck one to 'Jack the Stick'. He likes liquorice as well. Nice old boy, must be late sixties, grey hair, got trouble walking so the screws allow him to have a stick. Sometimes come across him on the landing 'cos he's slower than the rest of the cons who would either be in front or behind the Category 'A' prisoners.

He lifts his head and smiles. I watch him go and listen to the clunk, clunk of his stick against the metal. Is this me in forty years time? The thought strikes horror deep into my soul. A sort of blinding realization of what my life has become suddenly hits me.

Back in my cell, staring at the dim red glow and wishing for freedom, something I'm not all that well acquainted with, I wonder how many more birthdays and Christmas's will be spent in nick? Settle down with Mandy when I get out, try again for a decent job so I can look after her. Maybe kids...

Been here four months now, got it all going on, nice little earner with the bacca, interesting chats with Bobby in the Mailbag shop and on exercise. We get on great. He tells me if I can do what I do in here I oughta be a millionaire on the outside. Me, I'm just doing my time and counting the days.

"Groom, follow me," comes the order from a screw in the exercise yard. Bobby raises his eyebrows, "see you later then Watt."

Could it be a shakedown? I smile inwardly. Nothing to hide, I'm not that daft. Then again for a shakedown there would be two screws, not just one.

"Get your stuff together," he growls.

Gathering up Mandy's letters, I'm taken to reception. My property box is placed on the counter. What's going on? For a split second the thought of release springs to mind. But no, I'm handcuffed and taken to a waiting Black Mariah. I'm being Shanghai'd!

What have I done? Has Crusher grassed? No, never in a million years. Haven't been up in front of the Governor, where are they taking me? Oh no, not Durham.

Two screws sit either side of me. "Can I ask Sir, where I'm being taken?"

"Walton Prison in Liverpool."

"Walton, but why?" starting to panic now. Mandy will never be able to visit, it's a long way to Liverpool.

"Simple Groom, it's due to the fact you seem to be getting on very well with a certain Prisoner, and the Governor thinks you might be plotting another breakout."

My heart sinks. Bobby had never mentioned anything about escape. Now I'll be stuck in a Prison miles away from Mandy and Crusher's got all my bacca!

Haven't been doing my workouts this sentence. I'll start 'em again when I hit Walton. Something to take my mind off things.

Walton Prison is like most others, same sort of cells, same sort of furniture and similar routines. There are eight of us wearing the old patches.

Next morning my cell door is opened for slop out and another 'A' lister stops on the landing directly outside. He fills the doorframe being 6'4" tall and very heavily built. "Watt isn't it?"

"That's me."

"I'm Jimmy, a friend of Bobby's."

I step forward. "Any friend of Bobby's..."

He nods and holds out his hand, palm downwards. I take the bacca gratefully 'cos I've only got half an ounce in my pocket.

I'm allocated to Mailbag repairs and spend my days darning worn out canvas bags. No baroning in here 'cos I don't know any of the ordinary cons.

Jimmy is also doing 'three life sentences' as Bobby would put it. We walk round together on exercise .Curiosity gets the better of me and one day I ask him about the robbery. "What can I tell you," he shrugs, "we didn't do it."

I might bemoan my fate but at least I can see light at the end of the tunnel. Can't get my head round the idea of anyone being sentenced to thirty years!

Feels good to be doin' the old exercise routines again. Keeping fit becomes a sort of religion, it fills my mind, body and spirit with focus and a kind of wellbeing.

I write to Mandy most weeks and she writes back occasionally, keeping me in touch with what's going on in her life. Pearl writes a couple of times with news of home. Life goes on as normal for everybody else.

12 months into my sentence I'm called to the Governor's office. What does he want me for? I've certainly kept my nose clean. No trouble of any sort. No baroning. Working hard, thinking of Mandy and paying my dues.

"Groom," he's smiling at me, "my Officers have given you a good report and I have decided to change your status to category 'B.'"

Relief floods over me. "Thank you Sir."

"I don't believe you will try to escape again?" The Governor raises his eyebrows. It's a sort of question.

"No Sir."

I'm taken to reception and change into ordinary prison garb, no more patches. My new cell is a single so I'm well pleased. I'll keep it nice and clean, scrubbed to perfection three times week. No red light either. Might even get a warm night's sleep at last, only two panes missing!

Are my ears playing tricks? Is that the sound of a guitar? Perhaps I can have mine in here. Be great if I could. Asking one of the screws he points out a long haired con by the name of Danny and I approach him during exercise.

"Hey Danny, play a bit then do you?"

"Yes mate, mainly jazz , bit of the old ragtime that sort of thing. You've heard me then?"

"You're good. Play a bit myself, Country stuff. Name's Watt."

"You can make an application to the Governor for a guitar in your cell. We could do a few tunes together then. Be great." Danny sounds excited at the prospect of a fellow guitarist.

He used to play in a small band. One night they turned up to a gig but another group of players were already set up. A double booking. Danny had stayed and listened to the opposition for an hour or so, then headed home. Unfortunately his missus was playing somebody else's fiddle, and in the marital bed!

"Didn't mean to…saw them together…couldn't help myself," explains Danny, "I smashed the bastard alright. You should have seen the look on their faces."

"Is that what you're in for? Can't believe the fucker went to the cops."

"Got twelve months, only six months and five days left."

Like us all, he's counting the hours.

"Anybody using the old ink?" Been fancying a tattoo. MANDY with some flowers an' that round it.

"Josh, on the second landing mate, did this for me," Danny rolls up his sleeve to reveal a lovely scroll with MOM in the middle.

Next day I'm sat in Josh's cell while he makes a start by drawing out the name bordered by entwined flowers. Looks brilliant. I write and tell Mandy that her name is indelibly on my hand for all to see, for life.

"Not another guitarist," the screw pulls a face when I make application to see the Governor. When it's granted and permission is given for me to have a guitar in my cell, I write to Pearl straight away asking her to send it in.

Within two weeks I'm sitting in Danny's cell and we're strumming away. He knows loads of chords, shows me the universal shapes and teaches me a few jazz numbers. He's not into Country music but soon picks up some of my songs. Most evenings we have a very appreciative, albeit captive, audience.

My letters from Mandy are becoming a bit thin on the ground. Re-reading the last one she wrote, it was dated eight weeks ago. That's a long time in nick. Her letters are a lifeline, a connection, some continuing hope, never had that before, never really needed it somehow, but now I do.

When it comes it's in a white envelope and as I pull out the one piece of folded paper, the pit of my stomach ends up somewhere at my feet. Looking up at the bars on the window, part of me doesn't want to read this letter. Deep breath.

'Dear Watt', her handwriting is exceptionally neat, 'I'm sorry…' might as well say 'Dear John'. I know what's coming. Don't want to read any more but my eyes are drawn to the page. I set my face hard. Got her fuckin' name tattooed on me an' all. 'Met somebody else… hope you'll be alright… we can still be friends….see you around when you get out.'

The letter crumples into a ball in my hand and I throw it against the wall. Now it lies next to the slop out pot. I kick the metal bedframe and punch the wall. The bible does levitation as my fist connects with the table.

I scoop up the ball, my fingers unravel the paper and her cruel words burn into my eyes. I rip it, rip it into the tiniest shreds, just like all my hopes and dreams.

'*Your Cheating Heart*' a Country classic comes to mind and I pick up my guitar. With some emotion the words come flooding back. As I sing the last line a couple of cons standing at the door start clapping. Danny sits looking at me. "Fuckin' hell mate, that was brilliant."

Need to brighten the mood. "One of yours now, c'mon, what about *The Darktown Strutters Ball*?"

Other cons are getting interested and three or four send for guitars. They are rank learners so Danny and me take to teaching 'em what we know.

Having some form of entertainment certainly helps to pass the time, what with work, exercise, and guitar playing it's not long before Danny is waving goodbye.

Pearl comes for a visit with Tom and Roy. She's excited about their new house, tells me her door is always open and I'm more than welcome to stay with them when I get out. What a star. Only got three more months to serve.

"You need to keep away from all your old mates Watt. There's a big new housing estate being built over the back and Tom can get you a job as brickie's labourer," she looks at me expectantly.

"It's a long contract, two years at least," encourages Tom.

"Seen Mandy?"

Pearl casts me a sideways glance, "never mind her, look at you, good looking, always was, you'll meet somebody else."

"You got a steady girl yet Roy?"

"Girlfriend yes, steady no, you know me Watt, love 'em and leave 'em."

We laugh together.

"Oh, one of your old schoolmates, David something or other, lived down by the Etheridge School, you'll never guess what. He's an actor. Was on the television last week" remarks Roy.

"Never! I remember him, one of the English teacher's favourites, like me."

"Gordon was asking after you. Came round when he got out saying for you to look him up."

Pearl tuts. "See what I mean, you come and stay with us," she's wagging her finger at me.

All things being equal perhaps Pelsall is the better option. Quite enjoyed it on the building site last time. "Sounds good to me our Pearl" reaching across I squeeze her hand.

Tom smiles, "I'll have a word with Moggie, get a job lined up for you."

I watch them leave, Pearl's face beaming as she waves and mouths 'not long now.'

The final three months are the hardest. At last the screw opens the gate, steps back, and I walk through into the real world. The sweet smell of freedom hits my nostrils.

Footsteps run behind me. The old weather eye is razor sharp. Instantly I'm ready. Adrenalin pumps, fists clench, muscles tense. On high alert I whip round. A suit dashes past, not even giving me a second glance. Deep breath. Lighting up a fag I walk along the prison wall. This time, for sure, I ain't *never* comin' back.

Here I am sitting on the train from Liverpool. On licence for the remainder of my sentence I've given Pearls new address for the Probation Officer to contact me. The fields and towns whiz by. There's a better life for me out there, somewhere, with someone.

'Jack the Stick' springs to mind. Don't want to end up like him. No way. I'm almost thirty years old. It's all out there for the taking. Right now I want a nice hot bath, a bacon sarnie, a cuppa with plenty of sugar and a bit of leg over. Not necessarily in that order.

Although the pre-fab was nice it hadn't got an upstairs and Pearl's new place is more like a proper home. She's got her eye on one of the Council Houses being built in Shireview Road, a prime spot in the village, and is hoping to be allocated one of them shortly.

Monday morning, its springtime, the birds are singing and the sun is shining as I make my way to the building site, a short five minute walk from our Pearls. Good to be alive. Great to be free.

I'm working with two old timers but they're fast bricklayers and we share the cheque. Hard graft but it keeps me fit. Getting a good tan an' all.

Got quite a nice little earner going on the side. I've discovered, by accident really and as a result of larking about, that I can carry a one hundredweight bag of cement to the top lift between my teeth. Nobody believes it at first and everyone lays a bet.

Whenever a new crew comes onto site I get 'em at it. Several workers think they'll have a go after watching me but fail miserably 'cos they can't get through the pain barrier. It's all in the neck muscles. As I'm to learn later in life, it didn't do a lot for my teeth!

Suppose it's inevitable I bump into Mandy and her new bloke. Tom nudges me as she walks into the Red Cow. Briefly our eyes meet. She lowers her gaze and hurries to a table in the corner. I turn my back and order another pint. Looks a bit of a wimp to me. Don't know what she sees in him. What on earth did I see in her anyway?

Looking at my left hand the reminder stares up at me. MANDY, her name encased within a scroll of entwined flowers. I must have been fuckin' mad.

Come the weekend, my pay cheque cashed and with the bit extra I've earned from bets, I'm feeling flush. Tom's told me about a racing certainty running in the 2.15 at Newmarket this afternoon. Looking at my watch, ten to one, I'll put the bet on and pop for a pint. "Just going up the bookies," I tell Pearl.

"Wait a minute Watt, can you nip in the Post Office and get me a couple of stamps? Marje's birthday next week."

"Yes. See you later."

Best get the stamps first in case I forget. The Post Office is situated on the main road not far from the bookies. Reaching into my pocket for some change I open the door and walk in. It has one of those little bells on it. There's no-one about.

I walk towards the counter. There, right in front of me, is a pile of cash. I'm gauging it's a couple of hundred at least, if not more. I'm riveted to the spot. What shall I do? I could sneak out with the loot and no-body would be any the wiser. It's the sweetest bit of business I've ever had handed to me on a plate.

The Post Office is totally silent. A pin could be heard dropping at twenty paces. My old heart is thumping. A wrestling match is going on in my brain. At this point I'm not certain which side is going to win. A notice on the counter says it's closed between one and two. Looking at my watch it's now ten past one. They've gone to lunch and left the front door unlocked! I can just reach through and grab this cash.

Another dilemma hits me. If I walk out minus the cash but somebody happens to see me…with the door unlocked anyone could walk in afterwards and snaffle it and I could end up taking the blame.

My hand reaches to touch the wad of notes and draws back. This might just be one of the hardest things I'll ever do. I turn round and stand by the front door. I daren't look at the money, temptation might be too much. A very long half hour later a middle aged lady comes bustling in with various bags of shopping.

She's startled and suspicious at first but I manage to convince her I came in for two stamps, found the door open and have been standing guard ever since. Counting the bundle of notes to satisfy herself, she sells me the stamps, says thanks and asks me not to report it. Well no, the thought had never entered my head.

Feeling very self-righteous I make my way to the bookies. The racing certainty looses. Only one winner at the betting office and that's the bookie.

Oh, I need a pint after all this. Downing a quick one in the Queens, I head back to Pearl's with the stamps and to tell her the tale. She can't believe it.

I can't quite believe it myself!

I'm sitting in the bath thinking I might go into Walsall after tea, see who's about.

"Don't forget Ann's party tonight. Says you can come if you fancy it," shouts Pearl up the stairs.

I've met Ann. She popped to see Pearl one of the evenings earlier this week. Classy, good looking blonde piece, talks posh, 'bout the same age as me, goes out with one of the chaps on the building site, big Pete, as he's known. Looks a bit like Elvis. Hard grafter.

"No, don't think so, going into town," I shout back.

"She's got a younger sister."

What is it with Pearl?

"I've ironed your best shirt, it's on the hanger in your room," Pearl's outside the bathroom door now. "You coming to Ann's or what?"

"Go on then." If it's a party then there'll be lots of people there. If I'm bored I can always walk to the Bush or the Queens 'cos Ann lives local, in Grove Crescent.

Better get dressed smart, never know. I put on my best suit and take ages choosing which tie to wear, eventually settling on the Italian silk number I'd bought in London. Cost a fortune.

Grabbing some breath freshener and my guitar, I walk the short distance from Pearl's to Ann's. Wonder what her sister is like, blonde with blue eyes like her perhaps? Ann is... vivacious... yes that's the word, bubbly and full of life. With a spring in my step now, might be a good night after all.

Approaching the flat my eyes are drawn to a sports car parked outside. It's dark green, with running boards and big headlamps. The hood is down and two red leather seats seem to invite me in. Lots of chrome-work, all highly polished, gleaming it is. I run my fingers across the long bonnet and look at the badge on the front. An MG. Wow, what a beauty. What I wouldn't give to own a car like that.

My head is still full of the car as I follow the sound of music and voices which lead to the party.

"Hello Watt, want a drink," asks big Pete, walking towards me along the hallway. "Glad you brought the guitar. Here, put it in the lounge."

"Pint of Mild would be good mate. Who does the sports car belong to then?"

"Oh, it's Barbara's, you know, Ann's sister."

Carrying my drink into the kitchen Ann greets me but I can't take my eyes off the girl with the legs. She's got her back to me, washing some tomatoes at the kitchen sink.

"This is my sister, Barbara," Ann smiles and goes back to cutting sandwiches.

The girl with the most fabulous legs I've ever seen turns round. She's the one with the sports car. I'm hooked.

Chapter 18

SHE WAS JUST SEVENTEEN

"Hello," Barbara smiles across the kitchen. Dark wavy hair frames her young attractive face. She reaches for the towel, dries her hands and brings the bowl of tomatoes to her sister who is busy preparing a buffet for later.

"This is Watt, put the tomatoes here," Ann points to a small space on the worktop.

Raising my gaze from her shapely legs, our eyes meet. I give her one of my specially nice smiles. Food looks good. Scenery is great. Glad I came now.

"Do you need me for anything else?" Barbara asks her sister.

"No, no, you go and see everyone's got a drink."

"I'll help if you like." Seizing the moment, I follow her tall, willowy figure to the crowded lounge full of chattering friends with happy faces.

She asks everybody what they want and I'm supposed to go get it. The booze is in a small bedroom near the front door. By the time I reach it I've forgotten! Grabbing a handful of bottles I head back.

Barbara spends most of the evening rushing around. With legs like hers there's bound to be a boyfriend but he doesn't seem to be here. Don't think she's ever going to sit down.

Ann and Pete are great fun. Lots of loud music, dancing, eating, jokes flying about, laughter fills every room, what a party.

Come half past twelve a few partygoers leave because of babysitters. Now there's more room and I park myself on the empty two seater sofa.

"Let's shut the music off," suggests Pete, "here, play us something on the guitar," he passes it to me from where I'd left it in the corner.

"Know any Elvis?" asks Ann. I can tell she's a fan because most of her records are by 'the King'.

"Not really," shaking my head, "but I'll give it a go."

Barbara makes an appearance after finishing the washing up and I pat the empty seat next to me.

"Why don't you sing one you know," she picks her way through several couples who are lounging on cushions scattered over the floor.

Everyone joins in when I start playing 'Take Good Care of my Baby' which makes for a great atmosphere. An hour later my limited repertoire is more or less exhausted.

Ann wants 'Love Me Tender' by Elvis. I've never played it before but she knows all the words. After a couple of trial runs Ann and big Pete sing it to each other while I strum the chords. My rendition of 'Goldmine in the Sky' is well received but I've had enough now. Boy, do I need a drink

The radiogram is back in business playing mellow love songs. Couples start slow dancing and snogging.

Barbara gets up to make a cuppa and asks if anyone wants one. Only me, so I follow her into the kitchen.

"Sugar?" She has a sweet smile, nice figure, hardly any make up, and there's a certain something about the way she moves…

"Two heaped spoons…is that your MG outside?"

"Oh my God, I've left the hood down," she dashes off and I'm hot on her heels.

There's a slight drizzle. "Thanks for reminding me."

She grabs hold of one side and motions me round the other. Together, we ease the hood into position onto the front windscreen. "Need to sit inside to secure it." Barbara opens the car door, I follow suit on the passenger side. She shows me how to clip it into place. "There, all done."

"Let's stay here for a bit," I suggest, eyeing the copious amount of leg on show and lighting up a fag. Barbara screws up her nose and immediately it's out the window.

Making small talk for the next ten minutes I find out she's seventeen and had the car for her birthday! Must be a rich bird. Works at a Bank in West Bromwich and lives in Great Barr. Never heard of it.

Somewhere towards Birmingham apparently. Well spoken, quiet and very shy, she just answers my questions. No serious boyfriend, although she's sort of going out with a copper, been on a couple of dates, he didn't want to travel all the way to Pelsall tonight. A copper eh?

Very different to her sister but she does have amazing legs and the most intriguing eyes. They're greenish with a sort of sparkle about them. The more she looks at me the more I get lost in 'em.

Barbara is not the type I'd usually go out with 'cos she ain't exactly pretty and, well, even if I don't fancy the pants off her, I sure fancy a ride in this car!

Leaning over I slip my arm round her shoulder, she turns to me and we kiss, a long lingering kiss. Nice. Her body stiffens as my kisses become more intense. Steady. Don't want to rush things.

It's early hours of the morning and by the time we get back inside the last few stragglers are bidding farewell. Big Pete offers me the sofa and Barbara goes off to sleep with one of Ann's kids in the middle bedroom.

Sunday morning dawns and Barbara brings me a cuppa on the sofa. Two heaped spoons. She remembered. Looks as fresh as she did last night, no paint and powder this one.

"Fancy some bacon and eggs?"

After breakfast we go for a spin in the MG. Hood down, wind in my hair, better than any motorbike. Everybody stares at the car as we whiz by. I'm liking this. She drives me up to Barr Beacon where her horses used to be kept. The last one was sold in order to buy this car. Much better than any horse if you ask me!

Bit windy here but we walk round the monument and through the heather as she tells me tales of the stables. I slip my hand into hers. Think she likes me. Perhaps I can persuade her to let me have a drive on the way back.

"You sure you've got a licence?" she seems concerned.

"Course," hope I sound convincing.

"Its got a racing clutch fitted."

"No problem, I can handle it."

A further five minutes of persuasion gets me into the driving seat. What a motor. The MG roars into life, a deep throaty exhaust fills the air and my grin spreads from ear to ear.

It's been a long time since I was behind the wheel and whether it's that, the racing clutch, or the amount of alcohol still in my body after last night's party, I mount the gutter and almost hit a lamp-post. The car is extremely fast, slightest touch on the accelerator pedal and it goes like a rocket. Barbara tells me in no uncertain terms to "STOP".

We swap places and she drops me at Pearl's. "Do you need glasses or what?"

We laugh together but inwardly I'm thinking perhaps I do. "Fancy a walk on the common this afternoon?"

Quick bath, lovely Sunday roast, and I'm back up to Grove Crescent with my boots blacked. The sun is shining and the common is full of lads playing football, families larking about and couples strolling along, just like us.

"Who's Mandy then?" Barbara is curious about the tattoo.

"Old girlfriend, she's history."

"Where did you get the tattoos done?"

I can't tell her the truth. A classy bird like this will dump me straight away if she knows I've been in nick. "In the Merchant Navy."

Now she wants me to tell her all about life at sea, which ships I've been on, for how long, what foreign Countries are like. There was a chap in Walton, he'd served on a ship. What I can't remember, I make up. She seems to believe me.

"Come back to Ann's and I'll drop you at your sister's on my way home."

Barbara collects her overnight bag, we load the car, one lingering kiss and she waves goodbye.

"You seem pleased with yourself," remarks Pearl.

"Got a date with Barbara, you know, Ann's sister, taking her to the pictures in Walsall on Wednesday night, can't wait. Have you seen her car, Tom, a beauty?"

He nods and goes back to choosing the next record, "listen to this one Watt."

Pearl smiles, "She seems a nice girl, bit young though."

"Old enough," I wink at Tom, "she's just seventeen."

Next day I ask Pearl to get me the forms for a provisional and book me an appointment with the local Optician. Barbara won't let me drive the MG again unless I've been checked out. She thinks I've got a full licence but at least with a provisional I can wave something in front of her nose.

Wednesday sees me outside the Savoy Cinema in Walsall. Barbara looks stunning in a mini skirt. I've dropped on my feet here.

Sitting in the back row, she snuggles into my shoulder. The copper was her only boyfriend and she says he never kissed her. I'm the first. She's young and innocent and I'm going to make her mine. New girlfriend, new job, new life.

Barbara tells me about the horses she used to keep, show-jumping, dressage and cross country, it's like a foreign language. I've read a lot of books in my time, being in nick for so long, but she uses words I ain't never heard of.

For the next couple of months I'm going steady with Barbara, or Barb, as she likes to be called. I take her to the pictures, local pubs to watch the entertainment and sometimes we just sit at Pearl's or Ann's where I strum the guitar and sing. She's got a good voice an' all, pure and sweet, just like her.

All the time she's buying me presents and stuff, a lovely shaving kit in a leather zip case, a new watch, aftershave, you name it. If she spots I need something, anything, it's there for me the next time we meet. For the first time in my life I feel cared for and it feels nice.

Some Sunday mornings she comes with me to the building site and we stack bricks ready for the brickie's on Monday morning. Not only is she a classy bird, she ain't frightened to get her hands dirty.

One Sunday I suggest a picnic by the river in Bridgnorth, I know this secluded spot. Haven't got much further than a kiss and cuddle. She's hooked alright but seems anxious, her body stiffening, when my hands start straying. Romantic riverside setting, sunny day, perhaps, who knows...

I'm now the proud owner of a provisional licence and some god awful black rimmed spectacles. Still, if it gets me driving this beast of a car, I don't care. Most of the time I'm posing in the passenger seat with my sunglasses on.

"Let me have a drive, got my specs" I wave them under her nose.

"Oh, go on then, but be careful."

We set off to Bridgnorth and walk along the river to where a huge weeping willow tree forms a leafy enclosure. Perfect. Been here before. With the rug lain out on the grass, we munch through the goodies Barb has prepared for our picnic. Never had anything like it, she's even got trifle keeping cool in a kind of icebox.

I'm watching her every move as she packs the wicker basket. "C'mon, leave that." I pat the red tartan.

Barb blushes as she crawls across to lie beside me.

"That's better, relax."

On our backs, hands behind our heads, we watch the willow leaves wafting in the breeze and listen to the rippling water. I recite 'The Glory of the Garden' poem. Seems appropriate. She loves it.

I prop myself up on one elbow. "Nice here isn't it?"

She turns towards me and sighs "wonderful."

I lean over and take her into my arms. The kiss is special, tender and tastes of strawberries. As my tongue finds the inside of her mouth she presses herself against me. I don't need urging twice. My hands are everywhere and there's no dreaded bra to contend with 'cos she don't wear one!

My fingertips sneak along her inner thigh. She catches her breath and stiffens slightly. I crush my lips to hers. The panties are gone and she sort of melts into me as I make her mine. It's deliciously satisfying and I cry out. Not only have I got the bird, I beat the copper to it. She's a virgin.

We're lying side by side, she has her head in the crook of my arm and I'm stroking her hair.

"Hold me," she murmurs.

I'm bursting for a fag and a cuppa but Barb needs reassuring. It's her first time after all. I tighten my grip around her shoulders and she snuggles closer.

Ten minutes later I ease her off me, "Need a fag. Any tea left?"

Barb straightens her skirt; she's studying me hard, "think so... you know who you remind me of?"

Oh no, not this again. I shake my head expecting, somebody, whathisname, actor bloke. Everybody tells me but nobody knows the geezers name.

"Michael Landon, he plays Little Jo in Bonanza."

Well at least I know who it is after all these years. "Good looking is he then?"

She laughs and thumps me on the chest. I scoop her into my arms and shower her with playful kisses. "Now, where's this tea?"

"Why don't we go away, I've got a week's holiday due, what about the week after next?"

269

Don't earn much, haven't saved any. Can I afford it? Barb notices my expression.

"We can go camping, somewhere in Devon, I can get the sleeping bags and a primus stove. It'll be fun."

I've never been camping but it sounds great. I'll have her all to myself for a whole week, plenty of shagging and plenty of showing off in the MG with the hood down. It's late June already so if we don't go soon we'll miss the sun.

"Leave it to me. I'll get hold of a tent. We'll travel on Sunday 'cos if I work some evenings and all day Saturday the brickies will have a few stacks to go at."

I'm driving back and we're almost at Pelsall when a blue flashing light comes up behind. What the fuck!

"Better pull over, nothing to worry about, everything's in order," says Barb smiling.

There may be trouble ahead.

Getting a ticket to produce our documents the copper seems satisfied and off we go. Seven days to D day. Then she'll know I've lied.

No L plates: that's all they can do me for, but she ain't gonna like it. I've probably blown it, again.

Still, during the next seven days we can't get enough of each other, meeting most nights and by the time I confess my 'little white lie' she's a bit cross but willing to forgive me.

I get a fine and endorsement but she gets done for aiding and abetting which is a source of regret 'cos she had taken my word.

Only known her a couple of months and already I've put a blot on her copybook. Just need some L plates on the car, that's all. Next time I see her, she has some stashed in the glove box.

Pearl's finally got her wish and been allocated a brand new Council House in Shireview Road. Three bedrooms, two big living rooms and a kitchen. Backs onto fields an' all. She's made up and so am I 'cos my room here is twice as big and it's nearer to the Ryders Hayes Estate, which is where I'm working.

I want to show Barb off to my mates so suggest a trip to Bilston. She can meet my family and we'll take a drive through the estate, maybe pop into the Table Mountain. The following Saturday she picks me up and off we go.

Most of Chantry Crescent come out to admire the MG. Mom

likes Barb, I can tell. 'A real lady', she tells me. I'm showing my new watch to Roy when he pulls me to one side and says Gordon has been round asking after me. He told Roy he'd phoned Pearl's a couple of times and left messages!

Time to head to the Table Mountain. We can't park outside so I make sure we ride past once or twice before finding a space round the corner.

Opening the door for her, all heads turn as we walk in. Elaine is standing at the Juke Box dressed in a very tight top and short skirt showing her generous curves and leaving little to the imagination.

"Hello Watt, long time no see, heard as you'd got fixed up with a posh bit." Elaine eyes Barb up and down.

There's no sign of Gary. I want to ask her what the fuck she was playing at telling him I'd shagged her while he was in nick but can't really. I manage to muster a smile. "How's your husband?"

"In nick."

I pull out the chair for Barb and Elaine laughs bitterly, "blimey, you've got him well trained luv, never did that for me."

Do I detect a touch of the green eyed monster here? Barb looks at me enquiringly but I try to ignore her gaze and order the drinks.

Elaine won't seem to take the hint and plonks herself at the next table. She wants to chat to Barb who is looking more uncomfortable by the minute. This isn't what I planned at all.

"You wanna watch him luv," Elaine points at me, "get's 'em up the duff and fucks off."

Barb turns a brighter shade of beetroot and Elaine seizes on this. "Bit shy ain't she, not your type Watt." She thrusts her breasts across the table at me. Barb ain't too well endowed in that department and is becoming more crimson by the second. She twists her hair and gazes at the table top.

Rob walks through the door with Maud and their little 'un, not so little now. I introduce Barb and Maud takes to her straight away, they sit chatting, trying to ignore Elaine. I'm just anxious to get out of here; somebody might slip something out about my long prison record, the escape, anything.

"She's a bit out of your league Watt," Rob raises an eyebrow as we stand at the Juke Box.

"Works at a Bank, educated, that's her M.G. on the corner," lowering my voice, "I was the first an' all... if you get my drift."

He laughs and nods. "Done well for yourself mate, don't fuck it up."

As I wait for my order I turn and stand with my elbows resting on the counter, studying Elaine and then Barbara. Elaine was very good in bed, knew *all* the tricks and I'll never forget the fun we had, but she's a tart. My Barb on the other hand is wide eyed and innocent.

Even though she wears short skirts, it's the fashion, there's a big difference, somehow she looks unapproachable, but she's mine.

Glancing across she catches my eye and we smile together, the intimate smile only lovers share.

After tea and toast we swiftly leave the café. This wasn't one of my better ideas. Gordon's on my mind. Been a good mate. He's trying to get hold of me. We're soon parking outside his house behind the two-tone Cresta.

He seems relieved to see me. Wonder what's up. Ushering Barb through to the lounge I collar him and his missus in the kitchen. "Look she don't know anything about, well, you know."

"If you're serious mate you need to tell her. She's gonna find out sooner or later."

I know he's right but I don't want to take the chance of loosing her. "I'm going straight Gord, so I'm not up for anything dodgy."

Gordon sends his missus into the lounge with some tea to keep Barb company. "Rung your Pearl's a few times, heard as you was out and living there. Ain't she give you my messages?"

I shake my head. Pearl's only trying to look after me, I know that. "Well, I'm here now, what's up?"

"Done a few jobs with Russ since he got out. We got copped. I'm on bail now but I'm up at the Quarter Sessions in a couple of months. My Brief says I'll go down for sure."

"What can I do mate?"

"I thought if I go down you could give my missus some money for the car so I know she'll be alright for a bit, help us out like."

We've done stuff together, go back a way, don't know what to say really. "How much would you want then?"

"Hundred, hundred and fifty, it's a good price."

"Look Gord, I'll do my best. If I can't buy it then I'll find somebody who will. Don't worry about your missus."

He smiles, "knew I could rely on you Watt."

With that we join the women and spend a pleasant afternoon. His missus almost slips up chatting about our caravan exploits but Gordon spills his tea at the appropriate moment. Oh, what a tangled web we weave.

Having worked double hard this week, evenings and all day Saturday, I'm knackered but excited about the prospect of our holiday. Barb arrives at Pearl's on Saturday night with the primus stove and camping gear. I've borrowed a tent. Difficult to squeeze it all in, but eventually we're packed and ready for an early start in the morning.

Not long after tea we take a short walk over the common for a quick drink in the Old House at Home. We're back for half nine and to bed!

This is our first night together and the fact that it's only a single bed doesn't matter to either of us.

A whole week of bliss lies ahead. The weather is glorious as we set off and gets better the further south we travel. Half way Barb sets up the primus in a leafy lay-by and we enjoy bacon and eggs. Hey, this camping lark ain't half bad.

I remember North Devon as being pretty; think Barb will like it there so we head in that direction. Along the coast road through Barnstaple and Bideford we follow a sign to Fairy Cross 'cos the name appeals to Barb.

Turning into a grassy field we pull up on a cliff-top with panoramic views of the ocean. Romantic or what? This will definitely do.

Pitch the tent, cup of tea then whiz into Westwood Ho for provisions and pop to a pub so we can wind down, Barb with her orange juice and me with a pint. Need to get back before dark else we'll never find the field again.

Been here three fun-filled days and three fabulous nights now. Everyone notices us tazzing about in the MG as we do a bit of sightseeing. Evenings are spent either walking arm in arm along the cliff-top or in Clovelly before retiring early! It's just about the best time I've had in my life. Turns out it will be the best time for the two of us for quite a while to come.

I awake with a start. Muffled voices outside! There's a myriad of lights playing on the roof of the tent. Barb's asleep in my arms and I gently ease her head off my shoulder.

Atuning my ears I hear a man whisper "surround the tent, wait for my signal."

What the fuck…

Barb is half asleep and rolls over murmuring. I give her a nudge and press my hand over her mouth as she wakes up, wide eyed now. "Sshh," taking my hand away, "there's somebody outside; it might be cops."

We sit and watch the torches surround us. There are beams of light holding steady on all angles of the tent. I've got my arms around Barb who buries her head in my chest. What do they want? There's lots of 'em, at least ten. What if it's not cops but some strange cult, I've read books…

Someone in the field clears their throat, sounds very close, Barb tightens her grip on me and I motion for her to get behind.

"You in the tent, come out with your hands on your head." Sounds like cops to me but I ain't going nowhere 'til I've asked.

"Who are you and what do you want?"

"Armed Police."

Fuck me. Armed Police. What do they think I've done? I'm just on holiday for Christ sake.

"My girlfriend is here with me," I shout.

"Both of you, come out with your hands on your head, you first," the cop commands.

"I'm naked."

"You coming out or have we got to come in and get you? For the last time, come out with your hands on your head."

Nodding at Barb, I crawl to the entrance, untie the loops, step through and stand bollock naked with my hands clasped on top of my head.

I'm blinded by the torch lights as most of them swoop towards me. A couple are still trained on the tent. I can't see a thing. Nobody makes a move.

"Now the girl," shouts the cop looking towards the open tent flaps.

"She's naked! Let her put some clothes on."

"Cover yourself and come out."

Hearing a scuffle behind me I turn my head slightly as Barb emerges wearing tousled hair, smudged mascara and my stripey blue shirt. She looks absolutely terrified as half the guns now train on her.

"Hands on your head," growls the uniform.

Barb starts to walk towards me. "Stay where you are," he yells. She stops dead.

My eyes have become accustomed to the dark and I can see a semicircle of about fifteen cops, some with guns and others with torches, standing about five yards away.

The main man takes a step forward, "Identify yourself."

"Walter Groom and this is my girlfriend, Barbara."

"I have reason to believe you are Ronald Biggs, an escaped prisoner. I will need to see some proof of identity."

Ronald Biggs, he's one of the Great Train Robbers. They think I'm him. No. Are they fuckin' blind or what?

"We have our driving licences," Barb pipes up.

"You," he gestures at her, "get them."

"Go with her" he barks at one of the officers.

Barb crawls into the tent and a gun toting cop sits on his haunches at the entrance watching her every move. They must think we've got a gun.

Another one walks over to the tent and crouches down. "Keep your hands in sight at all times, pass the bag to me."

Barb's holdall lands with a thud at his feet and he starts rooting through the contents.

"In the zip pocket at the side," I hear her say.

"Got one." Pleased with himself the cop hurries to show it to the main man who painstakingly reads every detail by torchlight and nods.

"Where's yours?" comes a shaky plea from inside the tent.

Where the fuck is it? Know I had it. C'mon. C'mon. Can't think straight. I know. "Look in the glovebox of the car."

"Keys" demands the armed cop still crouched by the tent.

"It's not locked."

He moves towards Barb's MG which is parked a few feet away and comes back with my licence. The main man studies it in silence. Standing right in front of me now he looks me up and down, stares at my face and seems to be comparing me with something on a sheet of white paper in his hand. I turn the right side of my face towards him. Surely he must see I have a birthmark and what about my tattoos. The torch flicks back and forth from me to the paper.

"Stand down," he shouts, "it's not him."

The rest of the coppers begin talking amongst themselves; some admiring the car as they cast their torches over it.

"If I were you I'd see the farmer in the morning, drop him a few bob for using his field, you can get milk and eggs off him as well. Poor chap was frightened to approach you."

With that he raises his arm and motions the 'squad' back up the field and away.

Barb's sitting in the tent. She's shivering so I pull her into my arms and we climb into the sleeping bag. Boy do I need a fag and a cuppa. Lighting the primus we get the old brew going.

The rest of the holiday goes without incident. We see the farmer and stay one more day. After that Barb wants to move onto the proper site a couple of miles down the road where we've been taking our showers.

We arrive back late on Sunday and although I want her to stay Barb has to dash home 'cos of work in the morning.

Her folks don't like me at all. Been to their posh house a couple of times and seen the way they look at my tattoos. It's even worse now 'cos somehow they've found out I've been to prison. Pearl must have told Ann and she must have told her parents.

Barb doesn't make a scene but is a bit upset and wants me to tell her the full story. Can't think she'd want to stay with me if I did, so I soften the edges, saying I did a bit of thieving once and got nicked. She believes in me and says everyone is entitled to *one* mistake, as long as I've learned my lesson! One mistake… if only she knew.

Poor old Ann gets it in the neck from her parents because she's the one who introduced us at the party. They blame her for years to come.

It isn't long before the inevitable happens. Well, I never did like using those wretched johnnies and Barb is so naïve, probably doesn't even know they exist. Me, I'm just selfish. I want what I want and that's it.

I'm waiting on the steps of the cinema in Walsall. We go to the pictures every Wednesday night. She's late tonight. I check my watch. Normally Barb would come running up and throw her arms around my neck. I'd span her tiny waist with my hands and plant a kiss on those sweet tasting lips.

I can tell by her face there is something terribly wrong. Tonight there's no smile and her eyes never leave the pavement as she approaches.

"Let's go to the café instead," she's standing at the bottom of the steps . This is it. She's gonna dump me. Knew it. "Tea?"

Barb nods and slides onto a seat in the quiet corner. Usually we'd sit near the window.

"I'm late," her eyes bore into mine.

Takes me a second to get her drift. Late? Only a couple of minutes. No, she doesn't mean that sort of late. *Late.*

"I'm pregnant!"

My grin almost splits my face in two. "A baby, my baby," I jump up and punch the air. Several couples look across and laugh.

Barb's face breaks into a smile. "I thought you'd dump me."

I gather her into my arms and shower kisses all over her sweet, beautiful face, "dump you? I love you."

She looks taken aback for a minute, "it's alright then?"

Phew. I need a fag.

"I'll look after you, don't worry. We'll get married, yes?"

"Yes" her eyes shine, she's excited and happy now.

"I'll get us a place, it'll be great," I promise.

"Don't think Mom and Dad will give permission."

She's right, they won't. We'll have to wait until she's 21. A few weeks later I'm telling one of the plumbers on site about it. He knows a couple who went to Gretna Green. Don't need permission there. Long as you've got your birth certificates, he tells me, and stay in the vicinity for three days, you can be married. Perfect.

Barb wants to get away from home. Her folks are making life miserable, so together we hatch a plan. She books two weeks holiday at at the Bank and I tell the brickies I'm getting married. Brilliant feeling. At last I can get settled with my own wife and family.

Need to start looking for a place to live. Barb earns £20 a week at the Bank which is good wages. With what I pick up we can rent a nice little flat.

I nip home to tell Mom the good news. She likes Barb and thinks it's the best thing that's happened to me. Walking up town to catch the bus I'm lost in my own little world, making plans, when a sideways glance stops me dead in my tracks. I'd know that hair and those legs anywhere.

It's Susie.

Our eyes meet and we stand on opposite pavements momentarily before she runs across, her dark hair swinging from side to side. She smiles. I step back.

Her blue eyes search mine. "Hello Watt."

"Hello yourself, how you keepin' then?"

I feel awkward. We're like two strangers. It's been a long time.

"I'm alright," she looks at the cracks in the paving stones, her smile gone. "You never got back in touch." A sort of accusation.

"No, never seemed like the right time," sounds a bit lame.

"Going for a cuppa?"

We're not a million miles from the Table Mountain but I need to get home 'cos I'm seeing Barb tonight. I shake my head "sorry, catching the bus."

"Oh, I see. Duncan died you know. Wasn't long after I saw you that time."

"Can't say as I'm sorry."

"I waited but you never..." she falters, "I sent you messages," her eyes are watering now.

"Messages?" I certainly never got 'em, she's making this up.

"I thought...well...you know...you wanted us to be together. I told Rosie."

"I ain't seen Rosie in years."

"She used to come in the dress shop. Said she'd ask Elaine to tell you, 'cos you were still in touch with her sometimes."

I shake my head. That cow Elaine. She never told me nothing. In fact I remember asking her about Susie and she denied all knowledge.

"Been in nick. Only got out a few months back."

"I'd have waited for you, you know that don't you?"

"Yes." I nod 'cos it's true, she would have. "You seeing anyone?" As soon as the words leave my lips I know it's the wrong thing to say. Her face brightens immediately and she shakes her head vigorously. Oh no. Felt sure she would be re-married by now or have a boyfriend at least.

"I was, but not any more."

Need to put things straight. "I'm getting married soon."

Susie's face drops, "I meant it when I said I loved you, I always have and I always will," her sad blue eyes are misting over as they search mine.

My bus is coming. "Nice seeing you again Susie, I've gotta go."

The biggest guilt feeling I've ever experienced overtakes me as I hop onto the bus, force a smile and wave. She's trying hard not to cry, I can see that, her chest heaves as she takes some deep breaths and looks away. Teardrops flood her eyes and tumble down her cheeks.

Can't bear this but can't bear to take my eyes off her either. Our eyes hold each other, mine from the backseat and hers from the pavement as she stands there, a forlorn figure. What might have been, what will never be. A final glimpse, she disappears from sight. I never set eyes on her again.

The week of our planned elopement finally dawns. This time next week I'll be a married man with responsibilities. All I want to do is look after Barb and the baby. Pearl has said we can stay with her for a couple of weeks after we're married 'til we sort out a flat of our own.

We spend a few days at Pearl's together before setting off. Barb confides in her Sister and they take a trip into town to buy a special frock and shoes.

Our bags are packed and we're ready to go. Her folks will have to accept me now. We need to get copy birth certificates so head to Wolverhampton first, for mine.

An hour later I'm walking out waving it in the air. We're happy and laughing, L plates on, I'm driving and Barb's directing me to West Bromwich where we'll get hers. She emerges from the Registry Office wearing a big grin and clutching the certificate.

Shoving it in the glove box on top of mine, Barb pulls a map from behind the seat. "I've planned the route, I'll navigate, you drive," she leans across to kiss me, a smile just for each other, I squeeze her hand and we're off.

"That's where I work, look," Barb points to an imposing building on the corner. "fancy a liquorice?" she always keeps some for me in the side pocket.

I nod and check the rear view mirror. Blue flashing lights are converging. Inwardly smiling, got the old L plates on, they ain't after me. Thinking they'll pass I carry on blithely. Barb throws the liquorice and laughs as I catch it in my mouth. I'm on top of the world.

My heart goes cold when one cop car swerves in front while the other blocks us behind.

Fuck me, what's going on?

"Step out of the car," says the uniform.

Keep calm. Don't panic. "What's wrong officer?"

"This car has been reported stolen. I am arresting you on suspicion…"

Stolen? What's he on about?

"This car belongs to me, it's not stolen" Barb is indignant in the passenger seat.

"Step out of the car please," another uniform opens the passenger door and Barb gets out.

I'm handcuffed and frogmarched to one of the cop cars. Still protesting my innocence I see Barb being led to another. At least they ain't handcuffed her. She looks across and mouths 'don't worry'.

Cops don't worry me but I have this horrible gut feeling she's going to find out the full truth about me and my past.

I'm held in the cells and sit worrying. This is like a bad dream. If they've put her into a cell I'll swing for somebody.

Eventually I'm released without charge. The car isn't stolen. It was a ploy by her folks to get us picked up. Well, I could have told them that!

None of the cops will tell me where Barb is or what's happening. I wait outside but they move me on.

Leaning against the wall on the opposite corner I can see both entrances. I know she's still in there 'cos her Dad's car is parked on the side street and the MG sits inside the gates of the police compound.

I'm bound to spot her when she comes out.

Half an hour later there's some movement at the rear entrance. Barb's mother gets into the MG and drives through the gates. Keeping her eyes firmly fixed straight ahead she doesn't give me a second glance.

Barb appears with her Dad. The tearstained face stares bleakly at the tarmac. He bundles her into the back of his car and drives past at speed.

I give chase, right up the middle of the High Street, dodging the traffic and shouting for him to stop. She hears me and turns. Her hands are on the rear window. She's sobbing and calling my name.

Three hours ago we were the happiest couple in the world. No way are they going to keep us apart. As the car speeds into the distance I stop running and stand in the centre of the road, oblivious to the screeching tyres and tooting horns.

I raise my hand and walk slowly to the pavement. If they want a fight, they've got one. I won't give up, *never*. That's my girl and she's carrying my baby.

Chapter 19

ANOTHER DAY, ANOTHER SHILLING

Glancing at my watch in the moonlight I can just make out the time.

One thirty. I've been waiting in this gulley behind Barb's parent's house for hours, pacing up and down and pretending to tie my shoelaces if a car drives past to access the garages.

What am I doing here? Don't know myself. Am I going to storm the bastion? They'd just call the cops. Suppose there's a vain hope Barb will come to me. This is where we've sat in her car and talked for hours on end when I needed to be with her 'til the last possible second, even though it meant missing the last bus and a two hour walk back to Pelsall.

The house has been in total darkness since eleven o'clock. I thought one of the curtains twitched about half an hour ago, but nothing since. What do I expect of her? She's pregnant, only eighteen, been cosseted all her life, what have I got to offer? Nothing, sweet F.A. that's what.

Turning up my collar against the cool night air and looking down the deserted gulley, this is me then, on my lonesome, might as well make a track.

I'll try phoning tomorrow. If only I could speak to her…

Was that a click? I listen again. Sounds like footsteps, hardly discernable but definitely hesitant footsteps.

Slowly the back gate creaks open and Barb's face peers through. My whole world lights up as she smiles at me. Taking the small case from her hand I gently ease the gate shut.

My heart does somersaults as we kiss. She pulls away, "we need to get going. They could wake up any minute and find me gone."

"What about the car?"

"Forget the car, they think you're only interested in me because of the MG They're going to sell it."

The bastards. I like the car, can't deny it made me feel good, all the posing. But that doesn't matter, nothing matters, only Barb and the baby.

She's studying me now. I've hesitated. I can see it in her eyes, "I don't want to go back," she looks towards the gate.

I pull her to me. "I love you… and the little 'un," I pat her tummy. "We'll stay at Pearls 'til we get a flat. It'll be alright."

We kiss. A passionate kiss that stirs me but there's something else, a fierce protective urge as I take her hand and set off. It's a long walk to Pelsall and we take a break on Barr Beacon.

Her head fits like a comfy glove as she nestles into my shoulder and I pull her closer. We're made for each other. She's stolen my heart. Even though it's chilly a warm glow spreads inside me. On this grassy knoll, as dawn comes up on the horizon, we make our future plans.

Barb shares her experiences of the cop shop and explains how they took her fingerprints. Somehow, I know what's coming next.

"Are there things you need to tell me?" she asks, her head not leaving the crook of my shoulder.

The police have certainly made Barb aware of my past in *all* its shabby glory. Bit of a shock seeing as how she thought I'd done a bit of thieving and gone to prison once. Now she wants to know everything and sits quietly as I recount tales of Rochester, Shrewsbury, my escape, Strangeways and Durham. "You sure you've left nothing out this time?"

"Nothing," I breathe the sweet smell of her and my body fills with warmth as we kiss. I'm relieved that she knows. "I'm going straight and I won't let you down."

"I love you," she murmurs and shivers. It's cold so I slip out of my jacket and wrap it round her shoulders for the rest of our trek.

Couple of days later there's a bit of a scene at Pearl's when Barb's parents arrive but she tells them she's not going home and eventually they leave. We decide to live at Pearl's until we've saved enough deposit for a private flat.

Barb will have to catch two buses to her job in West Bromwich and gets up earlier than me on her first day back. "Don't know how long it will take me to get home," she sounds apologetic whilst I lie on the bed watching her get ready. Never seen her dressed for work before. All smart in a black suit with a knee length skirt. It's what's underneath that grabs my attention though, stockings and suspenders. Does it for me. I try to pull her into bed but she laughs and pushes me off.

Finishing work at four, a short stroll brings me to our Pearl's where I saunter up the path, whistling, and feeling happy. Wonder what's to eat? The instant my feet step over the threshold I see Barb's handbag on the hall table. Something's wrong.

I find her in the back living room. She's sitting on the sofa staring at the fireplace with unseeing eyes. My stomach hits the floor. Oh no, not the baby. Please God, not the baby.

Pearl motions me though, shoves a cuppa in my hand and closes the door.

"I've lost my job."

I'm stunned but relieved. "What happened?"

"The Police went to the Bank after the MG was reported stolen," she studies her teacup, "they know about you being my boyfriend, though what it's got to do with them I don't know. Perhaps they think you want to rob the place. Anyway they asked me to resign, so I did."

This is a blow. It will take us a lot longer to save a deposit.

"I'm going to start showing soon then nobody will take me on," Barb looks anxious, her eyes searching mine. "I can work right up to a month before the birth. I'll register with an agency or something."

A week after this bombshell another one drops. My brickies have an argument with the main contractor over their cheque, down tools and move to another site, somewhere the other side of Lichfield. No way can I get there every day, so I'm fucked.

Gotta get some work, and quick. Barb's been luckier. One of the agencies has come up with a perfect job. A missus of mine working at the Magistrates Court! Never thought I'd see the day. She goes for interview and walks it. Good money, better than the Bank.

We manage to find a small ground floor flat in Tettenhall, a sort of bed-sit with a kitchen, in a large mansion type house. It looks very grand from the outside. Well, I've got to try and keep her in the style to which she is accustomed.

Part furnished they said! In reality it has a mattress on the floor, one chair, a three bar electric fire and an electric cooker with only two rings working. What it doesn't have would make a longer list, including curtains. The bathroom, shared with three other flats, is upstairs at the end of a long hallway.

We've got next to nothing when we move in; a tin opener, two plates and mugs, a bowl, couple of spoons, two old pillows and a blanket. I nick a fork from the chippie which they use for the pickled onions and that's it.

Everything needs cleaning and the shared bathroom is gross, so finding an old brush under the sink, I make a start by scrubbing it out on the first day.

One thing we have got is hot water from a sort of heater over the kitchen sink.

Something is whirring like the clappers…it's the electricity meter! Every half hour I'm feeding it money.

We don't have a wardrobe for our clothes. Underwear is kept in Barb's case and the rest is folded in piles on the scrubbed floorboards.

Barb gets home from work at half past five and I've got a loaf of bread and a tin of baked beans, which we heat up in the tin. Laughable, but true.

I'd got chatting to a bloke in the newsagents this afternoon who said they were looking for drivers at the Gas Works. The long walk into town paid off and I'm so busy with my own news of a job to start on Monday that I don't notice Barb's a bit down.

She's sitting on my lap stroking my hair and I'm gabbling on about how nice we can make this place. Putting her fingers to my lips, she leans down and kisses me.

I look into her eyes. "What's up?"

"They told me today my job is conditional upon passing a medical in six weeks time."

"So?"

"The baby silly, they'll know I'm pregnant. Not going to offer me a permanent position are they?"

"Suppose not," I puff out my cheeks.

"I'll work the six weeks, get a bit of money, then I'll have to make an excuse and leave."

My job at the Gas Works is long hours and poor pay but I quite enjoy it. Don't need a full licence because I'm only driving inside the compound. Trouble is my clothes stink of Gas and it makes Barb throw up.

It doesn't take long to dawn on me that on my wages alone we can't afford this flat. The electricity meter eats coins. My workmate's Mom lives in Castlecroft and she has a caravan in her back garden. He says she is willing to rent it to us.

Just before Christmas we move in. Much better equipped with all the bedding, crockery, cutlery and Barb likes the pretty curtains. Great, it's got a television too.

I've heard the local bakery is looking for casual night-workers. With Barb having to leave her job we need every penny. I'm determined to get some shifts.

And so it is I work six days a week at the Gas Works and two nights at the bakery. When I go to work on Friday morning I don't see Barb again until Sunday morning, going straight from one job to the other. Sunday's I tend to sleep all day and the treadmill starts all over again.

One perk of working nights at the Bakery is that we get loads of cheap bread and cakes. Always buy as much as I can and sell it on for a few coppers extra.

Our first Christmas Day as a couple finds me at the Gas Works from 8.am to 6pm 'cos it's double time. Barb decorates the caravan by making some streamers out of a roll of sellotape and old bread wrappers. I get home at half past six and she's cooked two pork chops with all the trimmings.

Boxing Day is my one day off so we head over to Pearl's on three buses. Feel's more like Christmas, what with the tree and everything. She cooks us a lovely turkey dinner and fruity pud with lashings of custard. Her friend with a car, who lives three doors away, is going to give us a lift back.

We're just saying our goodbyes when Pearl blurts out, "Gordon phoned for you last week. He sounded a bit desperate."

Dashing back in…what was his number? Racking my brains, eventually it comes to me. After exchanging seasonal pleasantries he tells me his date for Quarter Sessions has come through for mid February. I give him the telephone number of the old lady in the house who let's us use her phone in emergencies.

I promised. Can't let him down. Like it or not, we're buying a Vauxhall Cresta for one hundred pounds. All I need to do now is get the money to pay for it. One thing's for sure, it won't be by working for a pittance at the Gas Works or the Bakery, barely pays enough to survive.

Barb is doing her best eking out the money and buying 'bottom drawer' stuff each week ready for our own place. It's kept in a big box under the bed.

On top is a list she's made of what we'll need and very few items have the 'red' line marked through. In the not too distant future we'll have to start buying baby stuff as well.

This caravan will be no good for a newborn. It's so, so cold in the mornings and condensation drips everywhere.

Barb's got a job as a Clerk at a factory on the outskirts of town but looks glum and doesn't talk about it much. Apparently blokes on the factory floor whistle at the office girls and make lewd remarks as they walk through. Barb has only ever worked in a professional environment where that sort of thing doesn't happen. Putting on a brave face she sticks it out. "I have to wear a loose smock overall. We all do. It'll mean nobody will notice as I get bigger."

I nod agreement but I'm not happy about some loud mouth bastard making smutty remarks at my Barb, it makes me angry. I'm not having it. "Give 'em a week's notice," I tell her. I'll think of something.

She refuses point blank. "If we both work we'll get somewhere, it's the only way."

I'm trying to go straight, literally working myself into the ground but I can't face a lifetime of this. My mind wrestles with itself day by day. The wrong side comes out on top. Fuck it. We need money so I'll get us some.

Barb has talked to me at length, saying we have to earn our money honestly and stealing from people who have worked for it, just like us, is really bad.

Can't argue with that. Wouldn't rob off ordinary folk anyway. Never have and never will. Just the rich bastards who can actually afford insurance, they get it back anyhow. It's a sort of justification. Misguided, but a justification all the same.

There's another driver at the Gas Works, Larry, bit of a wide boy, he's got the old prison tattoos on his hands an' all. Tell 'em a mile off. We get chatting and he remembers me, was in Shrewsbury when I escaped. Small world.

Gordon's Court date is approaching. I'll just do the one job, set us straight, buy Gordon's car, the baby gear and put a deposit on a nice flat. That's it then. Finito.

Barb thinks I'm doing a double shift. Don't want to lie to her again but feel there's no other way. From the Gas Works I go home with Larry. He's got a mate with a van and a shop lined up on the Birmingham New Road.

Apparently it's full to the rafters with fags and booze and he's got a buyer who'll take the lot, no questions asked. No dogs, no bells, no watchman, sounds too good to be true.

I'm in business, alive again, body and mind on high alert, the old adrenalin rush is back as we jemmy the back door and four of us form a human chain from shop to van.

Next morning I'm looking at one hundred and seventy five pounds, my share of the black market value. Not too sure it's been divided up equally but hey, who cares, I'm out of a hole. Trouble is I've earned more in an hour than I can pick up working double shifts for a month!

Now I've got another problem. How can I suddenly come into money without Barb being suspicious? Lies lead to more lies. It's a never-ending spiral once it starts.

Four days later the old lady comes rushing down the path to our caravan, she's breathless. "A lady on the phone, says it's urgent, something about her husband." She pulls me to one side, "I think your friend may have died. I didn't want to say anything because of your wife's condition."

Of course the old lady thinks me and Barb are married. Unmarried mothers are frowned upon and considered the lowest of the low. Barb has taken to wearing a ring we bought in Woolworths for two bob.

Inwardly I smile. Don't know what Gordon's missus has said to the old dear but when I pick up the receiver she's crying and tells me Gordon got four years. "Can you come for the car tonight?" she asks.

I make my way to the caravan and an anxious 'wife'. "You're not going out again," Barb pulls a face, "I get frightened here on my own at night, thought you weren't doing any more night shifts."

"I'll only be gone a couple of hours. Watch the tele or read your book."

The Cresta runs just as I remember it. Still a nice looking car. Being two- tone it's eye-catching and pulls admiring glances. I hand over the money and shoot back to the caravan. A big grin spreads across my face. Barb will be pleased with this. How wrong can a man be?

She's standing with her hands on her hips glaring at me. "This car belonged to your friend, what was his name, Gordon wasn't it?"

A few seconds ago I'd been happier than I've been for ages, the car has given me a lift but I'm frowning now.

"And you've driven it on your own, without L plates, without proper insurance?"

Deep down I know she's right. I shouldn't have taken a chance. "So fuckin' what?" I slam the car door and storm into the caravan.

Barb is hot on my heels. "Where did you get the money from, we can't afford bus fare let alone a car, we need to save up, what possessed you?"

All these questions. Nag, nag, nag. Not only does she want to try and change the way I speak, always telling me not to drop my 'H's' and moaning every time I leave the toilet seat up, now she wants to deny me a bit of pleasure. I need a fag and a cuppa. I'm sulking. Our first real tiff. No woman is going to tell *me* what I can and can't do. I've been told what to do and when to do it for the last fifteen fuckin' years. Had enough of that thank you very much. We don't speak for the rest of the evening.

Rather pointedly she pulls out her box from under the bed and stares at the list. I know the hundred pounds would have bought all them things on her list.

I'm angry with myself but I grab it and rip the paper into tiny shreds. Her dismayed face crumples into tears as I laugh, a harsh hollow laugh, and switch on the television.

I turn the sound up, knowing full well it's disturbing her. She scowls at me over the top of her book. Who will be the first to break? Not me. I roll another fag. The ashtray is full of dog-ends. I've smoked one after the other knowing how much she hates it. Out of the corner of *my* eye I watch her watching me out of the corner of *her* eye. Do I detect a sparkle? My eyes soften and hers crinkle. We break into a fit of laughter at the same time and fall into each others arms.

I promise to insure the car and put in for my driving test. Telling Barb I've had a pay rise at the Gas Works she goes shopping for maternity clothes. Her hours have been cut at the factory offices but

I'm not sorry and would rather she packed it in altogether. One of the older ladies has sussed the pregnancy but helps cover it up.

Barb visits her parents on the odd occasion. I drop her at the top of the road and kill an hour in the local pub. They don't want to see me. I don't want to see them either, so it works both ways. Barb needs to talk to her Mom, especially being pregnant an' all but it always seems to end in tears. She's asking them again tonight for permission to get married.

Baby is due at the end of June. It is springtime and light nights as I sit smoking and waiting a few yards from the house. Barb comes rushing out of the gate in tears. If they keep upsetting her like this I ain't bringing her again.

She climbs into the passenger seat as the engine purrs into life. "What is it this time?"

Already they've tried to bribe her with a new car, another horse, you name it. Why can't they just accept me, accept the fact we love each other?

"Want me to consider adoption for the baby. Mom says it's for the best. Dad says you'll never be able to provide for us."

What right have they got? This is *my* baby they're talking about. We want to get married but they still won't give permission. Provide? I'll show 'em who can provide.

Larry's got another job planned.

He's heard as I can crack safe's and knows where there's one for the taking. Easy access, big house, out towards Stafford. On Friday morning I tell Barb that I'll see her tomorrow after my nightshift at the Bakery. She'll be expecting some bread and cakes. Must remember to nip and buy some on the way home so she won't suspect anything.

At the end of the path I glance at Barb. She stands on the steps to the caravan, blows me a kiss, smiles and disappears inside. In another half hour she'll be locking the door and making her way to work. Not for much fuckin' longer. This time next week we'll be tucked up in a cosy warm flat with no dripping condensation and surrounded by all that stuff on her ever increasing list.

It's a normal day at the Gas Works except that today I'm driving the wagon round with a big stupid grin on my face. Towards knockin' off time Larry gives me a wave from his wagon and my pulse begins to race. He tells me more about the job as I drive him home. The lookout with a car has deafed it at the last minute. This means we need to use mine. I shrug my shoulders. No other option is there.

Setting off a bit late for my liking, its eleven thirty, I drive towards Stafford following Larry's directions. Seems a long way. By twelve thirty we're sitting opposite a very large house in a country lane. Trouble is the place looks like Blackpool illuminations, every light is on, music blaring, voices, laughter. They're having a fuckin' party!

I punch the steering wheel. No way am I going back empty handed. Need this money, well not necessarily *this* money. Heading through Stafford and into Wolverhampton, me and Larry decide to do a bit of ad-hoc burglary. Pick a quiet, leafy Avenue, house in darkness, take pot luck.

Cutting the engine and lights I glide to a halt. The Avenue has trees along the pavement, a sure sign of prosperity. Big sweeping drives lead temptingly to sprawling black and white timbered houses. This is more like it. This is what I want for me and Barb one day.

Larry keeps look out. Patting my pocket to check the 'equipment', I clamber over the six foot timber gate which gives access to a manicured back garden. Noticing how neat everything is, all the shrubs and small trees stand like soldiers, gently swaying in the wind, my eyes search for any open windows. A top-light which is not quite flush and patterned glass without drainage underneath means it's probably a pantry or cloaks cupboard.

My finger sneaks through and pushes up the latch. The wire is inserted and wends its way to the bottom stay. Once that's hooked it swings open and I'm into a cloakroom full of fancy coats. Rifling through the pockets I transfer the monetary contents of a wallet, about fifty pounds, grab an empty shopping bag and move on.

The hallway is square and spacious. Moonlight shines through fancy glass on the front door making patterns on the polished wooden floor. I listen intently for a few moments before creeping through an open door into the largest lounge I've ever seen, and I've seen a few.

Silverware gleams from every corner and it soon finds a new home in my shopping bag. One piece clinks against another and I hold my breath. All quiet. I take the bag and lower it to the ground through the cloakroom window.

My eye is taken by a pretty silver bangle lying on the hall table as I make my way back to the lounge. Into my pocket it goes.

Gently, very gently I ease open the cabinet drawers, switch on my torch and start scanning the contents. I stop dead. Was that a car? My heart stops beating.

Slowly, I inch my way to the lounge window and peer through. Can't see anything, come to that can't see Larry either. Where the fuck is he? The stupid bastard is supposed to be keeping watch.

There's movement by the hedge. Shadowy figures crouch low. A car without lights glides slowly past. In a flash I'm head first through the cloakroom window and doing a forward roll. My foot catches the bag of loot. Silverware clatters and clinks as it spills onto the slabs around me.

Like lightening I'm ditching the incriminating 'going equipped' stuff and legging it across the back garden and through to the next and the next. No more gardens. A road. Stop running. Look natural. A cop car hurtles round the corner and screeches to a halt. Four uniforms surround me.

I'm trying hard to appear bemused. "What's wrong Officer?" Well, they can't do me for just taking a walk.

One uniform cuffs me while another carries out a search of my pockets. The bangle, the fuckin' silver bangle. How could I have been so dumb? I'm arrested and taken to Bilston cop shop. No sign of Larry. He's got clean away.

Turns out the posh house had a telephone in the bedroom. They'd heard something and called the cops.

This is one of the longest nights of my life. What will Barb think? Will she stand by me? What about the baby? Bet her parents think they've won. She's bound to go home.

I'm *questioned* on Saturday morning. Who am I working with? How many other jobs have I done? There are lots of tic's they want me to admit. A savage punch to my gut has left me aching all afternoon. Lost my appetite. I sit on the bed and, head in hands, stare into the nothingness of the concrete floor.

Late Saturday afternoon old Flanagan comes to my cell, "got a visitor for you Watt."

I stand up as a tearful Barb walks in. Oh thank you sweet Jesus. Flanagan gives me one of those father figure sort of looks and says he'll leave the door open as I envelop her into my arms. Leave the door open, that's a first!

Wrenching herself free, she lowers her gaze. "Is it true? Tell me it isn't."

I take hold of her hands and she raises her face. Our eyes meet. What can I say? "I did it for us."

She shakes her head, "don't tell me that. You promised. Remember?"

Yes, of course I remember. "I know I've let you down but I won't do it again." What if she dumps me, I'll never see her again, never set eyes on my baby.

"How can I believe your promises? You keep breaking them," pulling her hands free she stands with her back to me. "No more lies, that's what you said."

I've got to persuade her to wait for me. It's not looking good. Her tone is accusing and the body language distant.

Ever the practical one, "have you got a Solicitor?"

I nod, my old faithful Solicitor, has an office round the corner. He'll be here on Monday. Another day, another shilling for him. Another day, end of my life for me.

Chapter 20

THE SILENT PROMISE

I know bail won't be forthcoming, not with my record, but my pay-packet from the Gas Works is still in my jacket. Least I can do is ask the Custody Sergeant, Flanagan, if Barb can have it. She'll need some money to sort herself out.

Barb turns and takes a deep breath, trying to hold back her tears. "Mrs. Harris wants us out. The Police came to search the van this morning," she clings to me burying her head in my chest, "it was horrible."

My arms close tightly around her. She's crying but I'm smiling. Everything will be alright. There is still an 'us'. That's all I wanted to hear.

"Look, I'll ask Flanagan to give you my wages and the keys to the car which will be in the compound. You go to Pearls. Yes?"

What have I done? I'm here again in these four walls, frustrated, angry, powerless. Fuckin' idiot.

Old Flanagan comes back all too soon. I ask him and then plead with him to make sure Barb gets my pay packet. He smiles at her. "C'mon my dear, I'll see what I can do."

Monday afternoon and my Solicitor calls to see me. Suppose I'm keeping somebody happy, he seems chirpy. "Guilty plea then, get it over?"

I nod. He sighs. We go through the paperwork and he's just leaving as Flanagan brings Barb to the cell. My Solicitor does a double take. "Is this your girlfriend?"

"Yes Sir, this is Barbara." I'm proud to introduce her.

"Why didn't you say anything about all this?"

What does he mean…all this? Then it dawns. Of course, the baby, our baby.

"Makes a big difference. Mitigation. Might be able to get you a lesser sentence. Are you getting married?"

"Her parents won't give permission."

"Gets better, the Magistrates will love it, struggle and strife," he winks at me. "I'll be back tomorrow and you can fill me in with the details." He turns to Barb. "When is the baby due?"

"30ᵗʰ June."

"Your case is listed for hearing on Friday. No point in a bail application at this stage but we can try for it then. They'll either remit the case to Crown Court or put it off for reports. If we go to Crown Court be prepared not to get bail." With that he's gone. Barb doesn't really know what he's just said but I do.

The case will go to Crown Court if the Magistrates feel I should get a longer sentence than they have the power to give. If it's adjourned for reports then I might just get a short sentence or even Probation. As I've never been lucky enough to get either of the latter my feeling of gloom and despondency deepens.

Barb seems more relaxed. The radio she brought for me has too many wavelengths and Flanagan tells her to bring a more basic one.

"I've moved out of the caravan and taken our stuff to your sister's. Pearl says I can stay."

Visits in police cells are short and only old Flanagan gives us extra time and leaves the door open when Barb visits, which she does every day. I'm worried, really worried, that I'll get a lengthy sentence, well, lets face it, all my sentences right from the start have been either three or four years. How will she cope with a baby on her own? I've fucked everything up.

We've talked it through. "I love you and I'll wait for you," she reassures me. Outwardly my face smiles but inwardly, deep inside my heart, a cruel voice tells me, 'they all say that.'

"She seems a nice girl," old Flanagan comments on Thursday, which is the last day before Court, "do right by her. If you walk tomorrow I don't want to see you in here again."

Barb has brought me my best Italian suit, a crisp white shirt and stripy tie so as to make a smart impression. Fuck me. I'm better dressed than my Brief!

After the guilty plea he moves onto mitigation, saying as how I want to wipe the slate clean, make a fresh start. The Magistrates seem well impressed when Barb takes the witness stand. I'm bowled over as she tells them, unfaltering, in a clear strong voice about the baby, our plans to be married once she comes of age and her faith in my ability not to commit further offences.

The Magistrates grant bail and put my sentencing off for reports. We rush into each others arms. This might be a chance for me. Three weeks later I'm given twelve months Probation. Only have to report regularly and keep my nose clean. It's a breeze. Relief washes over me. I'm fit to burst and plant a smackeroo on Barb as we race down the courthouse steps. Freedom, I'm gonna grab it with both hands.

Barb books me a driving test and says I ought to have a couple of lessons beforehand, because I'm self taught. Nah, I can do it. My failure comes as a bit of a shock. But I've been driving big wagons!!

I've lost my job at the Gas Works, not because of what happened but because they closed it, just like that, gone, capput. Barb is still working at the factory but can't continue much longer, less than a month to the birth.

Scouring the newspaper for jobs there's a big box staring at me from the middle of the page. £23 a week, Night-shift, Delta Metal, West Bromwich. Not too many turn up for the open interviews and I'm offered one of four vacancies. The job involves testing sample metal pieces visually and on a machine for any faults such as cracks or ripples.

In the same paper I'd seen a three storey, two bed town house for rent close to West Bromwich. Brand new, good location, all mod. cons. £8 a week. It backs onto a beautiful park, has something called a waste disposal unit and all white goods are included. State of the art, an absolute dream, what a place.

Got the job, got the house. I'll show 'em. We're gonna live like kings. Probation Officer will be pleased too.

When Barb gets back from work I whisk her over to see our new home. I'm so excited. We move in double quick, she quits her job and starts sewing curtains and stuff that women do. Ann, Pearl and their mates chip in with some odd bits of furniture and Moggie collects it in his van.

Barb tells me she's frightened on her own at night, probably because there's nothing but fields opposite and a park behind so I go to the local pound for a dog. Not one of my better ideas as it turns out.

A loveable young Boxer jumps on me and licks my hand. Well, it's more of a slobber really. I'm putty in his paws!

We call him Cassius, Cass for short. He's a good watch and barks at anything that moves but is very boisterous. It costs me a fortune every time we go for a walk 'cos he loves to play, especially with footballs or kiddie's toys. And there's no holding him if he spots a cat!

29th June 1967 and Barb starts her labour pains mid-afternoon. I'm frantic and want to take her to hospital straight away but we wait until they are every five minutes.

She's registered at Hallam Hospital in West Bromwich for the birth as Miss Baker and they won't allow me to stay. The nurses look down their noses at her. Their attitude is clear by the way they speak to us.

Barb's mother strides into the waiting area as I'm on the verge of leaving. Stern faced and tight tipped, she ignores me but I manage to catch a glimpse of Barb and a flash of turquoise as a nurse ushers her through

A few minutes later I'm outside lighting a fag when she rushes past towards her car. Barb has told me she'll do this thing on her own, and she will. I want to be there to hold her hand but it's not to be. To see your child born is wonderful and something I experience first hand the following year.

To keep my mind occupied I go to work as usual and next morning the Hospital beckons. Am I a proud Dad or what? No, not yet. A difficult and long labour. I sit in the Cresta and pop in every couple of hours.

"A baby boy, 9lb.12oz," the nurse announces sourly, "mother and baby are doing fine."

They won't let me see Barb or the baby 'cos we're not married. Discharge is in seven days, all being well. In between times I nip home to tell Mom and take my brothers out for a drink. We have to wet the baby's head. It's a tradition.

What's he like? What colour are his eyes? I can only tell 'em the weight. A big 'un according to Mom. On the seventh day I'm waiting, straight off my night shift.

"What time's discharge then?"

"It's certainly not *this* early, come back at eleven o'clock."

Barb appears at the Hospital doors with a bundle in one arm and her case in the other. Carefully, very carefully I take our baby in my arms. A tiny scrap with light hair and tightly shut eyes. I bend and kiss his forehead, this little part of me. Never felt so proud. Feel like this glow inside has taken over my whole being and will burst out of me any second.

I'm dying to show Barb the baby gear I've bought while she's been in hospital and throw open the front door. Cass bounds down the stairs to greet us, tail wagging, wanting to smell our bundle of joy. A big boisterous dog and a tiny new born are not the best combination.

"You'll have to put Cass in the garage," yells Barb turning her back on him. He's jumping up trying to get a sniff of the little 'un. Yanking his collar I drag him into the 'dog house' and his yelps can be heard for at least twenty minutes. Now it's just me, Barb and…"have you thought of a name?"

Barb smiles. "Only if you like it though. Jason".

It'll do for me. Anything she wants. I watch them both as she lays him carefully into his pretty yellow trimmed crib which sits proudly on the wooden floor by the fire. A silent promise. I won't ever let you down.

Drinking a cuppa, we sit watching him sleep, mesmerized by his every movement, gurgle or yawn.

In bed later, with the crib at my side, Barb tells me that the Adoption Agency had visited the Hospital trying to get her to sign over our baby. "They wouldn't believe you were going to stand by me. Went on and on. Anyway, I kept saying no, I wouldn't sign and that's that. They didn't come back."

Pulling her close she snuggles into my shoulder. "Oh, I've missed this," she murmurs. I've missed her too. My hand strays onto her milk laden breasts. She laughs and pushes me away. "Not for another six weeks."

Her parents finally relent and give permission for us to marry. Ann tells us they won't attend the ceremony and will go abroad on holiday instead.

Barb has been crocheting a dress in her spare time for the last four or five months, a pretty turquoise colour. She started it when I was working all those double shifts and left her alone so many nights, finishing it off whilst in labour at the hospital.

"I'll get married in this," she announces, "so many tears have been sewn into it. Perhaps I won't have to shed any more."

The date is set.12ᵗʰ August 1967.

Everyone rallies round and Ann offers to give us a bit of a 'do' at her place in Paddock Lane afterwards. Great stuff.

Arrangements are made for my brother Mike, who has a car, to collect Pearl and then Ann. My brothers, Roy and Malcolm will come from Bilston on the bus. Our next door neighbour has said she will look after Jason during the ceremony and we can pick him up afterwards.

The wedding is booked for eleven o'clock at West Bromwich Registry Office. Me and Barb arrived a bit early and have been here for half an hour already. She looks lovely in her turquoise dress which sits just above the knee. Her white slip shows through all the holes and she has a pair of white strappy shoes and a bag to match. Our neighbour gave her a posy of pretty white flowers this morning when we dropped Jason round. They smell amazing. We have no camera so this very special picture of her goes straight to my memory bank. Something I will always be able to recall down to the last detail.

The clock ticks. No sign of anyone. An officious lady keeps pestering us. If we don't go in soon then we'll miss our slot. I keep rushing up and down the stairs and looking up and down the road. At ten past we are told if we want to get married today we will need two witnesses within the next five minutes.

Barb is becoming tearful as I nip onto the street and ask a middle aged couple who happen to be walking past. It seems to brighten their day as they trundle up the stairs, shopping bags in hand.

The four of us are ushered into a small wood panelled room with a dozen or so blue upholstered chairs facing a leather top desk. Long as we get married I don't give a shit. A tall, smart woman introduces herself as the Registrar and asks me for the ring. We're using the one from Woolworths which Barb has been wearing for months and I place it onto a little blue cushion in front of me.

The marriage ceremony begins. A lot of jumbled words. My eyes hold Barb's as the Registrar asks us to turn and face each other. A commotion outside and slow hushed footsteps tread the wooden boards as Roy and Malcolm take a seat next to our two strangers.

It's over in moments and I'm kissing my wife. Outside and down the stairs, I thank the couple who go off to continue their shopping.

My brothers missed the bus which made them late. Oh well, what can you do?

Barb's standing by the Cresta, all dressed up but looking dejected. A horn beeps and the four of us turn. Ann jumps from Mike's car, breathless, "it was Pearl's fault. We had to wait ages for her."

Pearl strolls across. "Not that late are we? It's only just half past."

I wave the certificate. "It was eleven o'clock not half past."

Pearl and Tom laugh. Ann is seething and comforts Barb. Roy and Malcolm offer the fags round.

What a wedding. Barb puts on a brave face, "doesn't matter, it's only a piece of paper."

Might only be a piece of paper but it means I've won. Nothing and no-one ever beats me. I got the girl. She belongs to me. We're married now.

We troop back to Ann's for a lovely spread. She's had some good news.

Been offered a new house. It's the one next door to our Pearl in Shireview Road. Given what's just happened, the atmosphere as well as the small wedding cake, can be cut with a knife.

Two months later I'm made redundant. We can't afford this place. Nothing else for it but to give notice. Cass, who has spent more time in the garage since Jason arrived, is given to one of the builders up the road. We head to Pearls and put our names on the Housing List at the Council.

"Coming down the Jumble Sale this afternoon, might pick up something for your Jason," Pearl loves markets and jumble sales.

Barb looks up from feeding. "He's growing so fast."

There's a lot of quality gear at the Church Hall but owing to the fact that a local primary school is also holding some sort of fete the turnout is poor. Seeing the pile of second hand clothes reminds me of Mom's neighbours sifting through the dry cleaning stuff. Can't help but smile to myself.

"What are you going to do with this lot?" I ask the Vicar as the sale dwindles to a close at four o'clock.

He surveys the groaning tables and looks perplexed. "I really don't know."

"What say I drop you a few bob for the Church fund and take if off your hands?"

"Would you, oh how kind, we've nowhere to store it you see."

Barb and Pearl walk home as I fill the Cresta with bric-a-brac and second hand clothes. Ten trips later the Vicar calls me round back. "Don't forget this furniture will you."

There are wardrobes and beds, dressing tables and chairs, you name it.

Racing back to Tom I ask him to ring Moggie who brings the van.

"I'm not having all this in my house," Pearl is indignant and won't be swayed.

Ann offers and for days her back garden and front room are piled high and when I say piled high, I mean floor to ceiling. Once word gets round people come from all over the village. I stand on the door dishing out prices and collecting the dosh. When's the next jumble sale?

We are re-housed in a small end terrace on the A5 in Brownhills. Bit off the beaten track and a long walk to any shops. I manage to get work at one of the nearby factories. Barb is now pregnant with our second child.

The job is on nights but I know it's not for me on the first shift. My work entails lifting heavy stuff from one conveyor belt to another. When the bell for break sounds I have to finish transferring what is already on the conveyor before making my way to the tea area. Soon as I get there the bell goes for end of break which means there's no time for me to have a drink. The foreman doesn't seem impressed when I complain. Why don't they just extend the fuckin' conveyor belts so that they meet? Don't make sense to me. I'm off.

'Paint sprayer required' the ad says. I can do that. How hard can it be? At least it's not nightshift. I say I've done it before and land the job spraying fire back-plates and suchlike. Fumes overtake me a bit but the pay is decent and it's a sort of skill which I become quite good at. All in the wrist action.

Three months later the plant switches operations and redundancy beckons. I ain't been here very long so there's nothing extra in my pay packet. Barb suggests I try and make use of my baking skills.

"Look, they want someone at this place in Walsall," she waves the newspaper in front of me.

"They won't fuckin' have me 'cos of these," I wave my tattoo covered hands at her. What is it with women, they just don't listen. To satisfy her I go for an interview which is in two parts. First task is to make a loaf, by hand, not machine. That's what I'm good at. My spirits lift as the Manager says mine tastes the best and has the nicest texture. Might be in here.

Three of us wait to see the Boss. He takes one look at my hands. "I'm sorry Walter, but this new Hot Bread Shop venture involves bread being baked in small shops where customers will be able to see the process. Your tattoos" he shakes his head, "wouldn't be good for business."

I knew it all along. Don't know why I even bothered. On the way home my blood boils. Fuckin' tattoos. Do they matter that much? Why can't people see past my hands? I'm supposed to be the breadwinner. That's a laugh. Picking up a newspaper I sit and scour the ads. Must be a well paid job in here somewhere.

Barb can't work, looking after little Jason and pregnant with another. Money is tight and we fall behind with rent and bills.

Some days we walk with the pram to Ann's in Pelsall, a good eight miles there and back, to borrow enough money for a tin of baked beans and a loaf of bread. Barb is mortified when I nip into a cabbage field on the way home. There's millions in here, farmer won't miss one.

Morals are all very well but they don't stave off the hunger pangs at night. It crosses my mind more than once that I can get us some money. The way I know best.

This time, when the raging battle in my head finally comes to a conclusion, my silent promise wins. So we struggle on with me working a few odd days here and there on local building sites.

We've done our best with this terrace house. Scrimped and saved to buy paint and tidied it up. There's a problem. Vermin. Two adjoining houses are empty and this place backs onto a canal. Barb spends hours at the Council Offices asking to be re-housed and contacts the Health Department because of the risk to Jason. Our second child is due in May, four months away.

We can't afford petrol so I'm walking miles every day, trying for work. Purely by chance, I pass a Wheelbarrow Company on the bridge in Mob Lane. 'Vacancies' reads a large sign at the entrance. No time like the present.

A Manager shows me the work. It involves dipping parts into a vat of paint and hanging them onto hooks which then travel through the stove enamelling plant. I'm offered the job to start tomorrow. Its piecework so the faster I go the more I'll earn. Great.

Within a week I've figured out a way to load the hooks with double the amount the other blokes are doing on their lines. I'm working flat out but I'll be quids in come pay day. The foreman can't believe it. He checks and re-checks but the quality is spot on. I'm feeling dead chuffed as I stand in line to collect my first pay packet at the end of the second week. Having calculated my earnings to the last penny I know exactly how much it should be.

"Sign here," orders the foreman pushing a clipboard towards me.

I start to sign and glance at the amount. "This is wrong mate."

"You'll have to take it up with the office."

Grabbing the packet I walk briskly across the yard to the Managers office. His Secretary smiles at me but I ain't in no smiling mood. What are they playing at?

The Manager can't quite look me in the eye. "We've had to lower your piecework rate."

Open mouthed I stare at him. Can't quite take this in. "What do you mean?"

Not raising his eyes from the desk, "we can't have you shop floor workers earning more than the Managers, can we?"

Is he serious? Is that a question?

"There's nothing wrong with my work is there?"

He shakes his head.

"I want my money then. You told me the rate. You can't just alter it. I figured out how to make the machine carry more and I've worked fuckin' hard."

He holds up his hands. "I know, I know but it's up to the owner, not me. Nobody thought the plant was capable of producing that much until you came."

"Has everyone else's rate been dropped?"

He won't answer. My rate has been cut in half. I bang my fist on the desk. "So, I get less 'cos I've doubled your output. It's fuckin' unbelievable." He won't pay me any more. That's it then. "I want my cards, I'm leaving." Despondent, I make my way home.

I've heard on the grapevine Fafnir Bearings in Hednesford are holding open interviews for toolsetters tomorrow. 12 hour night-shifts. Excellent money. If I could just get one of them jobs we'd be set.

Might as well try, nothing to loose.

Ann comes with me for a ride over to Hednesford. The room is heaving with applicants. Lucas's, a big employer in Birmingham, has recently made a large number of toolsetters redundant. Looks like they're all here. I've got no chance.

Most of the blokes can't take their eyes off Ann. Long blonde hair, big blue eyes, legs that go all the way up to her armpits and very, very pretty. They think she's my missus and we laugh about it together.

When my name is called, Ann gives me the thumbs up, and I walk in. A pleasant looking bespectacled middle aged man sits at a desk. Asking where I did my apprenticeship I tell him Johnny Fellowes. Well, I did a fortnight there when I was fifteen, but he don't know that. He doesn't ask for my papers or anything. When he wants my job history and experience I make it up. Simple as that.

I'm told the job will involve reading plans, setting up machines in readiness for the women on dayshift and also learning to operate a new computerised welding machine. I tell him I can read plans and he asks me to wait outside.

Half an hour later the rest have gone. There's just me, Ann and another chap. He talks funny and tells us he's Polish. Can't get my mouth round his real name.

"Just call me Lukik" he tells me

The bespectacled man motions us both in together. We've landed the two nightshift jobs and start tomorrow. Ann can tell as soon as I walk out of the interview room. I'm trying not to look too enthusiastic but as soon as we get outside, *"yes"* I jump up and punch the air. Got it.

More good news waits for me at home. A letter has arrived from the Council inviting us to view a house in Brownhills. Barb's hard work badgering them has paid dividends and my bluffing skills have landed me a job, long as I can hold onto it that is. Feeling happy I pick up my guitar and strum a few tunes. Haven't done that in ages.

We accept the house immediately. The spacious three bed sits on a corner plot and lies back from the road, being approached across a lovely green. It has a living room and large dining kitchen. Perfect.

My job is a bit more problematic. The foreman greets me and Lukik on the first night. He shows us where the plans are kept and points out the computerised welder. Being such a new concept we will both receive training on it next week. Saying he'll be back just before clocking off time he disappears to another section.

Lukik walks over to the plans and checks a list which has been left of what runs we've got to make on the machines. "Which ones do you want to do?" he asks.

I've got to think of something fast. Might have thought I could blag my way through this but looking at these machines it doesn't take Einstein to figure I'll be sussed tonight and loose the job. I've got to tell him the truth.

"I can't set any of these machines. I've never done any toolsetting, only two weeks about sixteen years ago."

Lukik laughs. "You're kidding me." He turns to pick up the plans and holds out a set towards me.

I don't move a muscle.

"You're not kidding me?"

I shake my head. "Nope."

Lukik shrugs his shoulders. "You better see the foreman. He went that way."

"Look, I've got an idea. You help me, show me what to do and I'll give you half my wages for as long as it takes." Money, it's the greatest pull. I'm praying he'll go for it. We can survive on half my pay for a bit, won't take me long to pick it up.

"Seven years apprenticeship I served to learn how to do this job… and you… you think you can just *pick it up*?" Lukik turns his back and starts walking towards the door. He's gonna fetch the foreman. I pull him back by his khaki overall.

"Just give me a chance. Half my wages. Think about it. Got to be worth your while hasn't it?"

Slowly he turns, pulls a face, shuffles about a bit. I've got him now.

"How do I know you will pay me?"

"Look, I need this job, got a little 'un, another one due any minute, if I don't pay you I loose the job…right?"

Lukik nods. "Alright then. C'mon, let's get started."

We settle into a routine and he's laughing all the way to the bank as I hand over half my wages come Friday. The following week a specialist comes in to show us how to operate the computerised welder. I pick it up much quicker than Lukik and within a couple of months my welds are twice as good as his. He just can't get the hang of it and I end up doing *all* the computer welds. I have also learned how to set and operate every machine in the place. For the life of me I can't believe how it can take anyone seven years to learn this job.

Richard is born on 12th May 1968. A mass of dark brown hair with the longest eyelashes the midwife has ever seen. Gonna be handsome like his Dad. He weighs in at 10lbs. Another big 'un as my Mom would say. We need a twin pram so take out a Provident loan and splash out on a beautiful blue Silver Cross with big spoked wheels. We're having difficulty making ends meet. I need all my wages to survive.

"Shall we call it quits now then Lukik? I'm covering for you on this computerised machine. You've had a fair whack. I'm as good as you, admit it. How about I keep my full wages from now on?"

He's not too keen. Who can blame him? Got used to the extra money. I lay it on thick that my kids are starving and he reluctantly agrees.

Two and a half years I work as a toolsetter. During this time Barb has secured a position with a firm of Architects on a fixed term contract in Wolverhampton. Soon as I come in from nightshift she goes off to work dropping Jason and Richard at Nursery. We spend half an hour together because she's back at just turned six and I leave the house at half past.

Weekends we have taken to singing in local clubs and pubs to earn a few extra pennies. At first she was very shy but Barb has a stunning voice, sounds just like Judith Durham from the Seekers.

Pretty soon, with folks shouting for more, she loves it as much as me. The buzz is akin to adrenalin rushes I've had in the past, but this time, I ain't up to no good.

I take my driving test for the second time. Bearing in mind the examiner had said my performance was timid on the previous occasion, I whiz round. He says it's much better and thankfully I pass.

Barb's contract comes to an end but she immediately takes another secretarial job, working for a Psychologist. This is a permanent position, more pay, and she really enjoys it.

"Might train to be a Psychologist myself," she declares, "doesn't seem that hard to me."

Fafnir Bearings announces its impending closure and on the last night our foreman comes for a chat and a game of darts during break.

Lukik tells him what I'd done. Don't think he believes it. "You could never just *pick up* toolsetting. It's a trade. You have to serve a long apprenticeship."

This is the third redundancy for me but I've never had any severance before. With this payout I'm going to start my own business. No more night work. We can start to have a proper life and see a bit more of each other. Barb brings home a good wedge and with what I can earn in my new business venture we can save for what Barb's always wanted, a deposit on a house of our own.

The redundancy money sits in front of me. We've had a telephone installed and placed an advertisement in the Walsall Observer. I'm just off to buy a roof-rack for the car, some tools and a ladder for my roofing business. The ad offers general roof repairs, pointing ridge tiles, chimneys, replacing lead and re-roofing.

I took the first call last night and went straight to an address in Pleck. They want a new roof. Was hoping to start with a bit of re-pointing first. Wonder if I've priced it right, they seemed to snatch my hand off a bit quick when I gave 'em the quote.

There's loads of money in this roofing lark, or so I'm told. Still young and agile, I've climbed on a few roofs in my time and all those hours spent on building sites hasn't been wasted.

Barb looks doubtful but has bought a big thick book outlining everything to do with house building and repairs. She sits pouring over it underlining sentences with a red pen. Good job one of us likes the academic stuff. We've come through a lot together. She's my rock. Better add a box of red pens to that mental list of stuff to get.

My eyes wander across the room to Richard who is sitting on a sort of red plastic bus with wheels, tazzing round the place crashing into everything and laughing his head off. With big brown eyes and a shock of dark hair he's a chip off the old block alright. Jason's white blonde hair flops forward as he sits on the floor by the fire, next to his Mom. Glancing up from the colouring book, he smiles at me, his blue eyes full of love and trust. This is my family. I'm proud. It's what I always wanted and now I'm gonna build us a future.

Anticipation sets my nerve ends tingling. I feel as if I'm on the brink. Bursting with hope and full of dreams. Roofing might lead to other things like extensions...maybe one day I'll build us a home of our own....maybe I'll become a big house builder....

A smile plays about my lips. Me? I can do *anything* if I set my mind to it.

Now… where's my liquorice?

THE END

Postscript

The rocky road that followed led me through many ventures, some good, others not so good, but that's another story....

I was driven by a passionate desire for the trappings of wealth, born from the eyes of a little boy who stood peering into a different world as he begged for food and cast-offs on the doorsteps of those big houses on the main road.

With the help and support of my wife and two sons I built a successful business and finally got to live the dream. It took many years of real hard graft, dogged determination and self belief to achieve the lifestyle to which I aspired.

My musical career blossomed alongside the business ventures. Offers were flooding in when Barb announced she wanted to give it up and follow her own professional ambitions.

Eventually an uneasy truce came to pass between myself and Barb's parents. We buried our misgivings for the sake of the children. My resentment and hurt remains just beneath the surface. I may forgive but I'll never forget.

Of all the girls I loved before, only two ever crossed my path again. In 1983 who should step off the pavement in front of me but 'The Shape'. Recognition dawned immediately and truth to tell there was still a spark as our eyes met and we laughed together. She never married.

I've met Jean twice, once in 1970 when we shared memories and a cuppa with two heaped spoons in the Table Mountain and again in 2001.

In 1976 I finally quit smoking, much to Barb's relief and probably due to her constant nagging. One of my better decisions.

During the 70's bread strikes my oven was never switched off. Friends and neighbours didn't seem to bother about my tattooed hands as they clamoured for a fresh baked loaf.

In 2003 my tattoos were removed by laser, much more painful than having them on in the first place.

I have six grandchildren and seven step-grandchildren. My sons, you see, are not as fortunate as me because their marriages didn't work out and they had to try again. I only hope the choices they've made now will bring them the happiness they truly deserve.

Me and Barb? I still love her to bits and count my blessings every day. I married a remarkable young lady. She saved me from myself.

In these twilight years I have come to reflect on my life and how I lived it. There are many people whose lives I touched and maybe affected along the way. To those I hurt, I would like to say sorry and to those I gave some pleasure, well, I hope you enjoyed it, 'cos I sure as hell did!

Why have I chosen to tell my story? My past was kept hidden for years and I spent a long period of my life being ashamed. I was ashamed of my tattooed hands and ashamed of being in prison. With age comes realization. It's what I went through that makes me who I am. We get one life and live it how we see best for ourselves. Fate takes a hand but ultimately *we* make the decisions and, oh boy, did I make some bad ones.

I'm not proud of the crimes I committed but having paid my debt to society I can hold my head up high. Think of me what you will. This is my story.

This is *my* life.

And at 81 years young I'm looking forward to the next chapter...

*****